W9-CUK-506

DIFFUSION KINETICS FOR ATOMS IN CRYSTALS

DIFFUSION KINETICS FOR ATOMS IN CRYSTALS

by

JOHN R. MANNING

National Bureau of Standards

D. VAN NOSTRAND COMPANY, INC.

Princeton, New Jersey

Toronto *London* *Melbourne*

VAN NOSTRAND REGIONAL OFFICES: *New York, Chicago, San Francisco*

D. VAN NOSTRAND COMPANY, LTD., *London*

D. VAN NOSTRAND COMPANY (Canada), LTD., *Toronto*

D. VAN NOSTRAND AUSTRALIA PTY. LTD., *Melbourne*

Published simultaneously in Canada by
D. VAN NOSTRAND COMPANY (Canada), LTD.

Library of Congress Catalog Card No. 68-20921

PRINTED IN THE UNITED STATES OF AMERICA

Preface

Diffusion in crystals is basically an atomic process, with each atom following a more or less random walk. The large-scale migrations of matter which are observed result from many small jumps by individual atoms. By considering individual atom jumps, one can derive the equations which govern large-scale transport of matter. Most books on diffusion include at least a brief description of the simple random-walk equations. A more thorough and systematic treatment would seem desirable, however. The aim of the present book is to provide a systematic discussion of diffusion in crystals from an atomic random-walk viewpoint.

The equations governing diffusion are derived here by considering atoms which follow random walks or modified random walks. Important modifications of the simple random-walk equations result from driving forces, diffusion coefficient gradients, and correlation effects. These effects are discussed in detail, as well as possible combinations, such as correlation effects when there is a driving force.

In Chapter 1, basic equations and concepts are presented in a form consistent with kinetic theory. For a reader who wishes more background, recent books by Shewmon and Girifalco (see references at the end of Chapter 1, page 35) are recommended. Chapter 2 presents a thorough discussion of the uncorrelated random walk with constant diffusion coefficient. In Chapters 3, 4, and 5, major modifications of the random-walk diffusion equations are considered. In Chapter 6, thermodynamic continuum equations are discussed and compared with kinetic equations obtained earlier. General applications and several special topics are considered in Chapter 7.

The present atomic-kinetic approach requires a detailed tracing of individual atom and vacancy paths. Thus, a number of possible jump frequencies and jump probabilities must be defined. To aid the reader, a list of symbols is included.

The author accepts full responsibility for the contents of this monograph. The discussions presented here do not necessarily represent the views of any organization with which the author may be associated. Warm thanks for their very helpful comments on the manuscript are proffered to Professor H. B. Huntington (Rensselaer Polytechnic Institute), to Professor L. M. Slifkin (University of North Carolina) and to my colleagues at the National Bureau of Standards, in particular Dr. D. B. Butrymowicz, Dr. A. D. Franklin, and Dr. R. E. Howard. The typing and editing assistance provided by Catherine Manning was greatly appreciated.

Contents

List of Frequently Used Symbols

A	Fractional increase in basic jump frequency resulting from a driving force (in Chapters 4, 5, and 7).
A	Matrix whose typical element A_{jg} gives the transition probability from site j to site g (in Chapter 3 only).
B	Fractional increase in vacancy flow factor resulting from a vacancy flux.
c	Concentration (number per unit volume).
d	Distance between neighboring planes.
D	Diffusion coefficient (usually *tracer* diffusion coefficient).
D^*	Tracer diffusion coefficient.
D^I	Intrinsic diffusion coefficient.
$\tilde{D}$	Interdiffusion coefficient.
D_i	Diffusion coefficient of species i.
D_{ik}	Partial diffusion coefficient, relating flux of species i to concentration gradient of species k.
D_{xy}	x–y component of diffusion tensor, relating flux along x-axis to concentration gradient along y-axis.
E	Electric field; or theoretical activation energy $(E_m + E_f)$.
$E_{f\alpha}$	Energy of formation at site α.
$E_{m\alpha}$	Energy of motion for a jump to site α.
f	Correlation factor.
f_i	Correlation factor for diffusion of species i.
f_α	Partial correlation factor for jumps of type α.
f_v	Correlation factor for diffusion of vacancies.

$f_v{}^i$	Partial correlation factor for diffusion of vacancies by exchange with atoms of species i.
f_o	Correlation factor for self-diffusion in a pure crystal.
F_α	Driving force for a jump of type α.
F_s	Fraction of dissociative jumps to site s which lead to eventual randomizing of the vacancy's position with respect to the impurity.
$G_\alpha = G_{0\alpha}$	Vacancy flow factor for a jump of type α (from site 0 to site α) $= \nu_{\pi\alpha}/w_{\alpha\pi}N_{v\alpha e}$.
H	Value of effective escape frequency $w_{\alpha\pi}$ in the absence of driving forces or diffusion coefficient gradients (in Chapters 3, 4, and 5); or effective barrier height (Chapter 7).
J	Flux of diffusing species (number crossing unit area in unit time).
M_o	Value of $\sum_s F_s$ in a pure crystal (equal to 7.15 in face-centered cubic crystals (fcc), 5.33 in body-centered cubic crystals (bcc), and 2 in crystals with the diamond structure).
$\langle n_p \rangle$	Average number of jumps a vacancy moves to the right in moving from a site α (on the right of the tracer) to an equilibrium site p.
n_α	Number of jumps of type α.
$N_\alpha{}^e$	Number of independent displacements of type α.
N_i	Mole fraction of species i.
N_v	Mole fraction of vacancies.
$N_{v\alpha e}$	Equilibrium mole fraction of vacancies at sites of type α.
q	Electric charge.
$q_\alpha{}^*$	Atomic heat of transport for an α jump.
$\tilde{q}_\alpha$	$= q_\alpha{}^* - E_{f\alpha}$.
Q_s	Experimental activation energy for diffusion of species s.
$Q_j{}^*$	Reduced heat of transport for species j.
$Q_j{}^{**}$	Measured heat of transport for species j.

u	Ionic drift mobility.
$\langle v \rangle$	Drift velocity.
w_i	Vacancy jump frequency for exchange with atom of species i.
w_α	Vacancy jump frequency for jump of type α (to a site α).
w_{gh}	Jump frequency for a vacancy jump from site g to site h.
w_{gho}	Value of w_{gh} in the absence of driving forces or diffusion coefficient gradients.
w_s	Vacancy jump frequency from site α (neighboring on the tracer) to a given nontracer site s.
$w_{\alpha T}$	Jump frequency for exchange of vacancy on site α with the tracer.
$w_{\alpha\pi}$	Frequency of jumps which begin the vacancy on a path from site α (neighboring on the tracer) to any equilibrium site p *without* return to site α or exchange with the tracer $= \sum_s w_s F_s$.
W	Average vacancy jump frequency. In a binary alloy, $W = N_A w_A + N_B w_B$.
$W(m, N)$	Distribution function giving the probability that after N jumps an atom will be displaced m jumps in the positive direction.
$W(X, \tau)dX$	Distribution function giving the probability that after time τ an atom will have been displaced a distance $X \pm \frac{1}{2}dX$.
x_γ	The x-displacement resulting from jump γ.
$\langle X \rangle$	Mean displacement.
$\langle X^2 \rangle$	Mean square displacement.
y	Number of nearest neighbors located on the next plane in the $+$ (or $-$) x-direction.
z	Number of nearest neighbors.
γ_i	Activity coefficient of species i.
Γ	Atom jump frequency between two neighboring sites.
λ	Jump distance.

μ	Chemical potential.
τ	Diffusion time (interval of time).
ν	Total atom jump frequency (summed over more than one Γ).

SUBSCRIPTS

When jump frequencies (w, Γ, ν), atom fluxes (J), and other quantities in the above list are discussed, subscripts often must be included, indicating for example the particular jump or type of jump.

Typical subscripts with their meanings are:

Jump Frequencies

$+$	Jump in the $+x$-direction.
$-$	Jump in the $-x$-direction.
1, 2, 3, 4	Vacancy jumps near an impurity.
L	Jump to the left.
m	Jump frequency associated with plane at midpoint of a jump.
o	Vacancy jump far from an impurity.
r	Reverse jump.
R	Jump to the right.
s	Vacancy jump with a solvent (nontracer) atom.
T	Vacancy jump with a particular (tracer) atom.
α, β	Jump to one site in a set of sites (set α or set β); type of jump.
γ, δ	γth or δth jump in a series of jumps.

Jumps may also be designated by their initial and final sites. For example, a jump from site 0 to site j can be designated by the pair of subscripts $0j$. This jump could also be designated by the single subscript j representing the final site alone. A jump from one site on plane 0 to another site on plane 0 is designated by the single subscript 0. A jump from plane 0 to plane α is designated by the two subscripts 0α.

Sites

0	Site occupied by the tracer atom.
g, h	Any site in the crystal.
j	A site neighboring on a tracer (impurity).
p	A site where equilibrium vacancy concentrations are maintained.
α	One of an equivalent set of sites (often taken as neighboring on the tracer).
π	Summed over all sites p.

Planes

0, 1, 2, 3	Neighboring lattice planes.
a	Plane to right of tracer.
b	Plane containing tracer.
c	Plane to left of tracer.
α	Plane containing the set of equivalent sites α.

Atom Species

A, B	Species in a binary alloy.
i	Any species; impurity species.
k, M	Any species.
s	Solvent species.
T	Tracer species.
ρ, σ	Two isotopes of the same element.

Coordinates and/or Components

x, y, z	Cartesian coordinates.
μ, ν	x, y, or z.
ξ	Component along diffusion direction.

Subscript 0

The subscript 0 may refer to:

1. The site or plane occupied by the tracer.
2. A case where the number of displacements N equals zero.

DIFFUSION KINETICS FOR ATOMS IN CRYSTALS

1. BASIC CONCEPTS

1–1. INTRODUCTION

There are two main approaches to diffusion theory: (1) the atomistic approach, where the atomic nature of the diffusing substance is explicitly considered; and (2) the continuum approach, where the diffusing substance is treated as a continuous medium and the atomic nature of the diffusion process is ignored. Many useful equations result from the continuum approach. For example, general thermodynamic equations can be found which relate diffusion fluxes to thermodynamic driving forces. This approach in one sense simplifies the problem since it directly relates the initial and final states, but also it is limited in its results since it ignores the details of the atomic motions.

A more complete picture of diffusion phenomena is obtained if the atomic motions are considered. Equations can be found relating macroscopic quantities, such as diffusion fluxes, to atomic quantities, such as atom jump frequencies. Often, several macroscopic diffusion quantities are related to the same atomic parameter. Thus, the atomic approach allows the various macroscopic quantities to be related to one another in ways not possible from a purely continuum approach.

In the following chapters, the atomistic approach is discussed in detail. Continuum equations are discussed to a limited extent in order to show the relationship between the two approaches.

1-2. DIFFUSION MECHANISMS

Any theory of atom diffusion must start with a consideration of diffusion mechanisms. One must answer the question, "How does this particular atom move from here to there?" In gases, where the molecules are widely separated, it is assumed that each molecule travels in a straight line until it collides with another molecule (or with the walls of the container). This collision changes the speed and direction of the molecule, and it then proceeds in the new direction until it collides with still another molecule, and so on. This approach has led to a satisfactory kinetic theory of diffusion in gases with the diffusion coefficient being related to the average velocity and mean free path of the molecule. In liquids, the situation is more complex. Here a molecule cannot move freely between the molecules immediately surrounding it. Its motion is probably best described as an irregular jostling motion. This is quite difficult to treat accurately. Diffusion in amorphous solids, with no regular arrangement of atoms, is also difficult to treat.

In crystalline solids, it again is possible to describe diffusion mechanisms in simple terms. The ordered crystal lattice restricts the possible atom motions and allows a simple description of each specific atom displacement. This contrasts with the situation in a gas, where a perfectly random arrangement of atoms is assumed, and in liquids and amorphous solids, which are neither really random nor really ordered.

In any crystal, there is a regular array of lattice sites which are energetically favored positions for atoms. The basic assumption made to explain diffusion is that each diffusing atom makes a series of jumps between the various equilibrium lattice sites. These jumps are in more or less random directions and allow the atoms to migrate through the crystal.

We are left with the problem of describing the elementary atom jump. A number of possible diffusion mechanisms can be distinguished, depending on the type of elementary jump which takes the atom from one equilibrium site to another. These mechanisms may be listed as follows:[1]

1. Exchange mechanism
2. Ring mechanism
3. Interstitial mechanism
4. Interstitialcy mechanism
5. Crowdion mechanism
6. Vacancy mechanism
7. Divacancy mechanism
8. Relaxion mechanism
9. Dislocation pipe diffusion mechanisms
10. Grain boundary diffusion mechanisms
11. Surface diffusion mechanisms

The present discussion will be concerned mainly with diffusion *in crystals*. Diffusion along dislocations or grain boundaries, where the regular lattice structure breaks down, will not be discussed in detail; nor will surface diffusion, where atoms diffuse over the outside surfaces of crystals. Instead, attention will be centered on *volume* diffusion in the interior of crystals and in regions having a regular lattice structure.

The first eight mechanisms listed above are possible means of volume diffusion. Of these, the vacancy and the interstitial mechanisms are most frequently encountered. The elementary jumps are illustrated in Figs. 1–1 to 1–8.

Exchange Mechanism

Possibly the simplest mechanism one can envision for the elementary jump is the direct interchange of two neighboring atoms as illustrated in Fig. 1–1. This mechanism is unlikely in crystals with tightly packed atom structures since each atom in this case is closely surrounded and hemmed in by its neighbors. The atoms would need to be considerably compressed before any two could squeeze past one another and interchange

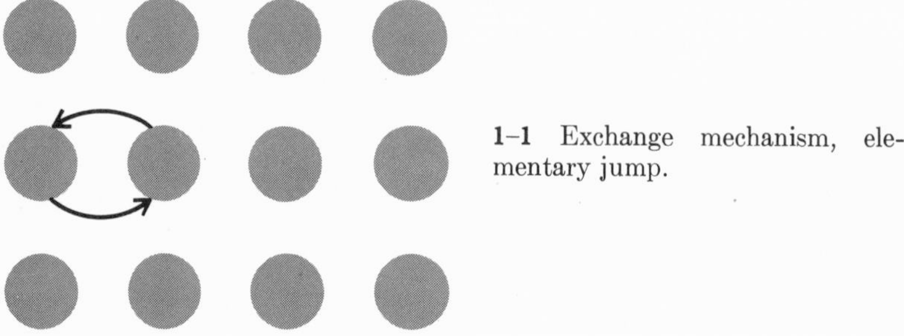

1–1 Exchange mechanism, elementary jump.

positions. On the other hand, this mechanism may be possible in very loosely packed crystals.

Ring Mechanism

A variation of the exchange mechanism is the ring mechanism, illustrated in Fig. 1–2. Here a number of atoms (three or

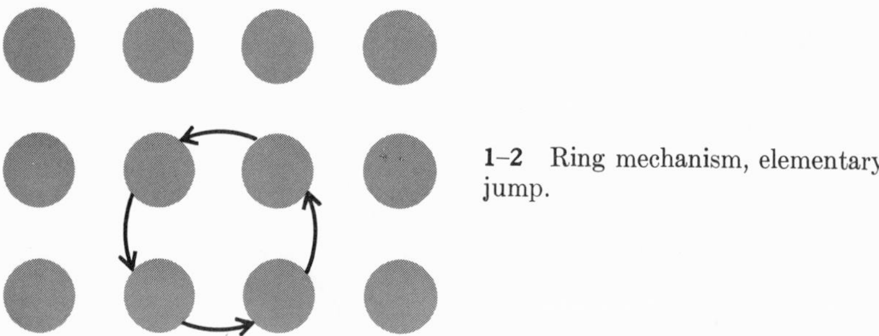

1–2 Ring mechanism, elementary jump.

more) which are situated roughly in a ring move together so that the whole ring of atoms rotates by one atom distance. The compressions required here are not as great as in a direct exchange mechanism. Nevertheless, this more complex mechanism also seems unlikely in most instances.

Interstitial Mechanism

The preceding two mechanisms are those which can operate in perfect crystals. When there are imperfections such as inter-

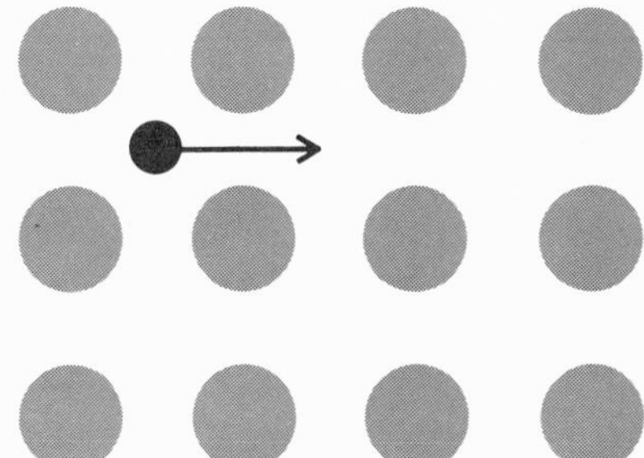

1–3 Interstitial mechanism, elementary jump.

stitial atoms, other mechanisms requiring considerably less energy can operate. One such mechanism is the interstitial mechanism, also called the direct interstitial mechanism. Here an atom moves through the crystal by jumping directly from one interstitial site to another, as in Fig. 1–3. This mechanism is particularly likely for diffusion of small impurity atoms, which easily fit into interstitial sites and in jumping do not greatly displace the solvent atoms from their normal lattice sites.

Interstitialcy Mechanism

When the interstitial atom is nearly equal in size to the lattice atoms (or to the lattice atoms on a given sublattice), diffusion is more likely to occur by the interstitialcy mechanism, also called the indirect interstitial mechanism. Here the interstitial atom does not move directly to another interstitial site. Instead it moves into a normal lattice site and the atom which was originally at the lattice site is pushed into a neighboring interstitial site. This is illustrated in Fig. 1–4. The cooperative

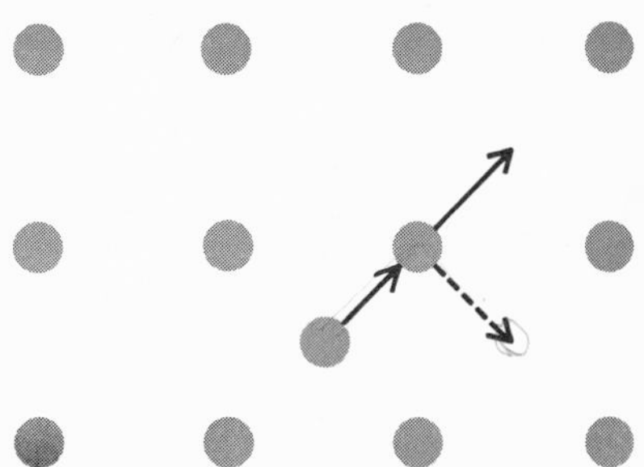

1–4 Interstitialcy mechanism. The solid arrows show displacements of the diffusing atoms during an elementary jump in a collinear interstitialcy mechanism. The dotted arrow shows an alternative (noncollinear) motion for the lattice atom.

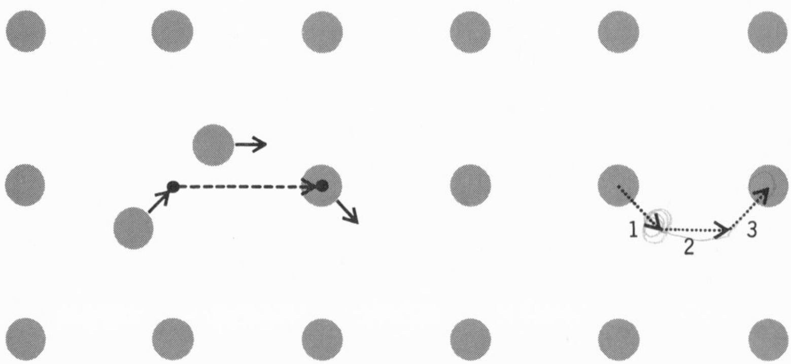

1–5 Dumbbell (interstitialcy) mechanism. On the left, the solid arrows show the displacements of the diffusing atoms during an elementary jump in the dumbbell mechanism. The dashed arrow gives the displacement of the (interstitialcy) imperfection. On the right, the dotted arrows show the three separate displacements necessary to move an atom from one lattice site to another in this mechanism.

motion of the two atoms moves the interstitialcy, i.e., the region containing the additional atom, from one interstitial site to another. However, the original interstitial atom now occupies a normal lattice site. Two jumps of the interstitialcy are required to move an atom from one lattice site to another. This mechanism seems to be important for diffusion of silver in the silver halides, where the silver ions are much smaller than the halogen ions. The most common type of interstitialcy jump is the collinear jump where the two atoms both move along the same line. However, noncollinear jumps whereby the atoms move at an angle to one another also can occur.

In some cases, the equilibrium configuration may be that for a "dumbbell interstitialcy". Here the interstitialcy is centered on a lattice site and two atoms occupy this site symmetrically in a dumbbell-like configuration, each being displaced by an equal amount from the normal lattice position. It can be said that three jumps of a dumbbell interstitialcy are necessary to move an atom from one lattice site to another. The first jump involves the arrival of the interstitialcy at the first lattice site and displaces the lattice atom into a dumbbell position; the second jump moves the interstitialcy and our atom to a dumbbell position at a different lattice site; and the third jump, where the interstitialcy moves away, allows the atom to relax into a normal lattice position at this second site. This is illustrated in Fig. 1–5.

Crowdion Mechanism

A third type of interstitial configuration is the crowdion (see Fig. 1–6). Here the additional atom is introduced into a more or less close-packed row of atoms. Each atom in the row, to perhaps ten atom distances from the additional atom, is displaced somewhat from the equilibrium lattice position. The crowdion configuration can move along this row. In passing down a row from one end to the other, the crowdion displaces each atom in the row one atom distance.

The crowdion and dumbbell interstitialcy mechanisms very likely aid in the annealing of nonequilibrium interstitials introduced upon radiation damage or cold work. However, in most cases of substitutional diffusion, with all atoms of approximately the same size, the vacancy mechanism seems to predominate.

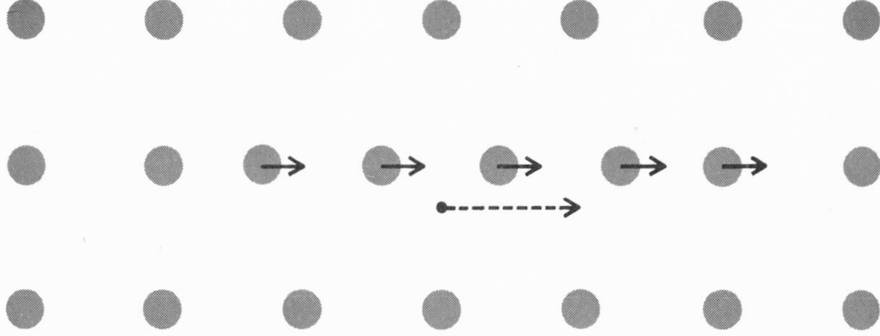

1–6 Crowdion mechanism. The solid arrows show the atom displacements during an elementary jump in the crowdion mechanism. The dashed arrow gives the displacement of the center of the (crowdion) imperfection.

Vacancy Mechanism

In thermal equilibrium, any crystal at a temperature above absolute zero contains a certain number of vacant lattice sites. These vacancies provide an easy path for diffusion. The elementary atom jump in the vacancy mechanism is the jump of an atom into a neighboring vacancy, as in Fig. 1–7. The site previously occupied by the atom then is vacant, so that in effect the atom and vacancy merely exchange positions. Each atom moves through the crystal by making a series of exchanges with the various vacancies which from time to time

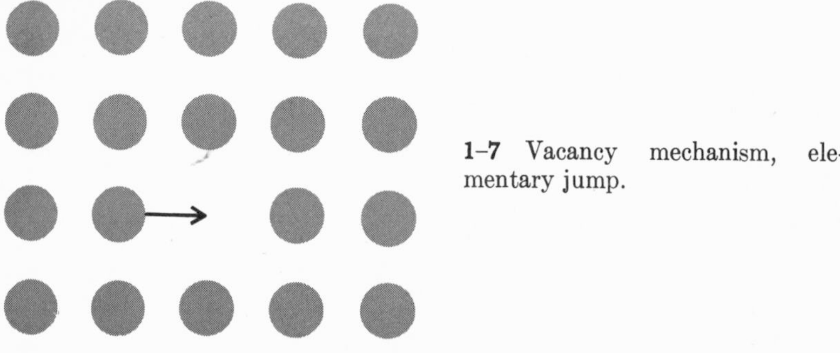

1–7 Vacancy mechanism, elementary jump.

are in its vicinity. In the following chapters, we shall pay particular attention to this mechanism.

Divacancy Mechanism

When there is a binding energy which tends to create divacancies (i.e., bound vacancy pairs), diffusion by means of divacancies may be appreciable, especially at high temperatures. Normally, however, diffusion by single vacancies predominates over diffusion by divacancies. Diffusion by means of bound trivacancies is even less common. Because of the binding and consequent lack of symmetry, diffusion by means of divacancies does not obey all the equations obtained for diffusion by single vacancies. Otherwise the two mechanisms are very similar.

Relaxion Mechanism

The relaxion mechanism is a modified vacancy mechanism. If the atoms in the region of a vacancy relax inward into the vacant lattice site to such an extent that the regular lattice structure in this region out to several atom distances disappears, the resulting region is called a relaxion. This might be compared with a localized melting, leading to disorder within this region. The atoms in this region can diffuse by an irregular jostling motion similar to that for atoms in a liquid. This is illustrated in Fig. 1–8.

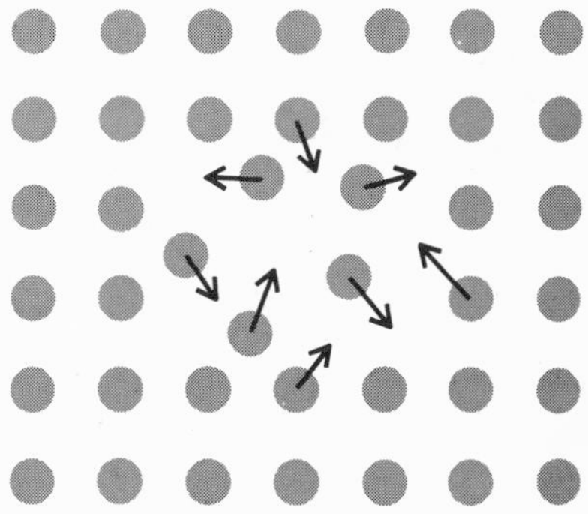

1–8 Relaxion mechanism. Atoms within the relaxed area move somewhat as in a liquid.

Dislocation Pipe, Grain Boundary, and Surface Diffusion Mechanisms

The last three mechanisms in our list are concerned with diffusion in regions where the regular lattice structure breaks down. They involve line or surface discontinuities in the crystal. It is clear that diffusion should occur more easily in the open regions of the crystal at dislocations, grain boundaries, and surfaces. However, the detailed atomic paths in each case will depend on the particular atom configurations at each line or surface defect. Thus, these mechanisms do not lend themselves easily to detailed kinetic analysis. Since the number of dislocations, grain boundaries, and surfaces is more or less independent of temperature, diffusion by these mechanisms might be expected to have a smaller temperature dependence than that for mechanisms involving point defects (vacancies and interstitial atoms), whose concentration increases with temperature. This does in fact seem to be the case. Line and surface mechanisms are relatively important at low temperatures but usually are not so important at high temperatures when compared to volume diffusion mechanisms. Because of these two factors, (1) lack of detailed models for the elementary jump and (2) relative lack of importance at high temperatures, these mechanisms will not be treated further here.

1-3. ENERGIES OF FORMATION AND MOTION

For each mechanism that requires an imperfection such as a vacancy or interstitialcy in order to operate, the rate of diffusion is proportional to the number of imperfections. In thermal equilibrium, the probability n of such an imperfection being at a given site is proportional to a Boltzmann factor,

$$n = \exp(-g_f/kT) \tag{1-1}$$

where g_f is the Gibbs free energy required to form the imperfection, k is Boltzmann's constant, and T is the absolute temperature. The Gibbs free energy can be expressed as

$$g_f = h_f - Ts_f \tag{1-2}$$

where h_f and s_f are the enthalpy and entropy of formation. Thus,

$$n = n_o \exp(-E_f/kT) \tag{1-3}$$

where $n_o = \exp(s_f/k)$ is the calculated value of n at infinite temperature and $E_f = h_f$ is the measurable energy of formation. The energy E_f can be measured experimentally by plotting $\ln n$ as a function of $1/T$.

Even when an imperfection is at a neighboring site, a certain thermal energy is required to cause an atom to jump. For example, when an atom jumps into a neighboring vacancy, it passes from one site which is favorable for atom occupation to a second such site. Since the region in between is not as favored as either the beginning or end point of the jump, an atom in this region must be in a higher energy state. If the potential energy is plotted versus position of an atom, a minimum will occur at each lattice site. The atom path between these two sites will pass through a region of maximum energy, usually at or near a saddle point in the three-dimensional potential diagram.

The difference between the Gibbs free energy of the crystal when the atom is at this saddle point and that when the atom is at a lattice site can be designated as g_m. According to rate theory, the frequency w with which the atom and a neighboring vacancy exchange is given by

$$w = w_o' \exp(-g_m/kT) \tag{1–4}$$

where w_o' is a constant. Also

$$g_m = h_m - Ts_m \tag{1–5}$$

where h_m and s_m are the enthalpy and entropy of motion. Thus,

$$w = w_o \exp(-E_m/kT) \tag{1–6}$$

where $w_o = w_o' \exp(s_m/k)$, and the measurable energy of motion E_m equals h_m. A similar equation can be written for the interstitialcy mechanism, where w in general equals the atom jump frequency if the necessary imperfection is assumed already available.

For a vacancy or interstitialcy mechanism, the jump frequency Γ of an atom to a given neighboring site is given by

$$\Gamma = wn \tag{1–7}$$

If there are z neighboring sites, each of which the atom can jump to with jump frequency Γ, the total atom jump frequency ν is given by

$$\nu = \Gamma z \tag{1-8a}$$

or

$$\nu = \nu_o \exp[-E/kT] \tag{1-8b}$$

where ν_o equals $w_o n_o z$, and

$$E = E_m + E_f \tag{1-9}$$

The quantity E is called the activation energy for diffusion.

A similar equation holds for self-diffusion by an interstitial mechanism. In this case, however, n equals the fraction of time that a given atom is an interstitial atom. For diffusion of impurities which are sufficiently small in size to always enter the crystal as interstitial atoms, n always equals unity. Thus, for these atoms, E_f equals zero. For diffusion by an exchange or ring mechanism, no imperfection is required. Therefore Γ simply equals w and again $E_f = 0$.

The energies of motion and formation can be calculated at least roughly from first principles.[2] The energy of motion for an exchange mechanism is found to be very large. Hence, this is not a likely diffusion mechanism. The energy of motion for interstitial diffusion is found to be smaller than that for vacancy diffusion. With a substitutional impurity, however, the energy to form an interstitial is usually much greater than that to form a vacancy. Thus, the vacancy mechanism usually is dominant for self-diffusion or for diffusion of substitutional impurities. An exception to this occurs in ionic crystals containing Frenkel defects. Here equal numbers of vacancies and interstitials are formed as one way to allow charge neutrality, and diffusion appears to occur at least in part by an interstitialcy mechanism. Other exceptions also can be found. For example, substitutional atoms may diffuse by a direct interstitial mechanism, such as Cu diffusing in the rather open Ge lattice (diamond structure). Means of determining diffusion mechanisms are discussed in Chapter 7.

1–4. ENERGY BARRIER DIAGRAMS AND JUMP FREQUENCIES IN A DRIVING FORCE

When there are no driving forces operating on the individual atoms, a jump in one direction between two given sites is just as likely as a jump in the other direction. This implies an energy barrier diagram along the diffusion path similar to that in Fig. 1–9a. The important feature in this diagram is its symmetry. The barrier for a jump to the right is the same as that to the left. A driving force upsets this symmetry and changes the barrier heights, as in Fig. 1–9b. Here the lower energy barrier for a jump to the right makes this jump more probable than one to the left.

The energy barrier diagram in Fig. 1–9b applies when a driving force F makes the atom jump preferentially to the right. The potential energy of the ion is lowered by λF when it moves a distance λ in the direction of the force. This is indicated in Fig. 1–9b by drawing a base line with slope $-F$. The height of the energy barrier equals the difference between the energy when the atom is at its original lattice site and that when it is at the saddle point. In most cases, the saddle point is at the midpoint of the jump, a distance $\frac{1}{2}\lambda$ from the equilibrium sites on either side. Thus, in a force F, the atom gains an energy $\Delta E_m = \frac{1}{2}\lambda F$ in moving to the saddle point.

The total energy which must be supplied to move the atom to the saddle point is $g_m = g_{mo} - \Delta E_m$, where g_{mo} is the barrier height in the absence of a driving force. The jump frequency is proportional to $\exp(-g_m/kT)$. Therefore,

$$\Gamma_+ = \Gamma_o \exp(\Delta E_m/kT) \qquad (1\text{–}10)$$

where Γ_+ is the jump frequency in the direction of the force

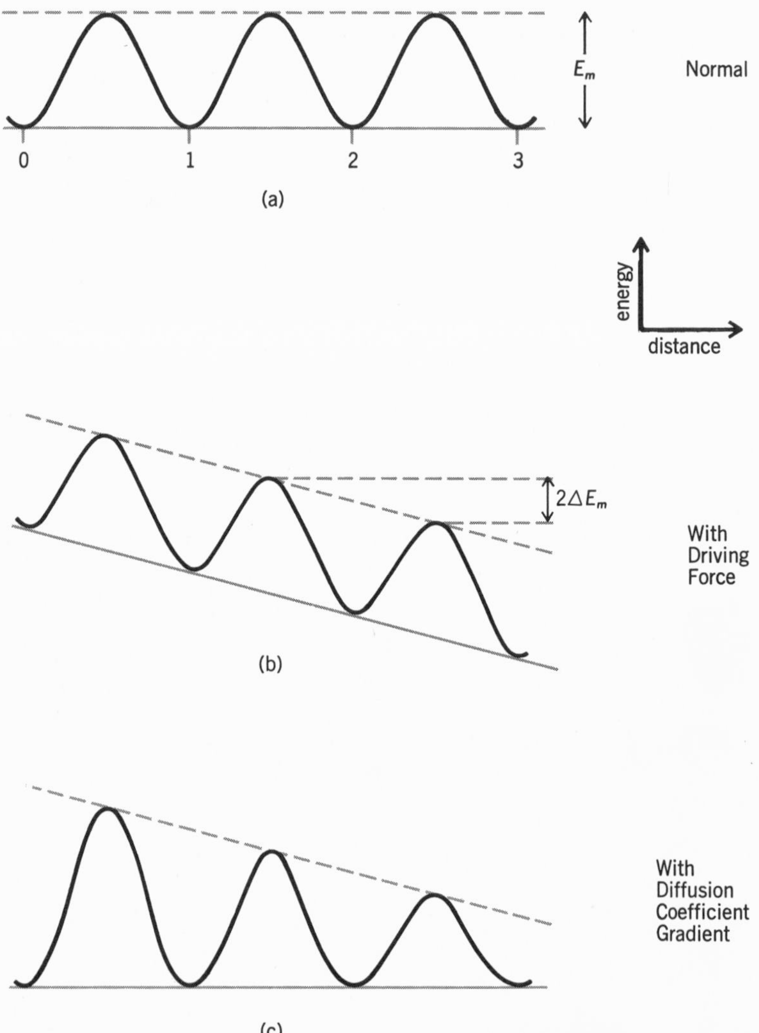

1–9 Schematic energy barrier diagrams. Energy of the crystal is plotted vertically and position of the diffusing entity horizontally in each figure. Equilibrium lattice sites are labeled 0, 1, 2, 3 and energy barriers separate neighboring sites. The jump frequency from one site to a neighboring site depends through a Boltzmann factor on the height of the energy barrier, i.e., the difference between the energy when the diffusing entity is at its original equilibrium lattice site and that when it is at the top of the energy barrier separating the two sites.

and Γ_o is that for a jump normal to the force or when the force is not present. Normally ΔE_m is much less than kT. Thus,

$$\Gamma_+ = \Gamma_o(1 + \varepsilon) \tag{1–11}$$

where ε is much smaller than unity. To first order,

$$\varepsilon = \Delta E_m/kT = \lambda F/2kT \tag{1–12}$$

Similarly, to first order, assuming the same force F,

$$\Gamma_- = \Gamma_o(1 - \varepsilon) \tag{1–13}$$

where Γ_- is the jump frequency in a direction opposed to the force.

The force F acts on the individual atoms. A typical example is the force $F = qE$ that an electric field E exerts on an ion of charge q. Other imposed forces could result from stress or gravitational fields. Also, when an atom for any reason has a frequency $\Gamma_+ = \Gamma_o(1 + \varepsilon)$ of jumping to the right and $\Gamma_- = \Gamma_o(1 - \varepsilon)$ of jumping to the left, an effective force F can be defined from Eq. (1–12). Thus, the analysis applies to chemical potential gradients in nonideal solid solutions and to thermal gradients, where the concept of a force exerted directly on the diffusing atom does not really apply.

The probability p of jumping in the direction of the driving force is given by

$$p = \Gamma_+/(\Gamma_+ + \Gamma_-) = p_o(1 + \varepsilon) \tag{1–14}$$

while the probability q of jumping in the opposite direction is given by

$$q = \Gamma_-/(\Gamma_+ + \Gamma_-) = q_o(1 - \varepsilon) \tag{1–15}$$

Here p_o and q_o are the probabilities in the absence of the driving force. In one-dimensional diffusion, where $p_o = q_o = \frac{1}{2}$ and $p + q = 1$, the same quantity ε must necessarily appear in

(1–14) as in (1–15), independent of the form of the energy barrier.

1–5. DEFINITION OF "DRIVING FORCE"

The term "driving force" can be used in several different ways in connection with diffusion. The "thermodynamic driving forces", which are discussed in Chapter 6, include not only forces on the individual atoms but also entropy of mixing terms, which give a "force" proportional to the concentration gradient of the diffusing species. Thus, the thermodynamic driving forces should be carefully distinguished from the driving forces F described above.

In this book, a driving force is defined as being any influence which makes the jump frequency for a jump in one direction between two given sites differ from that for a jump in the opposite direction between these same two sites. This is equivalent to saying that a driving force is any influence which makes the base line in the energy diagram Fig. 1–9b have a nonzero slope. Driving forces include not only actual forces, such as those from an electric field, but also effective forces from other sources. Effects which leave the base line in Fig. 1–9b unchanged are not considered to be "driving forces". In the literature, the concentration gradient of a diffusing species often is called a "driving force for diffusion". However, a simple concentration gradient does not make it any easier for a particular atom to cross a barrier in one direction than in the opposite direction. Hence, it does not contribute a driving force F, as defined above.

Even in the absence of driving forces the heights of the energy barriers may depend on position. This occurs, for example, in an alloy of variable composition if the energy of motion depends on the composition. The energy diagram may have the form shown in Fig. 1–9c. Then, the jump frequencies are the same for jumps in either direction across a given barrier;

but, for a jump from any given lattice site, the barrier to the right is easier to cross than the barrier to the left. This changes the diffusion equations in some respects, as discussed in Chapter 5. These effects are separate from effects due to driving forces.

1–6. DIFFUSION COEFFICIENTS

Fick's First Law

The diffusion coefficient D for planar diffusion is defined by the equation

$$J = -D(\partial c/\partial x) \tag{1–16}$$

Here J is the net number of atoms of the diffusing species passing through unit area of a plane normal to the x-direction in unit time, and c is the concentration of atoms of this species at this plane (number per unit volume). Since J has the units $(\text{time-area})^{-1}$ and $\partial c/\partial x$ has the units $(\text{volume-length})^{-1}$, the diffusion coefficient has units (area)/(time). Usually D is expressed in units of cm^2/sec. A minus sign appears in (1–16) because the flux usually is in the direction of decreasing concentration. In an isolated system, this tends to make the concentration gradient disappear.

Equation (1–16) is called Fick's First Law for planar diffusion and is analogous to the equation for heat flow, where the heat flux is proportional to the temperature gradient. As presented here, Eq. (1–16) applies specifically to the case where all fluxes, forces, and gradients are along one given diffusion direction, the x-direction in the present case. The concentrations and fluxes then have the same value at any position on a given plane normal to this direction, thus giving the name "planar diffusion".

Tracer Diffusion Coefficient

Equation (1–16) can be used to define a "diffusion coefficient" regardless of what forces or gradients are present. This leads to the definition of various kinds of diffusion coefficients.

A particularly simple situation is that for diffusion of a tracer isotope (in very dilute concentration) in an otherwise homogeneous crystal with no driving forces. Then the only factor that can lead to a net flow of tracer atoms is the concentration gradient of the tracer itself. A diffusion coefficient measured under these circumstances will be designated as D^* and will be called the "tracer diffusion coefficient". The term "self-diffusion coefficient" will refer to the special case where the tracer atoms are of the same species as the nontracer atoms in the crystal.

It of course is possible to introduce tracer atoms into nonhomogeneous crystals and measure their diffusion. We shall restrict the term "tracer diffusion coefficient", however, and have it refer only to diffusion in homogeneous crystals with no driving forces. This name seems appropriate since only tracer measurements allow diffusion coefficients to be measured directly in these crystals.

Effect of Driving Forces

When there is a driving force, atoms on the average have a greater than random probability of jumping in one direction, say the $+x$-direction, than in the opposite direction. The driving force thus gives each atom an average drift velocity $\langle v \rangle_F$ in the x-direction and contributes a term $c\langle v \rangle_F$ to the atom flux. The subscript F here indicates that only the drift velocity arising from driving forces is included. This distinction is necessary since a diffusion coefficient gradient (which is not a driving force) contributes to the drift velocity $\langle v \rangle$ but not to the atom flux J across any given plane. Effects from diffusion coefficient gradients can be seen from Fig. 1–9c and are discussed in Chapters 5 and 7.

If we include driving forces, the diffusion equation becomes

$$J = -D^*(\partial c/\partial x) + c\langle v\rangle_F \tag{1–17}$$

This is a basic equation which will appear many times in this book. The term $-D^*(\partial c/\partial x)$ arises merely because more atoms of the diffusing species are available on one side of the diffusion plane than on the other. The origin of this term is similar to that of the single term found for tracer diffusion with no driving forces. On the other hand, the term $c\langle v\rangle_F$ arises because the individual atoms have a preferred direction of jump.

The coefficient D^* in (1–17) does not need to equal the tracer diffusion coefficient except in the absence of driving forces; however, it almost always does equal this coefficient at least to first order in small quantities. Also, it has the same basic origin. Hence, it is reasonable to use the same symbol D^* for this coefficient as for the tracer diffusion coefficient. Other "diffusion coefficients" which may be conveniently defined are discussed below.

Intrinsic Diffusion Coefficients

In several important instances, the driving force F and hence the drift velocity $\langle v\rangle_F$ are proportional to $(\partial c/\partial x)$. Then it is useful to combine the terms on the right side of Eq. (1–17) so that

$$J_i = -D_i^I(\partial c_i/\partial x) \tag{1–18}$$

with

$$D_i^I = D_i^* - \frac{c_i\langle v\rangle_{Fi}}{(\partial c_i/\partial x)} \tag{1–19}$$

Here D_i^I is the intrinsic diffusion coefficient of species i, and the subscripts i indicate that the quantities are those for species i. Driving forces which are proportional to $(\partial c/\partial x)$ are those from (1) the diffusion potential in ionic crystals and (2) nonideal contributions to the chemical potential.

As an example, let us consider an ideal solid solution so that effect (2) goes to zero. Then let us consider interdiffusion of two species of cations in an ionic crystal where the anions remain fixed in position.[3] If diffusion on the cation sublattice occurs by a vacancy mechanism, the two species of cations can have different values of D^*. In the absence of driving forces, this would lead to a flux of cation A,

$$J_A = -D_A^*(\partial c_A/\partial x) \tag{1-20}$$

and of cation B,

$$J_B = -D_B^*(\partial c_B/\partial x) \tag{1-21}$$

With only two species of cations, $\partial c_A/\partial x = -\partial c_B/\partial x$. Then, if $D_A^* \neq D_B^*$, a net flux of cations might be expected, since according to (1–20) and (1–21),

$$J_A + J_B = (D_B^* - D_A^*)(\partial c_A/\partial x) \neq 0 \tag{1-22}$$

The net flux of electric charge, however, must equal zero in steady state, since otherwise local charge neutrality could not be maintained everywhere. Thus, when both cation species have the same charge q, there must be zero net flux of cations ($J_A + J_B = 0$). In practice, a "diffusion potential" arises, creating an electric field E_d just large enough to make the cation flux equal zero. The driving force F from this field equals qE_d, where q is the cation charge; and, in general, $\langle v\rangle_{Fi} = FD_i^*/kT$, as is found for example in Eq. (2–10). Thus, from Eq. (1–17),

$$J_A = -D_A^*(\partial c_A/\partial x) + qE_dD_A^*c_A/kT \tag{1-23}$$

$$J_B = +D_B^*(\partial c_A/\partial x) + qE_dD_B^*c_B/kT \tag{1-24}$$

Setting $J_A + J_B = 0$ and solving for E_d yields

$$E_d = \frac{kT}{q} \frac{(D_A{}^* - D_B{}^*)(\partial c_A/\partial x)}{D_A{}^* c_A + D_B{}^* c_B} \tag{1–25}$$

Thus, the driving force is proportional to $\partial c_A/\partial x$. For the atom flux, we obtain

$$J_A = -J_B = -\frac{D_A{}^* D_B{}^*}{N_A D_A{}^* + N_B D_B{}^*} \frac{\partial c_A}{\partial x} \tag{1–26}$$

where $N_A = c_A/(c_A + c_B)$ and $N_B = c_B/(c_A + c_B)$. The intrinsic diffusion coefficient $D_A{}^I$ is the coefficient of $-\partial c_A/\partial x$ in (1–26),

$$D_A{}^I = \frac{D_A{}^* D_B{}^*}{N_A D_A{}^* + N_B D_B{}^*} \tag{1–27}$$

Since $J_A = -J_B$ and $\partial c_A/\partial x = -(\partial c_B/\partial x)$, it also follows in this particular case that $D_A{}^I = D_B{}^I$.

In Eqs. (1–23) to (1–27) we see one example of a calculation of intrinsic diffusion coefficients in terms of tracer diffusion coefficients. Other examples for (1) nonideal solid solutions in metal alloys and (2) diffusion potentials when divalent ionic impurities diffuse in a monovalent sublattice are discussed in Chapters 5 and 7.

If we include nonideal solutions in the present treatment, an additional factor $[1 + (\partial \ln \gamma_i/\partial \ln N_i)]$ appears on the right-hand side of (1–27). Here γ_i is the activity coefficient of species i. The origin of this term is discussed in Chapter 5.

Interdiffusion Coefficients

When two species of atoms intermingle, their rate of mixing depends on the diffusion rates of both species. An interdiffusion coefficient can be defined to measure this rate of mixing, as in Eq. (1–30) below. For diffusion in an isolated system, this gives the rate at which the original concentration gradient disappears.

When the two species in an interdiffusion experiment have unequal intrinsic diffusion coefficients, there is a net atom flux across any plane in the diffusion zone. This causes the crystal to swell on one side of the diffusion plane and shrink on the other side. Each lattice plane in the diffusion zone thus acquires a velocity v_K with respect to a reference plane fixed at one end of the crystal. The flux J_i' of species i with respect to this reference plane is given by

$$J_i' = J_i + c_i v_K \tag{1–28}$$

where J_i is the flux of species i across the lattice plane in the diffusion zone. In general, J_i is given by (1–17). Thus,

$$J_i' = -D_i^*(\partial c_i/\partial x) + c_i\langle v\rangle_{Fi} + c_i v_K \tag{1–29}$$

The interdiffusion coefficient $\tilde{D}$ is defined in terms of J_i',

$$J_i' = -\tilde{D}(\partial c_i/\partial x) \tag{1–30}$$

In a two component crystal of constant dimensions and atom density, it is necessarily true that $J_A' = -J_B'$ and $\partial c_A/\partial x = -\partial c_B/\partial x$. For such a crystal, the same value of $\tilde{D}$ is found whether i in (1–30) is species A or species B.

In the situation treated in Eqs. (1–23) to (1–27), v_K equals zero. Thus, the intrinsic diffusion coefficient $D_A{}^I$ in (1–27) also is the interdiffusion coefficient. In metal alloy interdiffusion, however, v_K usually is not zero, and $\tilde{D} \neq D_A{}^I \neq D_B{}^I$ (see Chapter 5).

Discussion

There are three types of "diffusion coefficients" which can be defined from Eq. (1–16): (1) tracer diffusion coefficient,

(2) intrinsic diffusion coefficient, and (3) interdiffusion coefficient. Of these three, the tracer diffusion coefficient is the most basic, since it is directly related to the atom jump frequencies. In this book, we shall deal mainly with tracer diffusion coefficients. Unless it is explicitly stated otherwise, the term "diffusion coefficient" will always refer to the tracer diffusion coefficient.

Partial Diffusion Coefficients

In multi-component systems, it is not always convenient to use an expression such as Eq. (1–16) for the atom flux, since the "diffusion coefficient" then would be a very complex quantity, depending not only on concentrations, temperature, and pressure but also on the concentration gradients of various species. Instead, it is more convenient to use the expression,

$$J_i = -\sum_k D_{ik}(\partial c_k/\partial x) \qquad (1\text{–}31)$$

This equation explicitly allows for the possibility that the flux J_i of species i may depend on the concentration gradient $(\partial c_k/\partial x)$ of any species in the crystal. The summation includes all species k in the crystal including species i.

In this equation, the D_{ik} may be called "partial diffusion coefficients", since each separate term $-D_{ik}(\partial c_k/\partial x)$ contributes only part of the total flux J_i. Normally, the D_{ik} for $i \neq k$ are small compared to that for $i = k$. Still the cross-terms (where $i \neq k$) are not necessarily zero. Nonzero cross-terms arise whenever the driving force on an i atom depends on the concentration gradient of a different species k.

In general, the partial diffusion coefficients can be designated as either intrinsic or interdiffusion coefficients, depending on the reference axes used to describe the flux J_i. When fluxes are referred to the ends of the specimen, interdiffusion coefficients are obtained. If the diffusion plane is the reference plane, however, the D_{ik} are intrinsic diffusion coefficients. The full intrinsic diffusion coefficient as defined in Eq. (1–18) is given by

$$D_i^I = D_{ii}^I + \sum_{k \neq i} D_{ik}^I \frac{(\partial c_k/\partial x)}{(\partial c_i/\partial x)} \qquad (1\text{–}32)$$

A similar equation can be written for the interdiffusion coefficient. For a binary system, where $\partial c_A/\partial x = -\partial c_B/\partial x$, we find $D_A^I = D_{AA}^I - D_{AB}^I$.

We shall not really concern ourselves with partial diffusion coefficients in the remainder of this book. In Chapter 6, however, the cross-terms in the general thermodynamic equations are discussed. These thermodynamic cross-terms are closely related to those in (1–31).

1–7. OTHER BASIC DIFFUSION EQUATIONS

In our discussions, we shall deal mainly with planar diffusion and hence with equations similar to (1–17). These equations can be related to diffusion with arbitrary forces and concentration gradients and in anisotropic media as follows:

Diffusion Tensor

If we define mutually perpendicular axes, x, y, and z with concentration gradients along each axis, the flux J_x along the x-axis is given by

$$J_x = -D_{xx}^*(\partial c/\partial x) - D_{xy}^*(\partial c/\partial y) - D_{xz}^*(\partial c/\partial z) + c\langle v_x\rangle_F \qquad (1\text{–}33)$$

Here cross-terms proportional to the y and z concentration gradients have been added to Eq. (1–17). [Also the subscript

i used to designate the particular atom species is omitted here, and in (1–17), to simplify the notation.] Equations similar to (1–33) can be written for J_y and J_z, so that, in general,

$$\mathbf{J} = -\mathbf{D}^* \nabla c + c\langle \mathbf{v} \rangle_F \tag{1–34}$$

where $\mathbf{D}^*$ is the diffusion tensor and $\mathbf{J}$, ∇c, and $\langle \mathbf{v} \rangle_F$ are vectors.

Inasmuch as the diffusion tensor is always symmetric, in general $D_{\mu\nu}^* = D_{\nu\mu}^*$. Consequently, principal axes can always be found. When $\mathbf{D}^*$ is referred to these axes, the nondiagonal elements $D_{\mu\nu}^*$ (where $\mu \neq \nu$) are zero. Studies of planar diffusion along these axes allow a complete specification of the diffusion tensor. Random-walk calculations of the diffusion tensor are discussed in Chapter 2.

Diffusion Coefficient for Planar Diffusion in an Arbitrary Direction

The diffusion coefficient for planar diffusion in a direction which makes angles α, β, and γ with the x, y, and z principal axes can be calculated as follows: If the concentration gradient in the diffusion direction is $\partial c/\partial \xi$, the corresponding gradients along the principal axes are $\cos\alpha(\partial c/\partial \xi)$, $\cos\beta(\partial c/\partial \xi)$, and $\cos\gamma(\partial c/\partial \xi)$. The resulting fluxes across planes normal to the principal axes are

$$J_x = -D_{xx}^* \cos\alpha(\partial c/\partial \xi) + c\langle v_x \rangle_F \tag{1–35}$$

$$J_y = -D_{yy}^* \cos\beta(\partial c/\partial \xi) + c\langle v_y \rangle_F \tag{1–36}$$

$$J_z = -D_{zz}^* \cos\gamma(\partial c/\partial \xi) + c\langle v_z \rangle_F \tag{1–37}$$

The flux J_ξ across a plane normal to the diffusion direction is given by

$$J_\xi = J_x \cos\alpha + J_y \cos\beta + J_z \cos\gamma \tag{1–38}$$

Thus,

$$J_\xi = -D^*(\partial c/\partial_\xi) + c\langle v_\xi\rangle_F \tag{1–39}$$

where

$$D^* = D_{xx}{}^* \cos^2\alpha + D_{yy}{}^* \cos^2\beta + D_{zz}{}^* \cos^2\gamma \tag{1–40}$$

and

$$\langle v_\xi\rangle_F = \langle v_x\rangle_F \cos\alpha + \langle v_y\rangle_F \cos\beta + \langle v_z\rangle_F \cos\gamma \tag{1–41}$$

Here D^* is the diffusion coefficient for planar diffusion in our arbitrary direction.

In special cases, (1–40) simplifies. For example, in cubic crystals, $D_{xx}{}^* = D_{yy}{}^* = D_{zz}{}^*$, while, in general, $\cos^2\alpha + \cos^2\beta + \cos^2\gamma$ equals unity. As a result, D^* in cubic crystals is the same for planar diffusion in any direction. In hexagonal and tetragonal crystals, $D_{xx}{}^* = D_{yy}{}^*$ for the two principal axes in the basal plane. Then

$$D^* = D_{xx}{}^* \sin^2\theta_z + D_{zz}{}^* \cos^2\theta_z \tag{1–42}$$

where θ_z is the angle between the diffusion direction and the nonbasal principal axis (which is normal to the basal plane).

Fick's Second Law

The three-dimensional continuity equation

$$\frac{\partial c}{\partial t} = -\nabla \cdot \mathbf{J} \tag{1–43}$$

states that the change of concentration in any volume equals the net flow into this volume (assuming no sources or sinks). For planar diffusion (1–43) reduces to

$$\frac{\partial c}{\partial t} = -\frac{\partial J}{\partial x} \tag{1–44}$$

Applying this relation to Eq. (1–16) yields

$$\frac{\partial c}{\partial t} = \frac{\partial}{\partial x}\left(D \frac{\partial c}{\partial x}\right) \tag{1–45}$$

This is called Fick's Second Law. If D is independent of x,

$$\frac{\partial c}{\partial t} = D \frac{\partial^2 c}{\partial x^2} \tag{1–46}$$

The three-dimensional equation corresponding to (1–45) is

$$\frac{\partial c}{\partial t} = \nabla \cdot (\mathbf{D} \nabla c) \tag{1–47}$$

If diffusion is isotropic (so that $\mathbf{D}$ reduces to a scalar) and in addition $\mathbf{D}$ is independent of position, (1–47) becomes

$$\frac{\partial c}{\partial t} = D \nabla^2 c \tag{1–48}$$

This is the three-dimensional form of Eq. (1–46).

Other useful equations can be found directly from Eq. (1–17). Applying (1–44) to Eq. (1–17) gives

$$\frac{\partial c}{\partial t} = \frac{\partial}{\partial x}\left(D^* \frac{\partial c}{\partial x}\right) - c\,\frac{\partial \langle v_x \rangle_F}{\partial x} - \langle v_x \rangle_F \frac{\partial c}{\partial x} \tag{1–49}$$

When $\langle v_x \rangle_F$ is zero, this reduces to Fick's Second Law but with D specifically equal to D^*. The direct derivation of (1–45) from (1–16) allows D to represent any species of diffusion coefficient, i.e., tracer diffusion coefficient, intrinsic diffusion coefficient, or interdiffusion coefficient, depending on the physical condition of the experiment. Equation (1–49), however, is more limited.

If D^* and $\langle v_x \rangle_F$ are constants, but $\langle v_x \rangle_F \neq 0$, (1–49) becomes

$$\frac{\partial c}{\partial t} = D^* \frac{\partial^2 c}{\partial x^2} - \langle v_x \rangle_F \frac{\partial c}{\partial x} \tag{1–50}$$

1–8. SOLUTION OF DIFFUSION EQUATIONS FOR $c(x, t)$

The equations above can be solved[4] to give concentrations c as a function of x and t. When the initial distribution of the diffusing species at time $t = 0$ can be represented by a delta function at position $x = 0$, Eq. (1–46) when solved for $c(x, t)$ yields

$$c = \frac{S_0}{2(\pi D t)^{1/2}} \exp(-x^2/4Dt) \tag{1–51}$$

where S_0 is the original concentration per unit area at the plane $x = 0$. For diffusion in a driving force, solution of (1–50) with the same initial planar distribution gives

$$c = \frac{S_0}{2(\pi D^* t)^{1/2}} \exp[-(x - \langle v_x \rangle_F t)^2/4D^*t] \tag{1–52}$$

When the concentration at $t = 0$ is c_L for $x < 0$ and c_R for $x > 0$, it follows from (1–46) that

$$c = \left[\frac{c_L + c_R}{2} - \frac{c_L - c_R}{2} \operatorname{erf}(x/\sqrt{\pi D t})\right] \tag{1–53}$$

For diffusion in a driving force, solving (1–50) for these initial conditions leads to an equation similar to (1–53) but with x replaced by $(x - \langle v_x \rangle_F t)$ and D specifically equal to D^*.

In three-dimensions with an initial line source having L_0 atoms per unit length along the line $x = y = 0$, solution of

(1–48) gives

$$c = \frac{L_0}{4\pi Dt} \exp(-r^2/4Dt) \tag{1–54}$$

where $r^2 = x^2 + y^2$, and r is the distance from the line source at $x = y = 0$. For an initial point source of I_0 atoms at the origin, (1–48) yields

$$c = \frac{I_0}{8(\pi Dt)^{3/2}} \exp(-R^2/4Dt) \tag{1–55}$$

where $R^2 = x^2 + y^2 + z^2$, and R is the distance from the origin.

1–9. DEPENDENCE OF THE TRACER DIFFUSION COEFFICIENT ON TEMPERATURE AND PRESSURE

Over a wide range of temperatures, experimentally measured diffusion coefficients often fit a relation

$$D = D_o \exp(-Q/kT) \tag{1–56}$$

where both Q and the pre-exponential factor D_o are independent of temperature. Q and D_o depend on the identity of the diffusing element and the composition of the matrix crystal. Also, external forces and pressure can affect Q and D_o. Equation (1–56) is called the Arrhenius equation for diffusion. It applies best if D is the measured *tracer* diffusion coefficient D^*. Some published values of Q and D_o for tracer diffusion are listed in Table 1–1.

The exponential dependence of D^* on temperature follows naturally from kinetic theory. On an atomic scale, D^* is proportional to the atom jump frequency ν, which according to Eq. (1–8b) depends exponentially on temperature. In cubic crystals with a single diffusion mechanism, kinetic theory yields for the tracer diffusion coefficient D^*,

$$D^* = \tfrac{1}{6}\lambda^2 \nu f \tag{1–57}$$

where λ is the jump distance and f the correlation factor. [For example, see Eq. (3–2).] Then, for cubic crystals, (1–8b) yields

$$D^* = \tfrac{1}{6}\lambda^2 \nu_o f \exp(-E/kT) \tag{1–58}$$

By definition, the experimental quantity Q is given by

$$Q = -k[\partial \ln D/\partial(1/T)] \tag{1–59}$$

and is called the experimental activation energy. If λ, ν_o, and f are temperature independent (which should be a good approximation for self-diffusion) and there is only a single diffusion mechanism operating, $Q = E$ and $D_o = \tfrac{1}{6}\lambda^2\nu_o f$. For impurity diffusion, Q may differ appreciably from E. [For example, see Eq. (3–112).] Then, the experimental D_o values will differ appreciably from $\tfrac{1}{6}\lambda^2\nu_o f$.

Experiments also show that the tracer diffusion coefficient depends exponentially on pressure. According to thermodynamic theory,

$$\left(\frac{\partial G}{\partial P}\right)_T = V \tag{1–60}$$

where G is the Gibbs free energy of the system, P is the pressure, and V is the volume. It then follows from Eq. (1–1) that

$$-kT\left(\frac{\partial \ln n}{\partial P}\right)_T = \Delta V_f \tag{1–61}$$

where ΔV_f is the increase in volume of the crystal resulting from the introduction of an imperfection. From Eq. (1–4),

$$-kT\left[\frac{\partial \ln (w/w_o')}{\partial P}\right]_T = \Delta V_m \tag{1–62}$$

TABLE 1–1. SOME REPRESENTATIVE TRACER DIFFUSION COEFFICIENTS

(All values in this list were measured by radioactive tracer sectioning techniques)

Solvent	*Tracer*	*Temperature Range (°C)*	*Activation Energy Q (kcal/mole)*	*Frequency Factor D_o (cm²/sec)*	*Ref.*
SELF-DIFFUSION					
Antimony					
⊥ to trigonal axis	Sb^{124}	480–600	44.4	17.	*a*
‖ to trigonal axis	Sb^{124}	500–620	47.1	22.	*a*
Cadmium					
⊥ to *c*-axis	Cd^{115}	130–270	19.1	0.10	*b*
‖ to *c*-axis	Cd^{115}	130–270	18.2	0.05	*b*
Palladium	Pd^{103}	1057–1503	63.6	0.205	*c*
Phosphorus	P^{32}	0–30	9.4	1.07×10^{-3}	*d*
Platinum	$Pt^{195,199}$	1325–1600	68.1	0.33	*e*
Silver	Ag^{110}	630–935	44.09	0.40	*f*
Sodium	Na^{22}	0–94	10.45	0.242	*g*

TABLE 1–1. SOME REPRESENTATIVE TRACER DIFFUSION COEFFICIENTS—*Continued*

Solvent	*Tracer*	*Temperature Range (°C)*	*Activation Energy Q (kcal/mole)*	*Frequency Factor D_o (cm²/sec)*	*Ref.*
α-Thallium					
⊥ to *c*-axis	Tl^{204}	150–230	22.6	0.4	*h*
‖ to *c*-axis	Tl^{204}	150–230	22.9	0.4	*h*
β-Thallium	Tl^{204}	230–275	20.0	0.7	*h*
Tungsten	W^{185}	2660–3230	153.1	42.8	*i*
AgCl (pure)	Ag^{110}	160–350	20.5	1.46	*k*
AgCl (pure)	Cl^{36}	330–440	37.0	133.	*k*
IMPURITY DIFFUSION					
Silver	$Ru^{103,106}$	793–945	65.8	180.	*l*
Silver	Pd^{103}	736–939	56.75	9.57	*m*
Silver	Cd^{115}	592–937	41.7	0.44	*n*
Silver	In^{114}	613–936	40.6	0.41	*n*
Silver	Sn^{113}	592–937	39.3	0.25	*n*
Silver	Sb^{124}	468–942	38.32	0.169	*o*

Diffusion in Homogeneous Alloys

90.5% Ag–9.5% Al	Ag^{110}	700–800	42.9	0.83	*p*
99.1% Ag–0.9% Sb	Ag^{110}	569–890	42.6	0.30	*q*
93.5% Ag–6.5% Cd	Ag^{110}	571–908	42.6	0.31	*r*
93.5% Ag–6.5% Cd	$Cd^{115,109}$	571–922	40.5	0.33	*r*
72.0% Ag–28.0% Cd	Ag^{110}	505–740	37.3	0.16	*r*
72.5% Ag–27.5% Cd	$Cd^{115,109}$	526–795	36.0	0.25	*r*
98.2% Ag–1.8% Cu	Ag^{110}	700–850	44.8	0.66	*p*

[a] H. B. Huntington, P. B. Ghate, and J. H. Rosolowski, *J. Appl. Phys.* **35,** 3027 (1964).
[b] E. S. Wajda, G. A. Shirn, and H. B. Huntington, *Acta Met.* **3,** 39 (1955).
[c] N. L. Peterson, *Phys. Rev.* **136,** A568 (1964).
[d] N. H. Nachtrieb and G. S. Handler, *J. Chem. Phys.* **23,** 1187 (1955).
[e] G. V. Kidson and R. Ross, *Proc. First UNESCO Int. Conf. Radioisotopes in Scientific Research,* edited by R. C. Extermann (Pergamon Press, London, 1958), Vol. I, p. 185.
[f] C. T. Tomizuka and E. Sonder, *Phys. Rev.* **103,** 1182 (1956).
[g] N. H. Nachtrieb, E. Catalano, and J. A. Weil, *J. Chem. Phys.* **20,** 1185 (1952).
[h] G. A. Shirn, *Acta Met.* **3,** 87 (1955).
[i] R. L. Andelin, J. D. Knight, and M. Kahn, *Trans. Met. Soc. AIME* **233,** 19 (1965).
[k] W. D. Compton and R. J. Maurer, *J. Phys. Chem. Solids* **1,** 191 (1956).
[l] C. B. Pierce and D. Lazarus, *Phys. Rev.* **114,** 686 (1959).
[m] N. L. Peterson, *Phys. Rev.* **132,** 2471 (1963).
[n] C. T. Tomizuka and L. Slifkin, *Phys. Rev.* **96,** 610 (1954).
[o] E. Sonder, L. Slifkin, and C. T. Tomizuka, *Phys. Rev.* **93,** 970 (1954).
[p] R. E. Hoffman, D. Turnbull, and E. W. Hart, *Acta Met.* **3,** 417 (1955).
[q] A. H. Schoen, Thesis, University of Illinois, 1958 (unpublished).
[r] E. Sonder, *Phys. Rev.* **100,** 1662 (1955).

where ΔV_m is the increase in volume of the crystal resulting when an atom moves from an equilibrium site to a saddle point. Then, with $D^* = \frac{1}{6}\lambda^2\nu f$, one finds from (1–8a) for cubic crystals,

$$\Delta V = -kT\left[\frac{\partial \ln D^*}{\partial P}\right]_T + kT\left[\frac{\partial \ln (\lambda^2 w_o' f)}{\partial P}\right]_T \qquad (1\text{–}63)$$

Here,

$$\Delta V = \Delta V_m + \Delta V_f \qquad (1\text{–}64)$$

ΔV is called the activation volume, ΔV_m the activation volume for motion, and ΔV_f the activation volume for formation. If the second term on the right in (1–63) is small or corrections can be applied for it, measurements of D^* as a function of pressure at constant temperature yield ΔV.[5] Some published values of ΔV are listed in Table 1–2.

TABLE 1–2. ACTIVATION VOLUMES FOR SELF-DIFFUSION
(Radioactive tracer measurements)

Tracer	*Solvent*	ΔV *measured* *(cm³/mole)*	*Molar volume* *(cm³/mole)*	*Ref.*
Ag^{110}	Ag	9.2	10.3	*a*
Au^{198}	Au	7.2	10.2	*b*
Na^{22}	Na	12.4	24.	*c*
P^{32}	P	30.	68.	*d*
Pb^{210}	Pb	13.0	18.2	*e*
Br^{82}	AgBr	$\approx$44.	20. (vol. Br)	*f*

[a] C. T. Tomizuka, "Progress in Very High Pressure Research," edited by F. Bundy *et al.* (John Wiley and Sons, Inc., New York, 1961), p. 266.

[b] R. H. Dickerson, R. C. Lowell, and C. T. Tomizuka, *Phys. Rev.* **137,** A613 (1965).

[c] N. H. Nachtrieb, J. A. Weil, E. Catalono, and A. W. Lawson, *J. Chem. Phys.* **20,** 1189 (1952).

[d] N. H. Nachtrieb and A. W. Lawson, *J. Chem. Phys.* **23,** 1193 (1955).

[e] N. H. Nachtrieb, H. A. Resing, and S. A. Rice, *J. Chem. Phys.* **31,** 135 (1959).

[f] D. S. Tannhauser, *J. Phys. Chem. Solids* **5,** 224 (1958).

The preceding discussion has been based on Eqs. (1–1) to (1–9) obtained from simple reaction rate theory. More complex equations may be necessary to provide accurate theoretical expressions for the jump frequencies.[2] Still, the major features of an activation energy and a pre-exponential factor always appear. Since the present discussion is designed mainly to provide background for the kinetic theory in the following chapters, the calculation of jump frequencies from first principles will not be discussed further here.

REFERENCES

1. For further discussion of diffusion mechanisms, see, for example, L. A. Girifalco, "Atomic Migration in Crystals" (Blaisdell Publishing Co., New York, 1964); P. G. Shewmon, "Diffusion in Solids" (McGraw-Hill Book Co., New York, 1963).
2. Calculations of energies of motion and formation are discussed for example in the review articles: R. E. Howard and A. B. Lidiard, *Reports on Progress in Physics* **27,** 161 (1964); D. Lazarus, "Solid State Physics," Vol. 10, edited by F. Seitz and D. Turnbull (Academic Press, New York, 1960).
3. C. Wagner, *Z. physik. Chem.* **B11,** 139 (1930); W. Jost, "Diffusion in Solids, Liquids, and Gases" (Academic Press, New York, 1952), p. 146.
4. For a thorough discussion of mathematical solutions of diffusion equations, see J. Crank, "The Mathematics of Diffusion" (Oxford University Press, London, 1956).
5. See, for example, D. Lazarus and N. H. Nachtrieb, "Solids Under Pressure," edited by W. Paul and D. M. Warschauer (McGraw-Hill Book Co., New York, 1963), p. 43.

2. RANDOM-WALK DIFFUSION

2-1. INTRODUCTION

An atom can make a series of jumps through a crystal by one of the mechanisms described in the previous chapter. If the jumps are at random with no preferred direction, each atom follows a *random walk*. Crystal diffusion provides a particularly simple application of the random walk since the regular crystal lattice allows jumps having only certain discrete directions and lengths. In fact, the important case of planar diffusion can often be described in terms of a one-dimensional random walk with a single jump distance. The random-walk equations apply directly to diffusion by an interstitial mechanism and, with suitable modifications, to diffusion by other mechanisms.

In the present chapter, the simple random walk and the random walk modified by a constant driving force are considered together since the treatments are very similar. It is assumed that the driving forces F and jump frequencies Γ_o are not functions of position or time. Effects from variations in these quantities are considered in later chapters.

Random-walk theory can be discussed from three independent viewpoints: (1) Fluxes and concentration changes at a plane can be calculated in terms of jumps from neighboring planes. (2) It can be assumed that atoms which start on a particular plane at a given time t are distributed through the crystal at time $t + \tau$ according to a unique function $W(X, \tau)$. For many purposes, this function does not need to be known explicitly. (3) $W(X, \tau)$ can be calculated explicitly if Γ_o and F are independent of position and time. Then, conclusions can be drawn from the specific form of this function.

These three approaches are considered separately in Sections 2–2, 2–3, and 2–4, respectively. The aim is a comprehensive review of random-walk diffusion equations.[1] To simplify the equations, extensions to three-dimensional diffusion are delayed until the one-dimensional case has been treated thoroughly.

2–2. EQUATIONS IN TERMS OF JUMPS FROM NEIGHBORING PLANES

Fick's First Law. Simple Cubic Structure

The atom flux J between two neighboring atom planes can be calculated quite directly from random-walk theory. This leads directly to Fick's First Law [Eq. (1–16)] and gives a simple atomistic expression for the diffusion coefficient.

The basic results are most easily shown for diffusion in a simple cubic structure with the concentration gradient along a ⟨100⟩ x-axis. We can consider two adjacent {100} lattice planes normal to this axis, as in Fig. 2–1, and calculate the atom flux

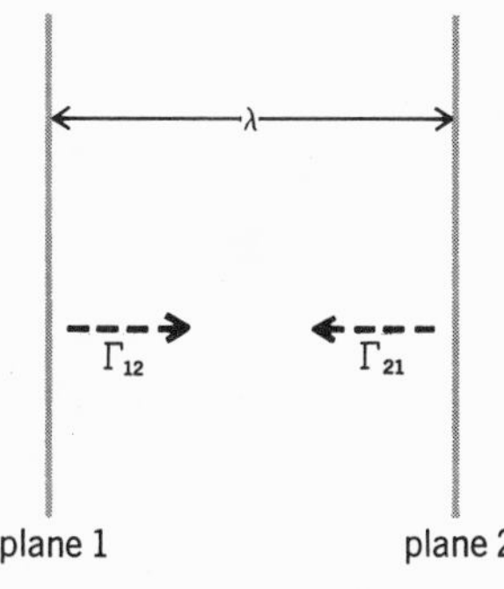

2–1 Neighboring lattice planes normal to the x-axis with jump frequencies Γ_{12} and Γ_{21}.

between these planes. The first plane contains n_1 atoms of the diffusing species per unit area, and the second plane contains n_2. If Γ_{12} is the jump frequency for atom jumps from a given site on plane 1 to the neighboring site on plane 2, the number of atoms per unit area per unit time which jump from plane 1 to plane 2 is $j_{12} = n_1\Gamma_{12}$. Similarly, the flux j_{21} of atoms jumping from plane 2 to plane 1 is given by $j_{21} = n_2\Gamma_{21}$, where Γ_{21} is the jump frequency for atom jumps from plane 2 to plane 1. The net atom flux J between these planes is

$$J = j_{12} - j_{21} = n_1\Gamma_{12} - n_2\Gamma_{21} \tag{2-1}$$

In the simplest case (simple random walk), the jump frequency does not depend on the direction of the jump. Then

$$J = (n_1 - n_2)\Gamma_o \tag{2-2}$$

where $\Gamma_o = \Gamma_{12} = \Gamma_{21}$.

The atom concentrations per unit area (n), which appear in Eq. (2–2), are related to concentrations per unit volume (c) by the equation $n = \lambda c$, where λ is the distance between neighboring planes. Also the concentration difference can be expressed in terms of λ and the concentration gradient. Thus,

$$n_1 - n_2 = -\lambda(\partial n/\partial x) = -\lambda^2(\partial c/\partial x) \tag{2-3}$$

Combining this with (2–2) gives

$$J = -\lambda^2\Gamma_o(\partial c/\partial x) \tag{2-4}$$

In a cubic lattice, all jumps to nearest neighbor sites are equally likely, and jumps to other sites are very unlikely. The total jump frequency ν therefore is given by

$$\nu = \Gamma_o z \tag{2-5}$$

where z is the number of nearest neighbors. In a simple cubic structure, $z = 6$, so (2–2) becomes

$$J = -\frac{1}{6}\lambda^2\nu\frac{\partial c}{\partial x} \tag{2–6}$$

This equation has the form of Fick's First Law [Eq. (1–16)] with $\frac{1}{6}\lambda^2\nu$ taking the place of the diffusion coefficient D. Therefore, one obtains the basic equation,

$$D = \tfrac{1}{6}\lambda^2\nu \tag{2–7}$$

which relates the macroscopic quantity D to the jump distance λ and jump frequency ν.

Here D specifically equals the tracer diffusion coefficient D^*, as described in Section 1–5. To simplify the notation, however, the asterisk is omitted both here and in other equations in this chapter. The "diffusion coefficient" D always equals the tracer coefficient.

In this derivation, diffusion in a given $\langle 100 \rangle$ direction was considered. Diffusion in cubic lattices is isotropic, however, and the diffusion coefficient is a scalar having the same value for all crystallographic directions. Therefore, (2–7) is valid regardless of crystal orientation.

Effect of a Driving Force

The preceding analysis can be modified to include the effect of a constant driving force. If the driving force is in the x-direction, (2–1) becomes

$$J = n_1\Gamma_+ - n_2\Gamma_- = \Gamma_o(n_1 - n_2) + \varepsilon\Gamma_o(n_1 + n_2) \tag{2–8}$$

Here Γ_+ and Γ_- are given by Eqs. (1–11) and (1–13). This then reduces to

$$J = -\lambda^2 \Gamma_o \frac{\partial c}{\partial x} + 2\varepsilon \Gamma_o c\lambda \tag{2-9}$$

where $c = \frac{1}{2}(n_1 + n_2)\lambda^{-1}$ is the concentration per unit volume. The term $-\lambda^2 \Gamma_o (\partial c/\partial x)$ is that found previously in (2–6). The additional term $2\varepsilon\Gamma_o c\lambda$ arises because of the driving force. Since this term is directly proportional to ε, it is directly proportional to the driving force. With (1–12), (2–5), and (2–7), this expression for J becomes

$$J = -D \frac{\partial c}{\partial x} + c \frac{DF}{kT} \tag{2-10}$$

Fick's Second Law

The rate of change of the concentration at plane 1 can be calculated by considering atoms which jump between plane 1 and the neighboring planes 0 and 2 to the left and right. Each atom which arrives at plane 1 adds one atom to the concentration on this plane and each atom that leaves substracts one. Thus the change in concentration Δn which occurs in time Δt is

$$\Delta n = \Delta t(\Gamma_{01} n_0 - \Gamma_{12} n_1 - \Gamma_{10} n_1 + \Gamma_{21} n_2) \tag{2-11}$$

$$\frac{\Delta n}{\Delta t} = \Gamma_+ (n_0 - n_1) - \Gamma_- (n_1 - n_2) \tag{2-12}$$

$$\frac{\Delta n}{\Delta t} = \Gamma_o (1 + \varepsilon) \left(-\lambda \frac{\partial n_-}{\partial x} \right) - \Gamma_o (1 - \varepsilon) \left(-\lambda \frac{\partial n_+}{\partial x} \right) \tag{2-13}$$

where $\partial n_- / \partial x$ is the concentration gradient between planes 0 and 1, and $\partial n_+ / \partial x$ is the concentration gradient between planes 1 and 2. Then

$$\frac{\Delta n}{\Delta t} = \Gamma_o \lambda \left(\frac{\partial n_+}{\partial x} - \frac{\partial n_-}{\partial x} \right) - \Gamma_o \varepsilon \lambda \left(\frac{\partial n_+}{\partial x} + \frac{\partial n_-}{\partial x} \right) \tag{2-14}$$

and, in the limit where Δt goes to zero,

$$\frac{\partial n}{\partial t} = \Gamma_o \lambda^2 \frac{\partial^2 n}{\partial x^2} - 2\, \Gamma_o \varepsilon \lambda \frac{\partial n}{\partial x} \tag{2–15}$$

where in terms of n and λ,

$$\partial^2 n/\partial x^2 = (n_2 - 2n_1 + n_0)\lambda^{-2} \tag{2–16}$$

$$\partial n/\partial x = \tfrac{1}{2}(n_2 - n_0)\lambda^{-1} \tag{2–17}$$

Finally, with $c = n\lambda^{-1}$ and Eqs. (1–12), (2–5), and (2–7) relating Γ_o and ε to D and F,

$$\frac{\partial c}{\partial t} = D \frac{\partial^2 c}{\partial x^2} - \frac{DF}{kT} \frac{\partial c}{\partial x} \tag{2–18}$$

where all quantities refer to values at plane 1. The second term on the right arises because of the driving force. In the absence of a driving force, this term equals zero and the result is Fick's Second Law with a constant diffusion coefficient [Eq. (1–46)].

It should be noted that the quantities $\partial n/\partial x$ and $\partial^2 n/\partial x^2$ which are defined in (2–16) and (2–17) are really first and second differences rather than first and second derivatives. Moreover, they are meaningfully defined only at discrete planes. However, if a continuum description of the crystal is adopted, these first and second differences become the corresponding partial derivatives. A similar problem does not arise in converting $\Delta n/\Delta t$ to $\partial n/\partial t$ since time is considered naturally continuous.

Alternate Calculation of Fick's First Law

In the preceding discussion, Fick's First Law was found by calculating the flux of atoms passing from plane 1 to plane 2. This equals the flux associated with the region between these planes. It is also possible to calculate the flux of atoms at the position of plane 1 itself. Each atom arriving at plane 1 contributes half an atom to the atom flux and each atom leaving plane 1 contributes half an atom. Thus, if plane 1 is a (100) plane in a simple cubic structure,

$$J = \tfrac{1}{2}(\Gamma_{01}n_0 + \Gamma_{12}n_1 - \Gamma_{10}n_1 - \Gamma_{21}n_2) \qquad (2\text{–}19)$$

The same quantities appear in this equation as in (2–11), but they appear with different signs. Equation (2–9) is obtained by combining these terms to first order.

Alternate Calculation of Fick's Second Law

The concentration in the region between plane 1 and 2 can be given physical meaning by defining it in terms of actual concentrations on planes 1 and 2,

$$c = \tfrac{1}{2}(n_1 + n_2)\lambda^{-1} \qquad (2\text{–}20)$$

Then Fick's Second Law can be found by calculating the time derivative of this concentration. We find

$$\frac{\partial c}{\partial t} = (J_1 - J_2)\lambda^{-1} \qquad (2\text{–}21)$$

where J_1 and J_2 are the fluxes at planes 1 and 2. Substituting values of J from (2–10) leads directly to Fick's Second Law (with constant driving force). Here it is assumed that c and $\partial c/\partial x$ are the only quantities which vary with position.

Both J and $\partial c/\partial t$ can thus be determined either at a lattice plane or between adjacent planes with comparable results.

Diffusion Coefficient in Other Structures

The discussion above is in terms of a one-dimensional random walk with a single jump distance. This applies in particular to diffusion along ⟨100⟩ directions in simple cubic crystals. The method can be extended to other structures and crystal orientations by allowing for jumps which lie at an angle to the diffusion direction. Jumps at different angles to the diffusion direction have different x-components and therefore contribute different amounts to the diffusion flux. For cubic structures with only nearest neighbor jumps allowed, these effects are easily taken into account. Then Eqs. (2–10) and (2–18) are again found with

$$D = \frac{1}{2}\Gamma_o\lambda^2 \sum_{j=1}^{z} \cos^2\varphi_j \tag{2–22}$$

Here the sum is over all nearest neighbors, φ_j is the angle between the x-axis and the jump vector for a jump to site j, and λ is the jump distance. For cubic structures, the summation over $\cos^2\varphi_j$ equals $\frac{1}{3}z$. Thus, it follows in general for these structures that

$$D = \tfrac{1}{6}\lambda^2\nu \tag{2–23}$$

where $\nu = \Gamma_o z$. In the face-centered cubic, body-centered cubic, and simple cubic structures, one also finds

$$D = s^2\Gamma_o \tag{2–24}$$

where s is the edge length of the unit cube. In the diamond structure, however (where there are two atom sites associated with each lattice point in the face-centered cubic space lattice), $D = \frac{1}{8}s^2\Gamma_o$. A very general derivation of (2–22) and corresponding expression for noncubic crystals are given in Section 2–3.

2–3. APPROACH ASSUMING A UNIQUE $W(X, \tau)$

Einstein Equation

Kinetic expressions for the diffusion coefficient can also be found by considering the density function $W(X, \tau)$. This function gives the probability that an atom which was at a position x at time t will be at $x + X$ at $t + \tau$. For the present, we shall assume that $W(X, \tau)$ does not depend on x or t. This restricts the analysis to homogeneous systems where the diffusion coefficients and any driving forces (such as electric fields) do not depend on position or change with time. The function $c(x, t + \tau)$ gives the concentration of diffusing species as a function of x at time $t + \tau$. This can be expressed in terms of $W(X, \tau)$ and the concentration function $c(x - X, t)$ at the earlier time t,

$$c(x, t + \tau) = \sum_{\text{all } X} c(x - X, t) W(X, \tau) \tag{2–25}$$

In this equation, the concentration at each position $x - X$ is multiplied by the probability $W(X, \tau)$ of displacement to position x, and the result is summed over all values of X. The rate at which the concentration is changing can be found by expanding $c(x, t + \tau)$ and $c(x - X, t)$ around $X = 0$, $\tau = 0$,

$$c(x, t) + \tau \frac{\partial c}{\partial t} + \cdots$$

$$= \sum_{\text{all } X} \left\{ c(x, t) - X \frac{\partial c}{\partial x} + \frac{X^2}{2} \frac{\partial^2 c}{\partial x^2} + \cdots \right\} W(X, \tau) \tag{2–26}$$

At time τ each atom must be at some position X so, by definition, the sum of the probabilities $W(X, \tau)$ over all X must equal unity. Thus,

$$\sum_{\text{all } X} W(X, \tau) = 1 \tag{2–27}$$

$$\sum_{\text{all } X} X^m W(X, \tau) = \langle X^m \rangle \tag{2–28}$$

Here the $\langle\rangle$ indicate an average over a large number of atoms. In particular, we shall be interested in the mean atom displacement $\langle X \rangle$ and the mean square atom displacement $\langle X^2 \rangle$ in time τ.

The derivatives $\partial c/\partial t$, $\partial c/\partial x$, $\partial^2 c/\partial x^2 \cdots$ have fixed values for the time t and the point x. In the limit where τ becomes very small, the higher order terms indicated by the dots on the left-hand side in (2–26) thus become negligible. Because of the nature of diffusion processes, the function $W(X, \tau)$ becomes more and more localized at $X = 0$ when τ becomes small. Therefore, for τ sufficiently small, the higher order terms indicated by the dots on the right-hand side of (2–26) become negligible. The terms $c(x, t)$ cancel, and the remaining terms give

$$\frac{\partial c}{\partial t} = -\frac{\langle X \rangle}{\tau}\frac{\partial c}{\partial x} + \frac{\langle X^2 \rangle}{2\tau}\frac{\partial^2 c}{\partial x^2} \tag{2–29}$$

For a simple random walk $\langle X \rangle = 0$, and

$$\frac{\partial c}{\partial t} = \frac{\langle X^2 \rangle}{2\tau}\frac{\partial^2 c}{\partial x^2} \tag{2–30}$$

In these equations, we have assumed that the diffusion coefficient and driving forces are constant. Similar equations allowing for variable diffusion coefficients and driving forces are given in Chapter 5.

Equation (2–30) has the form of Fick's Second Law [Eq. (1–46)] with $\langle X^2 \rangle/2\tau$ taking the place of the diffusion coefficient D. This leads to the basic Einstein equation,[2]

$$D = \lim_{\tau \text{ small}} \frac{\langle X^2 \rangle}{2\tau} \tag{2–31}$$

The derivation above is very general and $W(X, \tau)$ does not need to refer to a random walk. Thus, Eq. (2–31) is valid even for nonrandom-walk diffusion.

In the absence of driving forces, $\langle X^2 \rangle / 2\tau$ for a random walk does not depend on τ; therefore in this case the limit notation in (2–31) can be omitted. With driving forces present, however, the restriction on τ is important.

Kinetic Evaluation of $\langle X^2 \rangle$

Equation (2–31) can be evaluated to give a kinetic expression for D in terms of atom jump frequencies. The atom displacement X along the x-axis from a series of n elementary jumps is

$$X = x_1 + x_2 + x_3 + \cdots + x_n \tag{2–32}$$

where $x_1, x_2, \cdots, x_n$ are the displacements from the individual jumps 1 to n. It then follows that

$$X^2 = (x_1 + x_2 + x_3 + \cdots + x_n)^2 \tag{2–33}$$

$$X^2 = \sum_{\gamma=1}^{n} x_\gamma^2 + 2 \sum_{\gamma=1}^{n-1} \sum_{\delta=\gamma+1}^{n} x_\gamma x_\delta \tag{2–34}$$

To find the *mean* square displacement $\langle X^2 \rangle$, one must average X^2 over many series of jumps. Each jump in a random walk is independent of the others and has an equal probability of being in the positive or negative x-direction. As a result, the $x_\gamma x_\delta$ terms are equally likely to be positive or negative and, when averaged over many series of jumps, the contribution to $\langle X^2 \rangle$ from these terms goes to zero. For a true random walk, one thus obtains the simple expression,

$$\langle X^2 \rangle = \sum_{\gamma=1}^{n} \langle x_\gamma^2 \rangle \tag{2–35}$$

In many important diffusion situations, the atoms do not follow a true random walk. Then the contribution to $\langle X^2 \rangle$

from the $x_\gamma x_\delta$ terms does not go to zero. This is discussed in Chapter 3 on correlation factors and also in the section below on the effect of driving forces. At present, however, we limit ourselves to discussing Eq. (2–35).

If an atom can jump only to certain neighboring sites, for example to the z nearest neighbor lattice sites, (2–35) simplifies to

$$\langle X^2 \rangle = \langle \sum_{j=1}^{z} n_j x_j^2 \rangle \tag{2–36}$$

where n_j is the number of jumps in the direction of the jth nearest neighbor, x_j is the x-displacement for such a jump, and the summation is over all nearest neighbor sites. The summation and averaging processes in (2–36) can be interchanged. Also $\langle n_j x_j^2 \rangle = x_j^2 \langle n_j \rangle$ since, for a given j, there is only one value of x_j. From the definition of the frequency Γ_j,

$$\Gamma_j = \langle n_j \rangle / \tau \tag{2–37}$$

and thus

$$\langle X^2 \rangle = \tau \sum_{j=1}^{z} \Gamma_j x_j^2 \tag{2–38}$$

When this is substituted into Eq. (2–31) for D, one finds the very useful equation,

$$D = \frac{1}{2} \sum_{j=1}^{z} \Gamma_j x_j^2 \tag{2–39}$$

Here the requirement that τ is small has been omitted since none of the quantities in (2–39) depends on τ.

Equation (2–39) was derived for one-dimensional diffusion, where the only concentration gradient is that along the x-axis. However, for diffusion in cubic crystals or along principal axes in noncubic crystals, this equation is valid whatever the concentration gradients. For all crystals, this equation reduces to Eq. (2–22). A few examples will illustrate the use of Eq. (2–39).

Simple Cubic Structure

For a simple cubic structure with the x-axis in a $\langle 100 \rangle$ direction, (2–39) becomes

$$D = \tfrac{1}{2}[\Gamma_{100}(\lambda)^2 + (\Gamma_{010} + \Gamma_{001} + \Gamma_{00\bar{1}} + \Gamma_{0\bar{1}0})(0) + \Gamma_{\bar{1}00}(-\lambda)^2] \tag{2–40}$$

Here λ is the jump distance and the subscripts on Γ designate the coordinates of the neighboring sites to which the atom at (000) can jump. In each case the Γ_j are multiplied by the square of the x-displacement resulting from the jump. In a random walk, all nearest neighbor jumps are equally likely, so that $\Gamma_{100} = \Gamma_{\bar{1}00} = \Gamma_o$ and

$$D = \tfrac{1}{2}[\Gamma_o\lambda^2 + \Gamma_o(-\lambda)^2] = \Gamma_o\lambda^2 = \tfrac{1}{6}\lambda^2\nu \tag{2–41}$$

Hexagonal Close-Packed Structure

In the hexagonal close-packed structure, principal axes are the c-axis normal to the basal plane and the a-axes parallel to the basal plane. For diffusion along the c-axis, (2–39) gives

$$D_c = \frac{1}{2}\left[6\Gamma_n\left(\frac{c}{2}\right)^2 + 6\Gamma_b(0)\right] = \tfrac{3}{4}\Gamma_n c^2 \tag{2–42}$$

Here c is the height of the unit hexagonal prism, Γ_b is the jump frequency to a site in the same basal plane, and Γ_n is the jump frequency to a site in a different basal plane. The Γ_n jumps have sizable components along the c-axes but are not completely parallel to this axis. The Γ_b jumps, on the other hand, are always normal to the c-axis. For diffusion in a close-packed basal direction, where a is the nearest neighbor distance,

$$D_a = \tfrac{1}{2}\Gamma_b\left[(a)^2 + 2\left(\frac{a}{2}\right)^2 + 2\left(-\frac{a}{2}\right)^2 + (-a)^2\right]$$

$$+ \tfrac{1}{2}\Gamma_n\left[2\left(\frac{a}{2}\right)^2 + 2(0) + 2\left(-\frac{a}{2}\right)^2\right] \quad (2\text{–}43)$$

$$D_a = \tfrac{3}{2}\Gamma_b a^2 + \tfrac{1}{2}\Gamma_n a^2 \quad (2\text{–}44)$$

This expression is valid for diffusion in any direction in the basal plane.

$\langle X \rangle$ in a Driving Force

For a one-dimensional walk, the average value of X after N jumps is given by

$$\langle X \rangle = Np\lambda - Nq\lambda \quad (2\text{–}45)$$

where p is the probability of a jump to the right and q is that to the left. In the absence of driving forces, p equals q and $\langle X \rangle$ equals zero. In a driving force, it follows from (1–12), (1–14), and (1–15) that

$$\langle X \rangle = N\varepsilon\lambda = FD\tau/kT \quad (2\text{–}46)$$

where $D = \tfrac{1}{2}N\lambda^2/\tau$. This expression for D follows from (2–39).
When jumps in three dimensions are allowed

$$\langle X \rangle = \langle \tau \sum_{j=1}^{z} \Gamma_j x_j \rangle \quad (2\text{–}47)$$

where Γ_j and x_j are the jump frequency and x-displacement for a jump to site j. The sum is over the z nearest neighbor sites. In a force F,

$$\Gamma_j = \Gamma_o{}^j(1 + \tfrac{1}{2}Fx_j/kT) \quad (2\text{–}48)$$

where Γ_o^j is the value of Γ_j in the absence of the force. Because of the symmetry in regular crystal structures, $\langle \sum \Gamma_o^j x_j \rangle$ equals zero when averaged over all sites which can be occupied by an atom. Thus,

$$\langle X \rangle = \frac{F\tau}{kT} \left\langle \frac{1}{2} \sum_{j=1}^{z} \Gamma_o^j x_j^2 \right\rangle \tag{2–49}$$

where the factor $\langle\rangle$ equals D as in (2–39). This is valid in general and agrees with (2–46).

$\langle X^2 \rangle$ in a Driving Force

$\langle X^2 \rangle$ in a driving force can be calculated by including the $x_\gamma x_\delta$ cross-terms in (2–34). The terms in this equation can be arranged in a square matrix having n terms to a side, with $x_\gamma x_\delta$ being the term in row γ, column δ. In the simple case of one-dimensional diffusion with constant jump distance, the diagonal terms in the matrix each equal λ^2 and give a contribution to $\langle X^2 \rangle$ of $N\lambda^2$. There are $N(N - 1)$ nondiagonal terms. The probability that a given one of these terms is positive equals $p^2 + q^2$, and the probability that it is negative equals $2pq$. Therefore, the contribution to $\langle X^2 \rangle$ from these terms is

$$\lambda^2 N(N - 1)(p^2 - 2pq + q^2) = \frac{N - 1}{N} \langle X \rangle^2 \tag{2–50}$$

and

$$\langle X^2 \rangle = N\lambda^2 + \frac{N - 1}{N} (\langle X \rangle)^2 \tag{2–51}$$

In the limit where τ goes to zero, the term involving $(\langle X \rangle)^2$ becomes negligible, so that in this limit $\langle X^2 \rangle$ is independent of driving forces. A more detailed analysis allowing for jumps having different x-components confirms this result. Therefore D as defined in Eq. (2–31) is not changed by driving forces. This result illustrates the importance of the limit on τ in (2–31).

When $\langle X \rangle$ equals zero, $\langle X^2 \rangle$ is proportional to the number of jumps N, which in turn is proportional to Dt. This gives the parabolic relation between displacement and time, which is typical of diffusion phenomena.

Higher Order Moments

$\langle X^3 \rangle$ can be calculated by much the same method as $\langle X^2 \rangle$. The matrix of terms in this case contains N^3 terms. There are N terms having the form x_γ^3, $3N(N-1)$ terms having the form $x_\gamma^2 x_\delta$ and $N(N-1)(N-2)$ terms having the form $x_\gamma x_\delta x_\epsilon$ with $\gamma \neq \delta \neq \varepsilon$. The contributions to $\langle X^3 \rangle$ from these terms are, respectively, $N(p-q)\lambda^3$, $3N(N-1)(p-q)\lambda^3$, and $N(N-1)(N-2)(p-q)^3\lambda^3$. When added, these terms give

$$\langle X^3 \rangle = (3 - 2N^{-1})[N\lambda(p-q)](N\lambda^2) + N(N-1)(N-2)(p-q)^3\lambda^3 \quad (2\text{–}52)$$

The same method of calculating moments can be applied to $\langle X^4 \rangle$, $\langle X^5 \rangle$, etc. These higher order moments all involve higher order multiples of $N\lambda^2$ and $N\lambda(p-q)$ and hence can all be expressed in terms of $\langle X \rangle$ and $\langle X^2 \rangle$. An alternate and perhaps simpler method of calculating these higher moments is given in Section 2–5.

Three-Dimensional Diffusion—Diffusion Tensor

In three dimensions, the Taylor expansion of the concentration about the point (x, y, z) is, to second order,

$$c(x+X, y+Y, z+Z, t) = c(x, y, z, t) + \sum_\mu \mu \frac{\partial c}{\partial \mu} + \frac{1}{2} \sum_\mu \sum_\nu \mu\nu \frac{\partial^2 c}{\partial \mu \partial \nu} \quad (2\text{–}53)$$

where μ, ν refer to the displacements X, Y, and Z or to the corresponding coordinates x, y, and z, as appropriate. When this expression is substituted into the three-dimensional form of (2–25) and higher order terms are made negligible by allowing τ to become small, one finds by the same method as that leading to Eq. (2–29) that

$$\frac{\partial c}{\partial t} = -\sum_{\mu} \frac{\langle \mu \rangle}{\tau} \frac{\partial c}{\partial \mu} + \sum_{\mu} \sum_{\nu} D_{\mu\nu} \frac{\partial^2 c}{\partial \mu \partial \nu} \qquad (2\text{–}54)$$

where

$$D_{\mu\nu} = \lim_{\tau \text{ small}} \frac{\langle \mu\nu \rangle}{2\tau} \qquad (2\text{–}55)$$

Equation (2–55) is a general expression giving all nine components of the diffusion tensor. In all cases, $D_{\mu\nu} = D_{\nu\mu}$, so the diffusion tensor is always symmetric.

In three dimensions, with the diffusion tensor in general not diagonalized,

$$\langle \mu \rangle = \sum_{\nu} D_{\mu\nu} F_{\nu} \tau / kT \qquad (2\text{–}56)$$

where F_{ν} is the component of the driving force along the ν-axis. Then (2–54) becomes

$$\frac{\partial c}{\partial t} = -\sum_{\mu} \sum_{\nu} \left[\frac{D_{\mu\nu} F_{\nu}}{kT} \frac{\partial c}{\partial \mu} - D_{\mu\nu} \frac{\partial^2 c}{\partial \mu \partial \nu} \right] \qquad (2\text{–}57)$$

In the present chapter we assume that $D_{\mu\nu}$, the temperature T, and the driving force F_{ν} are independent of position. Thus they can be moved inside the partial derivatives with respect to μ. Also, inasmuch as the continuity equation states $\partial c/\partial t = -\sum_{\mu} (\partial J/\partial \mu)$,

$$J_{\mu} = \sum_{\nu} \left[\frac{D_{\mu\nu} F_{\nu} c}{kT} - D_{\mu\nu} \frac{\partial c}{\partial \nu} \right] \qquad (2\text{–}58)$$

The nondiagonal elements in the diffusion tensor can be

made to vanish by choosing the x-, y-, z-axes to be principal axes. Then the diagonal elements equal the diffusion coefficients along these principal axes. In general, $\langle X^2 \rangle \neq \langle Y^2 \rangle \neq \langle Z^2 \rangle$, and thus the diffusion coefficient can have a different value along each principal axis.

In the absence of driving forces, $W(X, Y, Z, \tau)$ has the same symmetry as that of the crystal. The symmetry properties of the crystal thus can be used to help determine principal axes for the diffusion tensor. For example, if there is mirror symmetry across the planes $X = 0$, $Y = 0$, $Z = 0$, all three cross-terms $\langle XY \rangle$, $\langle YZ \rangle$, and $\langle XZ \rangle$ are zero. Then the x, y, and z axes can all serve as principal axes. If there is mirror symmetry across the plane $X = 0$, the cross-terms $\langle XY \rangle$ and $\langle XZ \rangle$ are zero and the x-axis is a principal axis.

In cubic crystals, any set of three mutually perpendicular axes can serve as principal axes. Also it is always true that $\langle X^2 \rangle = \langle Y^2 \rangle = \langle Z^2 \rangle$ in cubic crystals, and Eq. (2–58) becomes (in vector notation)

$$\mathbf{J} = -D\nabla c + \mathbf{F}Dc/kT \tag{2–59}$$

Here

$$D = \lim_{\tau \text{ small}} \frac{\langle R^2 \rangle}{6\tau} \tag{2–60}$$

where $\langle R^2 \rangle = \langle X^2 + Y^2 + Z^2 \rangle = 3\langle X^2 \rangle$. Diffusion is isotropic in this case and the diffusion tensor reduces to a single scalar diffusion coefficient.

2–4. EXPLICIT EXPRESSION FOR $W(X, \tau)$

Random-Walk Density Function

Random-walk analysis can lead to a specific expression for the density function $W(X, \tau)$. For one-dimensional diffusion, we can assume that the atom starts at the origin and proceeds to make random jumps of length λ backward and forward along the x-axis. If the atom makes n_R positive jumps and n_L negative jumps, the total number of jumps N equals $n_R + n_L$, and the net jump displacement m equals $n_R - n_L$. Then

$$n_R = \tfrac{1}{2}(N + m) \tag{2–61}$$

$$n_L = \tfrac{1}{2}(N - m) \tag{2–62}$$

Also, if N is even, m must be even; and if N is odd, m must be odd.

We can define $W(m, N)$ as the probability that the atom has a net displacement m after N jumps. Of all possible jump sequences involving N jumps, the number which contain n_R positive jumps and n_L negative jumps equals $N!/n_R!n_L!$. This is the number of different ways in which N objects can be separated into two groups containing n_R and n_L objects, respectively. If the jumps are at random, each jump has probability one half of being in the positive x-direction and one half of being in the negative x-direction. Therefore, the probability that any one of these sequences will occur is $(\frac{1}{2})^N$, and

$$W(m, N) = \frac{N!}{[\frac{1}{2}(N + m)]![\frac{1}{2}(N - m)]!}\left(\frac{1}{2}\right)^N \tag{2–63}$$

This expression can be simplified by Stirling's approximation, which states for large n,

$$\ln n! = (n + \tfrac{1}{2}) \ln n + \tfrac{1}{2} \ln 2\pi - n + 0(n^{-1}) \tag{2–64}$$

If N is large and m much less than N, the factorials in (2–63) are given to very good accuracy even when the terms of order n^{-1} and higher in (2–64) are neglected. In the expression,

$$\ln\left(1 \pm \frac{m}{N}\right) = \pm \frac{m}{N} - \frac{m^2}{2N^2} \pm \frac{m^3}{3N^3} - \cdots \tag{2–65}$$

terms of order $(m/N)^3$ can be neglected if $N \gg m$. When these

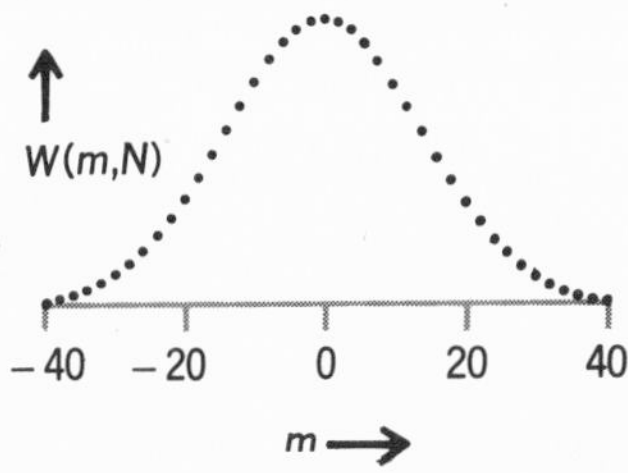

2–2 $W(m, N)$ as a function of m for $N = 200$ (see Eq. 2–67). Here m must be an even integer. Although m in this case may range from -200 to $+200$, $W(m, N)$ is very small except in the range from roughly -40 to $+40$.

relations are substituted into (2–63), one obtains

$$\ln W(m, N) = -\tfrac{1}{2}\ln N + \ln 2 - \tfrac{1}{2}\ln 2\pi - \frac{m^2}{2N} + \frac{m^2}{2N^2} + \cdots \tag{2–66}$$

and, neglecting all terms of order N^{-2} or higher,

$$W(m, N) = \left(\frac{2}{\pi N}\right)^{1/2} \exp\left(-\frac{m^2}{2N}\right) \tag{2–67}$$

In Fig. 2–2, $W(m, N)$ is shown as a function of m. Although $W(m, N)$ is a discontinuous function, the points in Fig. 2–2 form the outline of a smooth bell-shaped curve.

Density Function in Terms of the Continuous Variable x

Equation (2–67) is a reliable kinetic expression for $W(m, N)$ if N is large and m is much less than N. Often, however, it is more convenient to express the density function as a continuous function of x and t. Thus, we define $W(x, N)$ as a continuous function of x which is proportional to the discontinuous function $W(m, N)$ at all points $x = m\lambda$.

Since $W(m, N)$ is a probability, $\sum_m W(m, N)$ equals unity. Similarly, we wish to make $\int W(x, N)\,dx$ equal unity, so that $W(x, N)\,dx$ has the form of a probability. This is accomplished by letting the constant of proportionality between $W(x, N)$ and $W(m, N)$ equal $(2\lambda)^{-1}$, as can be verified by actually evaluating the integral.

Physically, if N is an even integer, m must also be even; and if N is an odd integer, m must be odd. Therefore, for a given value of N, only odd or only even values of m are allowed, and the distance between neighboring possible atom positions at a given time is always 2λ. Thus, to convert a probability $W(m, N)$ to a probability $W(x, N)\,dx$ covering the 2λ interval centered at $x = m\lambda$, it is reasonable to multiply $W(m, N)$ by dx and divide by 2λ.

By definition,

$$W(x, N) = (2\lambda)^{-1}W_c(m, N) \qquad (2\text{–}68)$$

where $W_c(m, N)$ is the continuous function obtained from (2–67) by replacing the discontinuous variable m by the continuous variable x/λ. This gives

$$W(x, N) = \left(\frac{1}{2\pi N\lambda^2}\right)^{1/2} \exp\left(-\frac{x^2}{2N\lambda^2}\right) \qquad (2\text{–}69)$$

The expressions for $W(x, N)$ and $W(m, N)$ are not identical, but they are very similar. The integral of $W(x, N)$ over an interval Δx does not in general equal the sum of $W(m, N)$ over this interval, even when Δx is a multiple of 2λ, since $W(x, N)$ is not a linear function of x. If N is large and $\Delta x \gg 2\lambda$, however, the fractional discrepancy between these two values is very small for ordinary values of x. The per cent error increases as x becomes large. However, the absolute magnitude of $W(x, N)$ is very small when x is large, and this large relative error usually is unimportant.

Diffusion Parameters and $W(x, t)$

If the atom makes ν_x jumps along the x-axis per unit time, the total number of jumps N is given by

$$N = \nu_x t \qquad (2\text{–}70)$$

where t is the time. Thus one finally obtains

$$W(x, t) = \frac{1}{2(\pi Dt)^{1/2}} \exp\left(-\frac{x^2}{4Dt}\right) \tag{2–71}$$

with

$$D = \tfrac{1}{2}\lambda^2 \nu_x \tag{2–72}$$

Since x and t are the distance and time as measured from the original starting position of the atom at $x = 0$ and starting time for diffusion at $t = 0$, they are equivalent to X and τ in Section 2–3. Thus, (2–71) with x and t replaced by X and τ gives the function $W(X, \tau)$ discussed in Section 2–3.

In a three-dimensional random walk along three mutually perpendicular x-, y-, z-axes, an atom is equally likely to jump in the x-, y-, or z-direction. Then, the total jump frequency ν equals $3\nu_x$ and

$$D = \tfrac{1}{6}\lambda^2 \nu \tag{2–73}$$

as was found earlier for the simple cubic and other cubic structures.

In the preceding analysis, we considered explicitly the random walk of a single atom, and $W(m, N)$ represented a probability referring to the particular atom. If the random walk were repeated a very large number of times, the values of m would be distributed as indicated by $W(m, N)$, or at least very nearly so. If N is sufficiently large, deviations from this distribution will normally be very small. Thus, if we consider a large group of atoms, all on the plane $x = 0$ at time $t = 0$, this analysis yields $c(x, t)$, the concentration per unit volume of these atoms as a function of x and t. When the original concentration is S_0 atoms per unit area on plane $x = 0$,

$$c(x, t) = S_0 W(x, t) \tag{2–74}$$

This, along with (2–71), agrees with the solution of Fick's Second Law, Eq. (1–51).

Expressions for $\langle X \rangle$, $\langle X^2 \rangle$, and $\langle | X | \rangle$ also can be calculated from $W(x, t)$. Since $W(x, t)$ for a random walk is an even function of x, the mean atom displacement $\langle X \rangle$ must equal zero. On the other hand, inasmuch as x^2 is an even function of x, the mean square displacement

$$\langle X^2 \rangle = \int_{-\infty}^{+\infty} x^2 W(x, t)\, dx \tag{2-75}$$

does not equal zero. With $W(x, t)$ given by (2-71), and D by (2-72), one finds

$$\langle X^2 \rangle = N\lambda^2 = 2Dt \tag{2-76}$$

The mean displacement from the origin regardless of direction is given by

$$\langle | X | \rangle = \int_{-\infty}^{\infty} | x | \, W(x, t)\, dx = (2N\lambda^2/\pi)^{1/2} = (4Dt/\pi)^{1/2} \tag{2-77}$$

Both $\langle | X | \rangle$ and the root mean square displacement $\langle X^2 \rangle^{1/2}$ measure the width of the density function $W(x, t)$. In general, this width is proportional to $N^{1/2}$ or $t^{1/2}$.

The values of $\langle X \rangle$ and $\langle X^2 \rangle$ above can be obtained directly from Eq. (2-63) for $W(m, N)$. [See Eqs. (2-98) and (2-104)]. Thus they are valid even for small values of N. This is not the case for $\langle | X | \rangle$, however.

Near the melting point in substitutional face-centered cubic (fcc) alloys, a typical value of D is $\approx 10^{-8}$ cm²/sec. Then, diffusion for one day near the melting point gives $\langle X^2 \rangle^{1/2} \approx$ 0.04 cm. For diffusion of small interstitial atoms near the melting point, a typical value of D is $\approx 10^{-5}$ cm²/sec. Diffusion for one day near the melting point then yields $\langle X^2 \rangle^{1/2} \approx 1.3$ cm.

Varied Jump Distance

When there is more than one jump distance, the equations must be modified. If all jumps are independent of one another, the final atom distribution from N_1 random jumps of length λ_1 and N_2 jumps of length λ_2 does not depend on the sequence in which the jumps are taken. Thus, we can pretend that each atom first makes N_1 jumps of length λ_1. The density function for these jumps is $W(m_1, N_1)$. If each atom then makes N_2 jumps of length λ_2, the probability that an atom has a final net displacement $m_1\lambda_1 + m_2\lambda_2$ is given by the product $W(m_1, N_1)W(m_2, N_2)$, where $W(m_2, N_2)$ is the density function for the N_2 jumps.

This expression can be written in terms of the continuous variables x and t. The net displacement x equals $x_1 + x_2$, where $x_1 = m_1\lambda_1$ and $x_2 = m_2\lambda_2$. The atom can arrive at x by various combinations of x_1 and x_2. Let us consider the probability that the final atom position lies between $x - \frac{1}{2}dx$ and $x + \frac{1}{2}dx$. For a given value of x_1, the probability is $W(x_2, N_2)dx_2$, where $x_2 = x - x_1$ and $dx_2 = dx$. The total probability that the final displacement is in the range dx at x therefore equals $W(x - x_1, N_2)dx$ multiplied by $W(x_1, N_1)$ and integrated over all values of x_1.

$$W(x, N_1, N_2)\, dx = \int_{-\infty}^{+\infty} [W(x_1, N_1)W(x - x_1, N_2)\, dx]\, dx_1 \tag{2–78}$$

Equation (2–69) gives explicit expressions for $W(x_1, N_1)$ and $W(x - x_1, N_2)$. When the integral in (2–78) is evaluated and the resulting expression is simplified, one obtains

$$W(x, N_1, N_2) = \left(\frac{1}{2\pi L^2}\right)^{1/2} \exp\left(-\frac{x^2}{2L^2}\right) \tag{2–79}$$

where $L^2 = N_1\lambda_1^2 + N_2\lambda_2^2$. This can be rewritten as

$$W(x, t) = \frac{1}{2(\pi Dt)^{1/2}} \exp\left(-\frac{x}{4Dt}\right) \tag{2–80}$$

with

$$D = L^2/2t = \tfrac{1}{2}\nu_1\lambda_1^2 + \tfrac{1}{2}\nu_2\lambda_2^2 \tag{2–81}$$

Here $\nu_1 (= N_1/t)$ and $\nu_2 (= N_2/t)$ are the frequencies with which the atom makes jumps of length λ_1 and λ_2.

If there is still a third jump distance, the same analysis as that leading to (2–79) will include the further atom displacements. Thus, (2–80) is valid in general with $2Dt = N_1\lambda_1^2 + N_2\lambda_2^2 + N_3\lambda_3^2 + \cdots$. For a continuous range of frequencies, with $n(\lambda)d\lambda$ being the number of jumps per unit time having lengths between λ and $\lambda + d\lambda$,

$$D = \frac{1}{2}\int_0^\infty n(\lambda)\lambda^2\, d\lambda \tag{2–82}$$

Applications of (2–81) occur when there is diffusion by two different mechanisms. For example, there might be simultaneous volume diffusion (jump distance λ_1) and diffusion along dislocations of random orientation (average length of dislocation segment λ_2). Since W in (2–80) shows the same functional dependence on x as that for volume diffusion alone (only the magnitude of D is changed), it is difficult to determine the contributions from these two effects separately. The measured diffusion coefficient is the sum of the diffusion coefficients for the two mechanisms operating separately.

Another application occurs in treating three-dimensional displacements. Jumps of equal length, but in directions making unequal angles with the diffusion axis, have different components along this axis. Thus, for diffusion along this axis, they are in effect jumps of different length, and

$$L^2 = \sum_{j=1}^{z} N_j\lambda_j^2 \cos^2\varphi_j \tag{2–83}$$

where the sum is over all neighboring sites to which the atoms can jump. Also, λ_j is the actual length of the jth jump, N_j is the number of these jumps, φ_j is the angle between the jth jump direction and the diffusion axis, and $\lambda_j \cos \varphi_j$ is the component of the jth jump along the diffusion axis.

Three-Dimensional Random Walk

In the preceding section, we have seen how two simultaneous random walks in the x-direction combine. Similarly, the density function for an atom which is making random jumps along two or more axes can be obtained by combining the separate probabilities for each axis. The net displacement along one axis is unaffected by jumps along a perpendicular axis. If an atom pursues random walks along the principal axes, x, y, and z,

$$W(x, y, z, t) = W(x, t)\, W(y, t)\, W(z, t) \qquad (2\text{–}84)$$

and

$$W(x, y, z, t) = \left(\frac{1}{2\pi}\right)^{3/2} \frac{1}{L_x L_y L_z} \exp\left\{-\frac{x^2}{2L_x^2} - \frac{y^2}{2L_y^2} - \frac{z^2}{2L_z^2}\right\} \qquad (2\text{–}85)$$

When $L_x^2 = L_y^2 = L_z^2 = 2Dt$, Eq. (2–85) is equivalent to Eq. (1–55).

For isotropic diffusion from a point source, the surfaces of constant concentration are spheres. In general, however, these surfaces are ellipsoids which obey the equation

$$\frac{x^2}{2L_x^2} + \frac{y^2}{2L_y^2} + \frac{z^2}{2L_z^2} = \text{constant} \qquad (2\text{–}86)$$

One interesting distinction between the three-dimensional and the one- or two-dimensional random walk is in the probability of return to a given site. In the one- and two-dimensional cases, the probability is unity that the atom will eventually return to its original site. Thus, it will return an infinite number of times. In a three-dimensional random walk, this probability is not unity. For a simple cubic structure,[3] the probability that an atom returns at least once is approximately 0.35; and the average number of times an atom revisits a site, counting multiple visits separately, is approximately 0.53 [equal to $\sum_{k=1}^{\infty} (0.35)^k$].

$W(x, t)$ with a Driving Force

When there is a driving force, the probability p of jump in the direction of the force will be greater than the probability q in the opposite direction. Then, Eq. (2–63) for $W(m, N)$ must be modified. The factor $(\frac{1}{2})^N$ must be replaced by $p^{(N+m)/2}q^{(N-m)/2}$ where $p = \frac{1}{2}(1 + \varepsilon)$ and $q = \frac{1}{2}(1 - \varepsilon)$. Since ε is much smaller than unity, the expression $\ln(1 \pm \varepsilon) = \pm\varepsilon - \frac{1}{2}\varepsilon^2 \pm \cdots$ can be used, and all but the first two terms in the expression will be negligible. This adds the following terms to the right-hand side of (2–66):

$$\tfrac{1}{2}(N + m)\ln(1 + \varepsilon) = \tfrac{1}{2}(N + m)(\varepsilon - \tfrac{1}{2}\varepsilon^2) \qquad (2\text{–}87)$$

and

$$\tfrac{1}{2}(N - m)\ln(1 - \varepsilon) = \tfrac{1}{2}(N - m)(-\varepsilon - \tfrac{1}{2}\varepsilon^2) \qquad (2\text{–}88)$$

When added, these two terms yield $m\varepsilon - \frac{1}{2}N\varepsilon^2$, so that (2–67) becomes

$$W(m, N) = \left(\frac{2}{\pi N}\right)^{1/2} \exp\left\{-\frac{(m - N\varepsilon)^2}{2N}\right\} \qquad (2\text{–}89)$$

This yields the same bell-shaped curve as (2–67), but now the center of the curve is shifted to the point $m = N\varepsilon$. The center

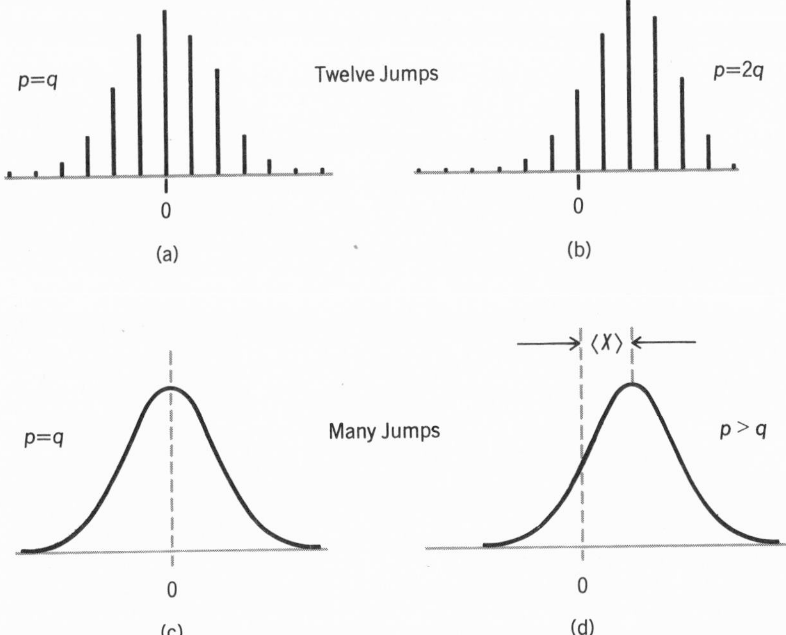

2–3 Effect of a driving force on $W(m, N)$ and $W(x, t)$. In each diagram W is plotted vertically and m (or x) horizontally. A driving force makes the probability p of jump to the right differ from the probability q of jump to the left, causing a shift in the position of the profile.
(**a**) $W(m, N)$ for $N = 12$ and $p = q$ (without driving force)
(**b**) $W(m, N)$ for $N = 12$ and $p = 2q$ (with driving force).
(**c**) $W(x, t)$ for N very large and $p = q$ (without driving force).
(**d**) $W(x, t)$ for N very large and $p > q$ (with driving force).
The horizontal and vertical scales in (**c**) and (**d**) differ from those in (**a**) and (**b**).

of gravity of the curve is shifted a distance $\langle X \rangle = N\varepsilon\lambda$ in the direction of the force, in agreement with (2–46).

In terms of x and t, (2–89) becomes

$$W(x, t) = \frac{1}{2(\pi Dt)^{1/2}} \exp\left\{-\frac{(x - \langle X \rangle)^2}{4Dt}\right\} \qquad (2\text{–}90)$$

Since $\langle X \rangle = \langle v_x \rangle t$, this equation is in agreement with Eq.

(1–52). The effect of a driving force on $W(m, N)$ and $W(x, t)$ is illustrated in Fig. 2–3.

2–5. SPECIAL TOPICS CONCERNING RANDOM-WALK DENSITY FUNCTIONS

The basic equations for $W(x, t)$ in a random walk are discussed in Section 2–4. In the present section, these equations are treated more fully, and several special topics are discussed. For the most part, these topics are not closely related to one another. However, they all are related to the random-walk density function, $W(m, N)$, $W(x, N)$, or $W(x, t)$, in some manner.

Exact Calculation of $\langle X \rangle$ and $\langle X^2 \rangle$ from $W(n_R, N)$

The random-walk density function in a driving force, when expressed in terms of the number of positive jumps n_R, is given exactly by

$$W(n_R, N) = \frac{N!}{n_R!(N - n_R)!} p^{n_R} q^{N-n_R} \tag{2–91}$$

The sum of $W(n_R, N)$ over all n_R has a form very similar to that obtained from the binomial expansion. If the dummy variable y (which later will be set equal to unity) is introduced,

$$\sum_{n_R=0}^{N} W(n_R, N) y^{2n_R-N} = \sum_{n_R=0}^{N} \frac{N!}{n_R!(N - n_R)!} (py)^{n_R} (qy^{-1})^{N-n_R} \tag{2–92}$$

$$\sum_{n_R=0}^{N} W(n_R, N) y^m = (py + qy^{-1})^N \tag{2–93}$$

where the relation $m = 2n_R - N$ has been used on the left and the binomial theorem on the right. Since $p + q = 1$, Eq.

(2–93) when $y = 1$ reduces to

$$\sum_{n_R=0}^{N} W(n_R, N) = 1 \tag{2–94}$$

as is expected since $W(n_R, N)$ is a probability.

By definition

$$\langle X \rangle = \sum_{n_R=0}^{N} xW(n_R, N) \tag{2–95}$$

Also, $x = \lambda m$, and

$$\langle X \rangle = \sum_{n_R=0}^{N} \lambda m W(n_R, N) \tag{2–96}$$

An expression similar to the right-hand side of (2–96) can be obtained by differentiating (2–93) with respect to y,

$$\sum_{n_R=0}^{N} mW(n_R, N) y^{m-1} = y^{-1}N(py - qy^{-1})(py + qy^{-1})^{N-1} \tag{2–97}$$

with $p + q = 1$ and $y = 1$, this becomes

$$\sum_{n_R=0}^{N} mW(n_R, N) = N(p - q) \tag{2–98}$$

and with (2–96),

$$\langle X \rangle = N\lambda(p - q) \tag{2–99}$$

An expression for $\langle X^2 \rangle$ can be found by multiplying (2–97) by y and then differentiating again with respect to y. This yields

$$\sum_{n_R=0}^{N} m^2 W(n_R, N) y^{m-1} = y^{-1}N(py + qy^{-1})^{N}$$
$$+ y^{-1}N(N - 1)(py - qy^{-1})^2(py + qy^{-1})^{N-2} \tag{2–100}$$

With $p + q = 1$ and $y = 1$, this becomes

$$\sum_{n_R=0}^{N} m^2 W(n_R, N) = N + N(N - 1)(p - q)^2 \quad (2\text{–}101)$$

By definition,

$$\langle X^2 \rangle = \sum_{n_R=0}^{N} x^2 W(n_R, N) \quad (2\text{–}102)$$

and, since $x = \lambda m$,

$$\langle X^2 \rangle = \sum_{n_R=0}^{N} \lambda^2 m^2 W(n_R, N) \quad (2\text{–}103)$$

Then, with (2–99) and (2–101),

$$\langle X^2 \rangle = \lambda^2 N + \langle X \rangle^2 \frac{N - 1}{N} \quad (2\text{–}104)$$

Higher Order Moments

Higher order moments of $W(n_R, N)$ such as $\langle X^3 \rangle$, $\langle X^4 \rangle$ can be found by repeated differentiation. The exact expression for $\langle X^3 \rangle$ is

$$\langle X^3 \rangle = 3\langle X \rangle \langle X^2 \rangle (1 - \tfrac{2}{3}N^{-1}) - 2\langle X \rangle^3 (1 - N^{-1}) \quad (2\text{–}105)$$

Here (2–104) has been used to express $N\lambda^2$ in terms of $\langle X^2 \rangle$ and $\langle X \rangle$. When N is large the terms in N^{-1} can be omitted.

Similarly

$$\langle X^4 \rangle = 3\langle X^2 \rangle^2 (1 - \tfrac{2}{3}N^{-1}) - 2\langle X \rangle^4 (1 - N^{-1})(1 - 2N^{-1}) - 4N^{-1} \langle X^2 \rangle \langle X \rangle^2 (1 - N^{-1}) \quad (2\text{–}106)$$

When N is large, this reduces to

$$\langle X^4 \rangle \approx 3\langle X^2 \rangle^2 - 2\langle X \rangle^4 \quad (2\text{–}107)$$

All higher order moments can be expressed in terms of $\langle X \rangle$, $\langle X^2 \rangle$, and N. In ordinary diffusion experiments, N is very large, and the moments of experimental diffusion profiles show no measurable dependence on N. Thus, the only information one can obtain from a random-walk diffusion profile concerns $\langle X^2 \rangle$, which is proportional to the diffusion coefficient, and $\langle X \rangle$, which is proportional to the driving force. If these two quantities are known, the profile for a given time and temperature is completely determined.

Value of N for Short Diffusion Times—Poisson Distribution

Atoms having a jump frequency ν cannot all be expected to make exactly νt jumps in time t. Instead there will be deviations. Some atoms will make more jumps than average and some will make fewer jumps than average. The probability that there will be N jumps in time t is given exactly by

$$W_N(t) = \frac{(\nu t)^N}{N!} e^{-\nu t} \tag{2–108}$$

This is the well known Poisson distribution which applies to many kinds of random events. The average number of jumps in time t equals $NW_N(t)$ summed over all N from zero to infinity. From (2–108), this equals νt, as expected.

For any time t, however short, the average number of jumps equals the jump frequency multiplied by t. Individual atoms, however, may vary drastically from this average when t is small. The probability that the atom will not jump at all in time t is given by

$$W_0(t) = e^{-\nu t} \tag{2–109}$$

This also equals the fraction of atoms that will not jump during time t. The average time τ which an atom spends between jumps is

$$\tau = \int_0^\infty t[-dW_0(t)/dt]\,dt = \nu^{-1} \qquad (2\text{–}110)$$

Therefore, the average time an atom stays at one site between jumps is just the inverse of the jump frequency.

At long diffusion times, Stirling's approximation can be used to evaluate $N!$ in (2–108). We can introduce the quantity $\Delta = (N - \nu t)$ and assume $|\Delta| \ll \nu t$. Then the approximation

$$-\ln(N/\nu t)^N = -N\ln[1 + \Delta/\nu t] \approx -\Delta - \frac{1}{2}\frac{\Delta^2}{\nu t} \qquad (2\text{–}111)$$

leads to

$$W_N(t) \approx \frac{1}{(2\pi N)^{1/2}}\exp\left[\frac{-(N - \nu t)^2}{2\nu t}\right] \qquad (2\text{–}112)$$

which is valid in the central region where $N \approx \nu t$. As a function of N, $W_N(t)$ has a maximum in this region. For large N, the width of this maximum increases as $N^{1/2}$, and the relative width decreases as $N^{1/2}/N$. When N goes to infinity the relative width goes to zero. Thus, for many purposes it is a good approximation to take $W_N(t)$ equal to unity at $N = \nu t$ and equal to zero at other values of N.

Value of W for Short Diffusion Time

In the evaluation of $W(m, N)$, Stirling's first approximation for $N!$ was used. This introduces very little error if N is large. For smaller values of N, however, a more accurate expression is given by Stirling's second approximation,

$$\ln n! = (n + \tfrac{1}{2})\ln n + \tfrac{1}{2}\ln 2\pi - n + \frac{1}{12n} + O(n^{-3}) \qquad (2\text{–}113)$$

which contains the additional term $+(12n)^{-1}$ and is accurate to the order of n^{-3}. This adds the terms

$$\frac{1}{12N} - \frac{2}{12(N+m)} - \frac{2}{12(N-m)} = -\frac{1}{4N} + O(N^{-3}) \tag{2-114}$$

to the right-hand side of (2–66) and if terms $O(N^{-3})$ are neglected, one obtains

$$W(m, N) = \left(\frac{2}{\pi N}\right)^{1/2} \exp\left\{-\frac{1}{4N} - \frac{m^2}{2N}\left(\frac{N-1}{N}\right)\right\} \tag{2-115}$$

In addition, one might be interested in cases where it is no longer true that $m \ll N$. Then the higher order terms in m/N in (2–65) and (2–114) must be included. One finally obtains

$$W(m, N) = (2/\pi N)^{1/2} \exp Q \tag{2-116}$$

where to sixth order in m

$$\begin{aligned} Q = &-\left[\frac{1}{4N} + O(N^{-3})\right] - m^2\left[\frac{1}{2N} - \frac{1}{2N^2} + \frac{1}{3N^3} + O(N^{-5})\right] \\ &- m^4\left[\frac{1}{(3)(4)N^3} - \frac{1}{4N^4} + \frac{1}{3N^5} + O(N^{-7})\right] \\ &- m^6\left[\frac{1}{(5)(6)N^5} - \frac{1}{6N^6} + \frac{1}{3N^7} + O(N^{-9})\right] \end{aligned} \tag{2-117}$$

Reflecting Barrier

The analysis in Section 2–4 for $W(x, t)$ can be extended with only minor modifications to a one-dimensional random walk which is restricted by a reflecting barrier at $m = m_b$. Without loss of generality, we can suppose that $m_b \geq 0$, since there is symmetry around the point $m = 0$. We then calculate the probability $W(m, N; m_b)$ that the atom under these conditions will be at position m after N jumps.

Because of the barrier, any atom which arrives at m_b has a probability unity of retracing its step to $m_b - 1$ when it makes its next jump. Any path which ordinarily would have ended at $m > m_b$ is merely reflected at the plane $m = m_b$. Plane m is a distance $|m_b - m|$ from the barrier. Its "image" point on the other side of the barrier is also $|m_b - m|$ from the barrier. Thus the image point is $2m_b - m$ from the origin. The effect of the reflecting barrier is taken into account merely by adding to $W(m, N)$ the probability $W(2m_b - m, N)$ of arrival at the image point after N steps,

$$W(m, N; m_b) = W(m, N) + W(2m_b - m, N) \qquad (2\text{–}118)$$

In the limit of large N and with the continuous variables x and t,

$$W(x, t; x_b) = \frac{1}{2(\pi Dt)^{1/2}} \left\{ \exp\left(-\frac{x^2}{4Dt}\right) + \exp\left(-\frac{(2x_b - x)^2}{4Dt}\right) \right\} \qquad (2\text{–}119)$$

The case $x_b = 0$ corresponds to diffusion into a semi-infinite medium, as when a layer of tracer atoms diffuses into a crystal from the surface. Then

$$W(x, t; 0) = (\pi Dt)^{-1/2} \exp(-x^2/4Dt) \qquad (2\text{–}120)$$

The concentration gradient of the diffusing species always vanishes at the reflecting plane, since (2–119) yields $(\partial W/\partial x)_{x=x_b} = 0$ for any value of x_b.

Absorbing Barrier

The problem of an absorbing barrier at m_b is very similar to that of the reflecting barrier. Here, any atom that reaches the point m_b is absorbed and cannot participate in the diffusion process any further. We wish to find the probability $W(m, N; m_b)$ that the atom will be at position m after N jumps. In the absence of the barrier, the probability that the atom will be at m after N jumps would be $W(m, N)$. To find $W(m, N; m_b)$, we must subtract the contribution of the "forbidden" jump sequences which involve an atom visit to m_b. As before, we can use the concept of reflection about a plane through m_b. In the absence of the barrier, one finds for every sequence where the atom first visits m_b and then arrives at m a sequence where the atom arrives at m_b and proceeds to the image point $2m_b - m$. The probability of arrival at this image point is $W(2m_b - m, N)$. Thus

$$W(m, N; m_b) = W(m, N) - W(2m_b - m, N) \qquad (2\text{–}121)$$

In terms of the continuous variables x and t with N large

$$W(x, t; x_b) = \frac{1}{2(\pi Dt)^{1/2}}\left[\exp\left(\frac{-x^2}{4Dt}\right) - \exp\left(\frac{-(2x_b - x)^2}{4Dt}\right)\right] \qquad (2\text{–}122)$$

At the absorbing barrier,

$$W(x_b, t; x_b) = 0 \qquad (2\text{–}123)$$

The atom flux at the barrier from atoms which start random walks at $x = 0$ at time $t = 0$ is given by

$$j(x_b, t) = -DS_0 \left.\frac{\partial W}{\partial x}\right|_{x=x_b} = \frac{x_b}{t}\frac{S_0}{2(\pi Dt)^{1/2}} \exp\left(\frac{-x_b^2}{4Dt}\right) \qquad (2\text{–}124)$$

Here S_0 is the number of atoms per unit area originally on the lattice plane at $x = 0$.

This result can be applied to diffusion of a species out of a crystal with the surface concentration maintained at zero. The number of atoms evolved at the surface per unit time if the concentration originally is uniform is given by

$$J(t) = \int_0^\infty d^{-1}j(x_b, t)\, dx_b = cD^{1/2}/(\pi t)^{1/2} \qquad (2\text{–}125)$$

where d is the distance between lattice planes while, for a uniform concentration, S_0 equals cd. The total amount evolved after time t is given by

$$\int_0^t J(t)\, dt = 2c(Dt)^{1/2}\pi^{-1/2} \qquad (2\text{–}126)$$

These equations for reflecting and absorbing barriers apply exactly only when driving forces are absent. With driving forces present, the equations are considerably more complex.[4]

Markoff Method

Another method of determining the density function $W_N(\mathbf{r})$ involves the use of Fourier transforms. If the jump probabilities $W_1(\mathbf{r})$ are the same for each jump, then

$$W_N(\mathbf{r}) = \frac{1}{8\pi^3}\int_{-\infty}^{\infty} A^N(\boldsymbol{\varrho}) \exp(-i\mathbf{r}\cdot\boldsymbol{\varrho})\, d\boldsymbol{\varrho} \qquad (2\text{–}127)$$

where

$$A(\boldsymbol{\varrho}) = \int_{-\infty}^{\infty} W_1(\mathbf{r}) \exp(i\mathbf{r}\cdot\boldsymbol{\varrho})\, d\mathbf{r} \qquad (2\text{–}128)$$

Here $W_N(\mathbf{r})$ is the probability that the atom after N jumps will be displaced by a vector $\mathbf{r}$ from its starting position. $W_N(\mathbf{r})$ must of course be real and is obtained by taking the real part of the expression in Eq. (2–127).

For diffusion in one dimension, these equations reduce to

$$W_N(x) = \frac{1}{2\pi}\int_{-\infty}^{\infty} A^N(\rho_x) \exp(-ix\rho_x)\, d\rho_x \qquad (2\text{–}129)$$

$$A(\rho_x) = \int_{-\infty}^{\infty} W_1(x) \exp(ix\rho_x)\, dx \qquad (2\text{–}130)$$

As a simple application of these equations, we can consider a one-dimensional random walk with jump distance λ. Then

$$W_1(x) = \tfrac{1}{2}\delta(x - \lambda) + \tfrac{1}{2}\delta(x + \lambda) \qquad (2\text{–}131)$$

The delta functions in this expression equal zero except when the expressions in parentheses equal zero. At these points, the deltas equal unity. The first term gives the probability of a jump to the right and second term that to the left.

Equation (2–130) then yields

$$A(\rho_x) = \tfrac{1}{2}(e^{i\lambda\rho_x} + e^{-i\lambda\rho_x}) \qquad (2\text{–}132)$$

which when raised to the Nth power is

$$A^N(\rho_x) = \left(\frac{1}{2}\right)^N \sum_{j=0}^{N} \frac{N!}{j!(N-j)!} (e^{i\lambda\rho_x})^j (e^{-i\lambda\rho_x})^{N-j} \qquad (2\text{–}133)$$

Now

$$(2\pi)^{-1} \int_{-\infty}^{\infty} \exp\,[i(x - x_1)\rho_x]\, d\rho_x = \delta(x - x_1) \qquad (2\text{–}134)$$

so that from (2–129)

$$W_N(x) = \left(\frac{1}{2}\right)^N \sum_{j=0}^{N} \frac{N!}{j!(N-j)!} \delta(2\lambda j - \lambda N - x) \qquad (2\text{–}135)$$

For discrete jumps $x = m\lambda$, and the delta function equals zero except for $j = \tfrac{1}{2}(N + m)$, and

$$W_N(m) = (\tfrac{1}{2})^N N!/[\tfrac{1}{2}(N + m)]![\tfrac{1}{2}(N - m)]! \qquad (2\text{–}136)$$

as found previously.

The Markoff method can be used with various $W_1(\mathbf{r})$ jump probability distributions to calculate $W_N(\mathbf{r})$ for either large or small values of N. It is especially useful when $W_1(\mathbf{r})$ is a continuous function of position. A number of useful examples have been treated by Chandrasekhar[5] and Torrey.[6]

REFERENCES

1. Many of the topics in this chapter are also discussed in standard reference works on random walks and diffusion. Useful references include: E. H. Kennard, "Kinetic Theory of Gases" (McGraw-Hill Book Co., New York, 1938); S. Chandrasekhar, *Rev. Mod. Phys.* **15,** 1 (1943), also reprinted in "Selected Papers on Noise and Stochastic Processes, edited by N. Wax (Dover Publications, New York, 1954); W. Feller, "An Introduction to Probability Theory and Its Applications," 2nd ed. (John Wiley and Sons, New York, 1957); P. G. Shewmon, "Diffusion in Solids" (McGraw-Hill Book Co., New York, 1963); L. A. Girifalco, "Atomic Migration in Crystals" (Blaisdell Publishing Co., New York, 1964).
2. A. Einstein, *Ann. Physik* **17,** 549 (1905).
3. W. H. McCrea and F. J. Whipple, *Proc. Roy. Soc.* (Edinburgh) **60,** 281 (1940).
4. See, e.g., W. Feller, "An Introduction to Probability Theory and Its Applications," 2nd ed. (John Wiley and Sons, New York, 1957), pp. 322, 391.
5. S. Chandrasekhar, *Rev. Mod. Phys.* **15,** 1 (1943).
6. H. C. Torrey, *Phys. Rev.* **92,** 962 (1953).

3. CORRELATION EFFECTS

3–1. CORRELATION FACTOR

In random-walk diffusion, it is assumed that the atom jump probabilities do not depend on the directions of previous jumps. In real crystals, however, the jump probabilities often do depend on the directions of preceding jumps. Then successive atom jumps are related (or correlated) to one another; and, instead of following a random walk, each atom follows a *correlated walk*. When correlation effects arise, the random-walk diffusion equations from Chapter 2 cannot be used directly. Instead, they must first be modified. This is accomplished by introducing a *correlation factor* into the diffusion equations.[1–3]

Detailed calculations of the correlation factor can be quite involved. In many cases, however, the correlated jumps can be considered to cancel in pairs; and the correlation factor can be given a simple physical interpretation. If the atom first makes a forward jump, and then a correlated reverse jump, back to its original site, neither the first jump nor the reverse jump in the pair is effective in causing random diffusion, as the two jumps merely cancel. The effective frequency of random jumps ν^e then differs from the actual jump frequency ν^a, and we can write

$$\nu^e = f\nu^a \tag{3–1}$$

where f is the correlation factor. The correlation factor then equals the fraction of jumps which are effective in causing random diffusion.

For self-diffusion by a vacancy mechanism, the correlation factor ranges between 0.78 for a face-centered cubic structure and 0.50 for a diamond structure.[3] For impurity diffusion by a vacancy mechanism, the correlation factor becomes almost zero for a fast diffusing impurity or almost unity for a slow diffusing impurity. A correlation factor near zero corresponds to a large correlation effect, whereas one near unity indicates that there are only weak correlations between successive jumps.

When Eq. (3–1) is valid, the correction to the equations in Chapter 2 is particularly simple. For example, in place of Eq. (2–23) for cubic crystals, we find

$$D = \tfrac{1}{6}\lambda^2\nu^a f \qquad (3\text{–}2)$$

Even this simple correction can considerably complicate the analysis of diffusion data, since the basic atomic quantity ν^a in Eq. (3–2) can be calculated from the experimental diffusion coefficient only if the correlation factor is known.

Methods of calculating or estimating the correlation factor are discussed in the remainder of this chapter. In a final section, applications to several types of experiments are described.

3–2. CORRELATION EFFECTS AND COMMON DIFFUSION MECHANISMS

Correlation effects arise whenever the atom jump probabilities depend on the directions of previous jumps. If the elementary atom jump requires a lattice imperfection at a neighboring site (as in the vacancy and interstitialcy mechanisms), correlation effects always arise. With other mechanisms, correlation effects may disappear. In addition, correlations arise if the crystal structure itself creates a lack of symmetry in the atom jumps from a given site. This is important for lattice sites with noncubic environments.

The effect of correlations on the diffusion equations is developed in detail in Sections 3–3 to 3–10. Before proceeding to this quantitative treatment, we first shall discuss qualitatively correlation effects for the various diffusion mechanisms. To simplify this qualitative discussion, we assume a crystal with each atom site normally in a cubic environment. Then only impurities or imperfections lead to nonrandom jumps.

Vacancy Mechanism

Let us consider the motion of a given (tracer) atom M when diffusion proceeds by a vacancy mechanism. The atom is not able to jump until a vacancy arrives at a neighboring site. In the absence of driving forces, vacancies migrate away from their sources (free surfaces, grain boundaries, dislocations) in random directions. Thus, they are equally likely to approach M from any direction, and the initial atom-vacancy exchange will be in a random direction. After a particular vacancy has exchanged with the atom, however, the atom-vacancy configuration is no longer random. Instead it depends on the direction of the initial jump. Immediately after the atom-vacancy exchange, the vacancy is in the proper position to allow a reverse jump, returning the atom to its original location. Therefore, the second exchange of M with a given vacancy is not random in direction. Instead, it has a greater than random probability of being in a direction opposite to the first jump. This is illustrated in Fig. 3–1.

There is a similar correlation between the second and third exchanges, or any two successive exchanges, of the atom with a given vacancy. In each case, the local symmetry is altered by the jump, the vacancy first being on one side of the atom

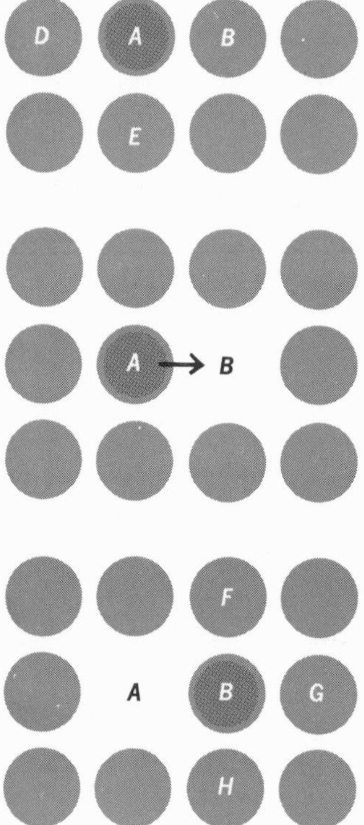

(**a**) The diffusing (tracer) atom is indicated by the double circle. The tracer cannot jump from site *A* until a vacancy arrives at a neighboring site *B*, *C*, *D*, or *E*. In the absence of driving forces, a vacancy is equally likely to arrive at any of the four sites *B*, *C*, *D*, or *E*. Thus, the next jump of the tracer atom will be in a random direction.

(**b**) A vacancy arrives at site *B* and the tracer atom then jumps to site *B*.

(**c**) After the tracer jumps to site *B*, the vacancy which used to be on site *B* is on site *A*. The tracer on its next jump therefore does not have an equal probability of jump to the four sites *A*, *F*, *G*, and *H* which neighbor on site *B*. Instead there is a greater than random probability of jump back to site *A*, causing a correlation between the directions of successive tracer jumps.

3–1 Correlation Effect with a Vacancy Mechanism.

and then on the other. This changing symmetry affects the atom jump probabilities and leads to correlations between successive jumps.

Interstitialcy Mechanism

In an interstitialcy mechanism, atoms move through the lattice by jumping first from a normal lattice site to an interstitial site, then from the interstitial site to a normal lattice site, and so on. When a diffusing atom M jumps from interstitial site i_1 to normal lattice site n, a lattice atom must move from site n into a second interstitial site i_2. This is illustrated in Fig. 3–2, where site i_1 is called B, site n is G, and site i_2 is K. During the jump, the interstitialcy imperfection itself moves from site i_1 to site i_2. The interstitialcy at i_2 after the jump is a nearest neighbor of the diffusing atom M at site n. Thus atom M has a greater than random probability on its next jump of jumping back to site i_1, and a correlation effect arises. Here, as in the vacancy mechanism, the elementary atom jump places an imperfection at a site neighboring on atom M. Thus, the local symmetry is altered and correlation effects arise.

If noncollinear jumps are allowed (where sites i_1, n, and i_2 do not lie on a straight line), the analysis is more involved than for collinear jumps, but the same principle applies. The diffusing atom always has a smaller than random probability of jumping to site i_2, and there is a correlation between the directions of successive atom jumps.

When a diffusing atom in a pure crystal arrives at an interstitial site, its surroundings always have the same local symmetry regardless of the direction of the n-i jump. Thus, in the absence of a driving force, the i-n jumps are in random directions and are not correlated to any previous n-i jumps. The correlated jumps in this case can be divided rigorously into correlated pairs. Each n-i atom jump is correlated to the preceding i-n jump, and no other correlations occur.

In impure crystals, a small correlation arises between the i-n jumps and previous jumps if the jump frequency depends on the species of the lattice atom participating in the interstitialcy jump. For example, an n-i solvent atom jump involving a fast diffusing impurity as the cooperating atom has a greater than random probability of being followed by a reverse jump.

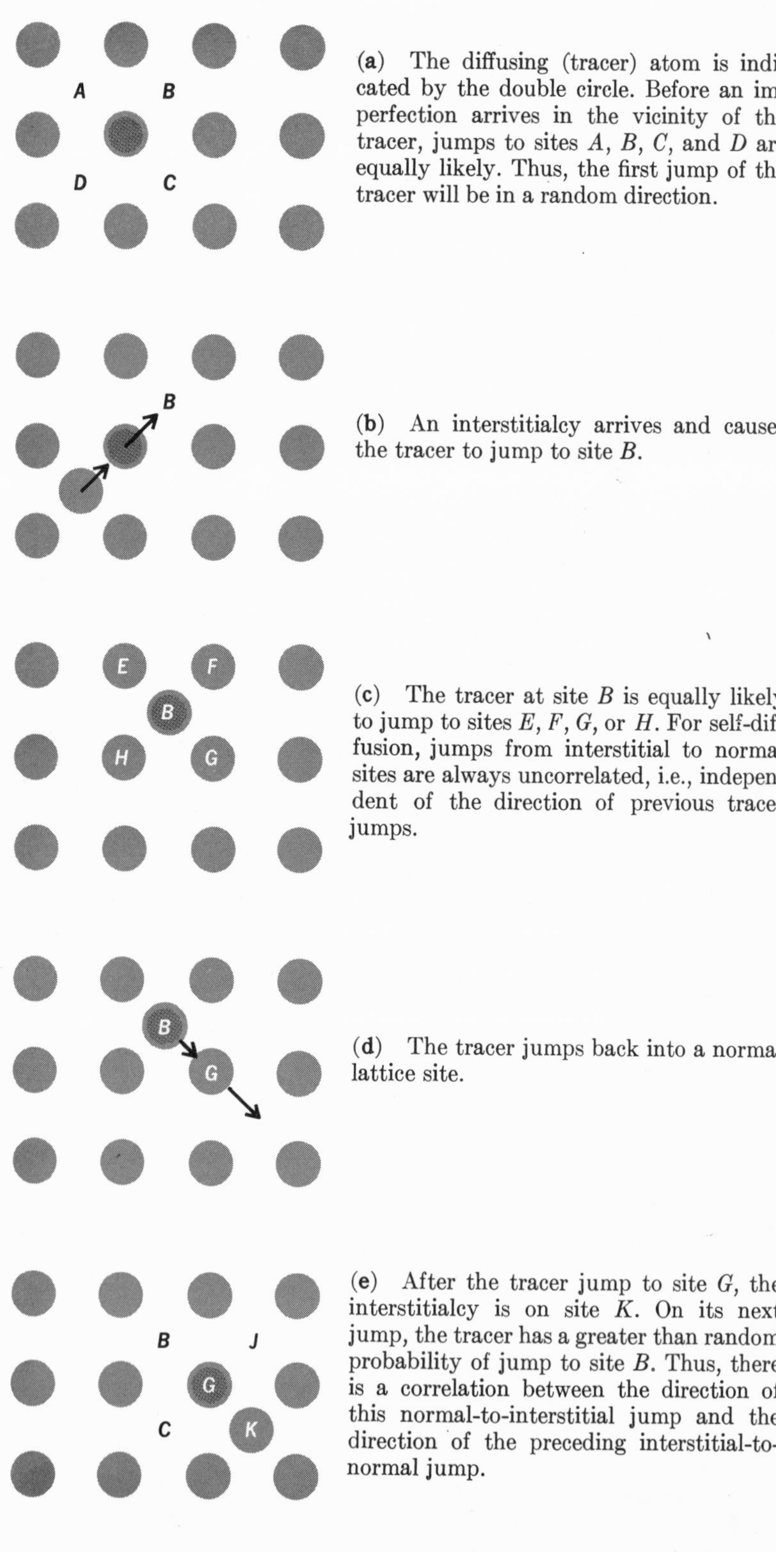

(**a**) The diffusing (tracer) atom is indicated by the double circle. Before an imperfection arrives in the vicinity of the tracer, jumps to sites A, B, C, and D are equally likely. Thus, the first jump of the tracer will be in a random direction.

(**b**) An interstitialcy arrives and causes the tracer to jump to site B.

(**c**) The tracer at site B is equally likely to jump to sites E, F, G, or H. For self-diffusion, jumps from interstitial to normal sites are always uncorrelated, i.e., independent of the direction of previous tracer jumps.

(**d**) The tracer jumps back into a normal lattice site.

(**e**) After the tracer jump to site G, the interstitialcy is on site K. On its next jump, the tracer has a greater than random probability of jump to site B. Thus, there is a correlation between the direction of this normal-to-interstitial jump and the direction of the preceding interstitial-to-normal jump.

Exchange and Ring Mechanisms

In a pure cubic crystal, with diffusion by an exchange or ring mechanism, correlations between successive jumps do not occur. When diffusion in an alloy proceeds by these mechanisms, however, small correlations often arise. The jump frequency for exchange of an A atom with a B atom in general differs from that for exchange of two A atoms or two B atoms. Thus, the jump probabilities for each atom depend on the identities of its neighbors. The two atoms participating in the exchange remain nearest neighbors. Therefore, the diffusing atom in some instances is more likely than random to jump back to its original site and in other instances less likely than random, depending on the identity of the second atom involved in the exchange. This disrupts the random walk and gives a diffusion coefficient which differs by a small amount from the simple random-walk expression.

It may be noted that a vacancy itself really diffuses by an exchange mechanism, since it jumps by exchanging places with neighboring atoms. Thus, a vacancy in an alloy also suffers this type of correlation. This is in contrast to vacancy diffusion in a pure crystal where the vacancy follows a random walk. This correlation normally should not be large; but, at present, calculations are available only for rather simple models.

Interstitial Mechanism

A single atom diffusing by an interstitial mechanism in a pure cubic crystal exhibits no correlations. Each jump is at random since the local symmetry does not depend on the direction of the previous jump. When the interstitial concentration becomes very large, however, an appreciable number of the allowed interstitial sites are filled. Then the lattice of interstitial sites is essentially a sublattice with a large number of vacancies, and much the same correlation effects are obtained as for diffusion by a vacancy mechanism. Normally, interstitial concentrations are small, however, and the diffusing interstitials do not interfere appreciably with one another. The correlation effects correspondingly disappear.

Crowdion Mechanism

A crowdion can move freely along only one direction. Thus, it normally pursues a one-dimensional random walk, and there is probability unity that it will return to its starting position if given sufficient time. This results in a strong correlation between the directions of successive atom jumps. For example, if a crowdion passes through a region by moving from left to right, and then retraces its steps to the left, the atoms all make reverse jumps back to their original positions. The final result is zero net diffusion and a correlation factor of zero.

Appreciable diffusion can be obtained from a crowdion mechanism only if the atom jumps are decorrelated in some manner. Disappearance of the crowdion at a sink, such as a grain boundary, or interference by a second crowdion moving in a crystallographic direction different from the first could accomplish this. Also a crowdion may rotate to a second crystallographic direction by reorientation of several atoms near the center of the crowdion. This would lead to a less correlated motion.

Relaxion Mechanism

Jump frequencies and jump distances cannot easily be described for a general relaxion mechanism. These would depend on the details of the atom motions in the relaxed region. If the motions in the relaxed region are more or less at random, correlation effects should be small. On the other hand, a very localized relaxion, allowing diffusive motion only at or very near its center, would give correlation effects similar to those for a vacancy mechanism.

Divacancy Mechanism

Correlation effects for diffusion by a divacancy mechanism arise for reasons very similar to those for a single vacancy mechanism, described above. However, the particular value of the correlation factor is usually smaller and more difficult to calculate. In the face-centered cubic structure, the correlation factor for self-diffusion by a divacancy mechanism[4] is approximately 0.47 compared to 0.78 for a single vacancy mechanism.

Dumbbell Mechanism

Correlation effects for the dumbbell mechanism are similar in origin and magnitude to those for the conventional interstitialcy mechanism described above.

3–3. GENERAL EQUATIONS FOR THE CORRELATION FACTOR

When there are correlation effects, the random-walk diffusion equations must be modified; and a correlation factor appears in the diffusion equations. The correlation factor f is defined by the equation,

$$D_{\text{actual}} = fD_{\text{random}} \tag{3–3}$$

Here D_{actual} is the tracer diffusion coefficient under actual conditions, where the atom follows a correlated walk, and D_{random} is the tracer diffusion coefficient one would obtain if the atom made the same number of jumps per unit time but successive atom jumps were independent of one another.

In general, inasmuch as D is a tensor quantity, f is a tensor also. For planar diffusion, however, both D and f are scalar quantities. For planar diffusion in the x-direction, $D = \langle X^2 \rangle / 2\tau$

in the limit where τ is small, as given in Eq. (2–31), and

$$f = \lim_{\tau \text{ small}} \frac{\langle X^2 \rangle_{\text{actual}}}{\langle X^2 \rangle_{\text{random}}} \qquad (3\text{–}4)$$

In general, f has a different value for diffusion in each direction. Notable exceptions to this rule occur in cubic crystals, where D and f are the same in every direction. Also, in hexagonal and tetragonal crystals, D and f are the same for every direction in the basal plane.

Equation (2–34) can be used to evaluate the $\langle X^2 \rangle$ in Eq. (3–4). The averages of the diagonal and cross-terms in (2–34) are independent of one another. Thus,

$$\langle X^2 \rangle = \sum_{\gamma=1}^{n} \langle x_\gamma{}^2 \rangle + 2 \sum_{\gamma=1}^{n-1} \sum_{\delta=\gamma+1}^{n} \langle x_\gamma x_\delta \rangle \qquad (3\text{–}5)$$

Also, for a random walk, the summations over $\langle x_\gamma x_\delta \rangle$ equal zero. It follows that[1]

$$f = 1 + \lim_{n \to \infty} \left(2 \sum_{\gamma=1}^{n-1} \sum_{\delta=\gamma+1}^{n} \langle x_\gamma x_\delta \rangle \Big/ \sum_{\gamma=1}^{n} \langle x_\gamma{}^2 \rangle \right) \qquad (3\text{–}6)$$

In order to include the full correlation effect, we let n in this equation go to infinity. Then all correlations, including those between widely separated jumps where $\delta \gg \gamma$, are considered.

The exact value of the correlation factor differs according to the particular lattice geometry and diffusion mechanism. It can be determined by calculating the $\langle x_\gamma x_\delta \rangle$ in each case. In Section 3–4, explicit expressions for diffusion by vacancy and interstitialcy mechanisms in cubic crystals are found.[2,3] These equations later are generalized in Section 3–6.

Restriction on τ

The restriction on τ in Eq. (3–4) calls for some discussion. To calculate the correlation factor accurately, we must allow an infinite number of exchanges n between an atom and a given vacancy, since otherwise not all correlations would be included. This would seem to require that τ go to infinity and be in conflict with the requirement that τ be small. This apparent difficulty can be resolved as follows:

(1) In the absence of driving forces $\langle X^2 \rangle$ is directly proportional to τ, and $\langle X^2 \rangle / 2\tau$ is independent of τ. Since there is no τ dependence, the upper limit on τ in (3–4) may be omitted in this case, allowing an infinite number of jumps.

The proportionality between $\langle X^2 \rangle$ and τ can be seen in the equations for a one-dimensional walk with constant jump distance λ and no driving forces. Then $\langle X^2 \rangle = N\lambda^2$, where N is the number of independent displacements. By definition, $N = \nu\tau$, where ν is the frequency with which the displacements occur. As a result, $\langle X^2 \rangle$ equals $\lambda^2\nu\tau$, where ν and λ are independent of τ, and $\langle X^2 \rangle$ is proportional to τ.

(2) When there is a driving force, $\langle X^2 \rangle$ is not simply proportional to τ, and $\langle X^2 \rangle / 2\tau$ is not independent of τ. Then some other line of reasoning must be used to allow an infinite number of jumps. From Eqs. (2–51) and (2–46),

$$\langle X^2 \rangle = N\lambda^2 + \langle X \rangle^2 \frac{N - 1}{N} = N\lambda^2 + \varepsilon^2\lambda^2 N(N - 1) \qquad (3\text{–}7)$$

Here, the term from the driving force, involving $\langle X \rangle^2$ or ε^2, is proportional to $N^2 = \nu^2\tau^2$. Thus, in a driving force, the restriction that τ is small must be maintained if we wish to obtain the correct values for D and f.

This does not limit the number of jumps n as strictly as might appear, however. In reality, we only require that the number of independent displacements N must equal 0 or 1, since then the ε^2 term in (3–7) becomes zero. Only one independent displacement N results from a series of exchanges between a given atom and a given vacancy, regardless of the number of jumps n in the series. Thus, n can go to infinity while N equals unity.

Treatment of Jumps Involving Different Vacancies

In summary, we can always let n go to infinity when there are no driving forces, since then the $\sum \langle x_\gamma x_\delta \rangle$ terms where jumps γ and δ are caused by separate vacancies always equal zero. (This is equivalent to saying that $\langle X \rangle^2$ equals zero.) In a driving force, these terms no longer are zero but, instead, yield the $\langle X \rangle^2$ term in Eq. (3–7). This $\langle X \rangle^2$ term must be eliminated if we wish to find the correct values for the correlation factor.

In the calculations below, it is assumed that an atom which exchanges with a given vacancy does not exchange with a different vacancy until the initial vacancy has moved away. This considerably simplifies the calculations since it allows correlations from the individual vacancies to be considered separately. Normally, the time required for an atom to complete a series of exchanges with a given vacancy is small compared to the time which elapses before a second vacancy visits the atom. Therefore this restriction usually is not important. A similar restriction can be applied when f for interstitialcy mechanisms is calculated.

Effect of a Driving Force

To first order, a driving force does not change the value of $\langle x_\gamma{}^2 \rangle + \sum \langle x_\gamma x_\delta \rangle$ averaged over jumps caused by a single vacancy. As a result a driving force does not change the tracer diffusion coefficient D, as given by Eq. (2–31), nor does it change the correlation factor. This is discussed further in Section 3–8. For the sake of simplicity, zero driving force is assumed in Sections 3–4 to 3–7. However, the results to first order are not affected by a driving force.

3–4. CORRELATION FACTORS IN CUBIC CRYSTALS

Vacancy Mechanism

Crystal symmetry properties quite often can be used to simplify calculations of the correlation factor. This is especially true for cubic crystals. Since all jumps in a cubic crystal have the same length, $\langle x_\gamma x_\delta \rangle = \langle x_\gamma^2 \cos\theta_{\gamma\delta} \rangle$, where $\theta_{\gamma\delta}$ is the angle between the γth and δth jumps. Also $\sum_{\gamma=1}^{n} \langle x_\gamma^2 \rangle = n \langle x_\gamma^2 \rangle$; consequently, Eq. (3–6) reduces to

$$f = 1 + \lim_{n\to\infty} \frac{2}{n} \sum_{\gamma=1}^{n-1} \sum_{\delta=\gamma+1}^{n} \langle \cos\theta_{\gamma\delta} \rangle \qquad (3\text{–}8)$$

or

$$f = 1 + \lim_{n\to\infty} \frac{2}{n} \sum_{\gamma=1}^{n-1} \langle \cos\theta_{\gamma,\gamma+1} + \cos\theta_{\gamma,\gamma+2} + \cdots + \cos\theta_{\gamma,n} \rangle \qquad (3\text{–}9)$$

where the displacements $x_1, x_2, \cdots$ are all caused by a given vacancy.

One can relate $\cos\theta_{\gamma,\gamma+2}$ to $\cos\theta_{\gamma,\gamma+1}$ and $\cos\theta_{\gamma+1,\gamma+2}$ by a trigonometric formula for spherical triangles,

$$\cos\theta_{\gamma,\gamma+2} = \cos\theta_{\gamma,\gamma+1} \cos\theta_{\gamma+1,\gamma+2} + \sin\theta_{\gamma,\gamma+1} \sin\theta_{\gamma+1,\gamma+2} \cos\psi \qquad (3\text{–}10)$$

Here ψ is the angle between the plane I, defined by the γth and $\gamma + 1$th jump vectors, and plane II, which is defined by the $\gamma + 2$th and $\gamma + 1$th jump vectors. For a given $\theta_{\gamma,\gamma+1}$ and $\theta_{\gamma+1,\gamma+2}$, the average of the second term on the right in (3–10) is proportional to $\sum P_\psi \cos\psi$, where the sum is over all allowed values of ψ, and P_ψ is the jump probability for a given ψ. If there is at least two- or threefold rotational symmetry around each jump vector (as in pure cubic crystals), this sum equals zero; and

$$\langle \cos\theta_{\gamma,\gamma+2} \rangle = \langle \cos\theta_{\gamma,\gamma+1} \cos\theta_{\gamma+1,\gamma+2} \rangle \tag{3–11}$$

In cubic structures in the absence of driving forces, the correlation between the γth and $\gamma + 1$th jump will not differ from that between the $\gamma + 1$th and the $\gamma + 2$th jump. Thus, $\langle \cos\theta_{\gamma,\gamma+1} \rangle = \langle \cos\theta_{\gamma+1,\gamma+2} \rangle$. Also the correlations are independent of each other, so that

$$\langle \cos\theta_{\gamma,\gamma+1} \cos\theta_{\gamma+1,\gamma+2} \rangle = \langle \cos\theta_{\gamma,\gamma+1} \rangle \langle \cos\theta_{\gamma+1,\gamma+2} \rangle.$$

This yields

$$\langle \cos\theta_{\gamma,\gamma+2} \rangle = (\langle \cos\theta_{\gamma,\gamma+1} \rangle)^2 \tag{3–12}$$

and, by iteration,

$$\langle \cos\theta_{\gamma,\gamma+m} \rangle = (\langle \cos\theta \rangle)^m \tag{3–13}$$

Here θ without subscripts refers to the angle between any two successive atom jumps.

Equation (3–9) summed over γ then becomes

$$f = 1 + \lim_{n\to\infty} \frac{2}{n} \{ \langle \cos\theta \rangle + (\langle \cos\theta \rangle)^2 + \cdots (\langle \cos\theta \rangle)^n \} (n - 1) \tag{3–14}$$

$$f = 1 + [2\langle \cos\theta \rangle / (1 - \langle \cos\theta \rangle)] \tag{3–15}$$

$$f = \frac{1 + \langle \cos\theta \rangle}{1 - \langle \cos\theta \rangle} \tag{3–16}$$

It should be noted that $\langle \cos\theta \rangle$ is always negative for a vacancy mechanism. Therefore f is always less than unity.

Equation (3–16) has been derived by assuming each jump is correlated to each preceding jump. Also there is the restriction that each jump vector must lie along an axis of two- or threefold rotational symmetry. Because of this latter restriction, (3–16) is not valid for diffusion in most noncubic crystals and, even in cubic crystals, is not valid for diffusion by means of bound vacancy pairs.

The presence of an impurity can also give rise to unsymmetric jump probabilities for other atoms in its vicinity. Although (3–16) is valid for diffusion of a dilute impurity in an otherwise pure cubic matrix, it is not valid for diffusion of a solvent atom near an impurity. Methods of treating these other cases are given in Section (3–6).

Interstitialcy Mechanism

In the interstitialcy mechanism in a pure crystal, only every other atom jump is correlated to the previous jump. Thus $\cos\theta_{\gamma,\gamma+m}$ equals zero if $m > 1$, and one half of the time $\cos\theta_{\gamma,\gamma+1}$ equals zero. In this case, (3–9) reduces to

$$f = 1 + \langle\cos\theta'\rangle \tag{3–17}$$

where θ' is the angle between the atom jump vector for an interstitial to lattice jump and the jump vector for the succeeding lattice to interstitial jump. This equation is valid for any cubic structure.

3–5. EVALUATION OF $\langle$COS$\theta\rangle$

General Equations

In (3–16) and (3–17), the problem of calculating f is reduced to one of evaluating the average cosine of the angle between successive atom jumps. This involves calculating the average vacancy or interstitialcy motion between the time when the imperfection causes an initial atom jump to the time when it possibly causes another jump by the same atom. If the probability that the imperfection will cause successive atom jumps with an angle θ_j between the directions of the two jumps is called T_j,

$$\langle \cos\theta \rangle = \sum_j T_j \cos\theta_j \tag{3–18}$$

where the sum is over all possible jump directions.

If p_{ng} is the probability that the imperfection will be at site g after n jumps, and b_{gj} is the probability that an imperfection at site g will on its next jump cause the atom to jump in the jth direction (toward site j),

$$T_j = \sum_g \sum_{n=0}^{\infty} p_{ng} b_{gj} \tag{3–19}$$

For vacancies, b_{gj} equals zero if $g \neq j$. In cubic crystals, if only nearest neighbor vacancy jumps are allowed, the nonzero values of b_{gj} are all equal and can be represented by a single constant b. For diffusion by an interstitialcy mechanism with collinear jumps, b_{gj} for a particular j will be nonzero for only one given g. For interstitialcies with noncollinear jumps, however, the two participating atoms do not move in the same direction. Then b_{gj} for a given j can have nonzero values for several values of g.

The p_{ng} are related to the $p_{n-1,g}$ by a set of linear equations,

$$p_{ng} = \sum_h p_{n-1,h} A_{hg} \tag{3–20}$$

where A_{hg} is the probability that the next jump of an imperfection from site h takes it to a particular site g. Repeated application of Eq. (3–20) eventually allows p_{ng} to be related to p_{0g}, which is known since it represents the original position of the imperfection immediately after the initial atom jump.

Equivalent Sites

The number of sites g which must be included in Eq. (3–20) and in the matrix A can be reduced by grouping all sites in the crystal into classes of equivalent sites. When the original jump vector lies along an axis of n-fold rotational symmetry, sites which can be brought into coincidence by any combination of rotations through angles $2\pi n^{-1}$ about this axis are equivalent sites. Also, when there is mirror symmetry across a plane containing the original jump vector, mirror sites on opposite sides of the plane are equivalent sites. An imperfection at any of these sites has the same effect on diffusion in the direction of original jump vector as an imperfection at any other equivalent site. Thus, we can treat these sites as if they were just one site whose probability of being occupied p_{ng} equaled the total occupation probability for the class (i.e., summed over all sites g in this class). Then, if A_{hg} is redefined as the probability of jump from a given site in class h to the whole class of sites g (summed over all sites in class g), Eq. (3–20) is again found.

When there is inversion symmetry through the site 0 occupied by our diffusing atom, the equations can be simplified still further. An imperfection at the inversion image from site g causes an atom at site 0 to have a displacement just the negative of that obtained from an imperfection at site g. Consequently, these sites are "negatively" equivalent to sites g. If there is mirror symmetry across the plane which passes through site 0 normal to the original jump vector, mirror sites from sites g are also negatively equivalent to sites g. These inversion and mirror symmetry sites form a class, which may be called class $\tilde{g}$. The classes g and $\tilde{g}$ can be combined into a single set g represented by a single term in the summations above. This simplifies Eqs. (3–19) and (3–20). The p_{ng} for set g will equal p_{ng} for class g minus p_{ng} for class $\tilde{g}$. Other quantities, such as the $\cos\theta_j$, b_{gj}, and A_{hg} are unchanged. Then, $\langle\cos\theta\rangle$ again follows directly from (3–18) to (3–20), but the number of individual sites g and directions j which are included in the summations are considerably reduced.

The principle of equivalent sites has general usefulness in kinetic calculations of diffusion. The same principle can be applied to planar diffusion when there is either rotational symmetry around an axis in the diffusion direction or mirror symmetry across planes containing site 0 and parallel to the diffusion direction. Negatively equivalent sites can be included if there is inversion symmetry through site 0 or mirror symmetry across a plane containing site 0 and normal to the diffusion direction. For diffusion along the [100] directions in many cubic structures there are enough planes of mirror symmetry so that sites in only one-sixteenth of the actual crystal volume need to be included in the matrix A. All other sites are either equivalent or negatively equivalent to these sites.

Detailed Methods of Analysis

Equations (3–18) to (3–20) give a complete recipe for the calculation of $\langle\cos\theta\rangle$. A considerable number of papers have been published applying these equations in detail to diffusion in various structures. Most treatments can be grouped under four general headings:

(1) Diffusion of Probability: In this quite direct approach, the p_{ng} are determined by first setting up a lattice diagram representing all the various sites in the crystal. The probability that the imperfection will be at the various sites in this diagram is then followed in a step-by-step process, starting with the known values of p_{0g}. This approach requires repeated application of Eq. (3–20) and was first used by Bardeen and Herring[1] in their original quantitative calculations of correlation factors. In principle, the imperfection can be followed for as many jumps as desired. Extensive numerical calculations are required if one wishes extreme accuracy; however, accuracy to two significant figures can be obtained rather easily by this method.[6,7] Since the b_{gj} and $\cos\theta_j$ can be found almost by inspection, $\langle\cos\theta_j\rangle$ is easily obtained when the sum over n of the p_{ng} is known.

(2) Matrix Methods: Quite often, correlation calculations can be simplified by use of matrices and matrix algebra. In matrix notation, (3–20) becomes

$$\mathbf{p}_n = \mathbf{p}_{n-1}\mathbf{A} \tag{3–21}$$

where $\mathbf{p}_n$ is a row matrix having components p_{ng}. Also, $\mathbf{p}_{n-1}$ is a row matrix having components $\mathbf{p}_{n-1,g}$ and $\mathbf{A}$ is a square matrix containing the elements A_{hg}. If the concept of equivalent sites is used, A_{hg} is the probability that a given vacancy on a site in class h will jump to a site in class g, summed over all g. (If a jump to class $\tilde{g}$ is possible from h, this makes a negative contribution to A_{hg}.) By iteration

$$\mathbf{p}_n = \mathbf{p}_0\mathbf{A}^n \tag{3–22}$$

Normally, $\mathbf{p}_0$ will have one component equal to unity and all other components equal to zero, since the imperfection must be on one specific lattice site immediately after causing a given atom jump. (The probability for this site then is unity and that for all other sites is zero.)

If the row matrix $\mathbf{T}$ has components T_j and the square matrix $\mathbf{b}$ has components b_{gj}, (3–19) becomes

$$\mathbf{T} = \mathbf{p}_0 \cdot (\mathbf{1} + \mathbf{A} + \mathbf{A}^2 + \cdots) \cdot \mathbf{b} \tag{3–23}$$

Also, a column matrix $\boldsymbol{\tau}$ having components $\cos\theta_j$ can be defined. Then Eq. (3–18) reduces to $\langle\cos\theta\rangle = \mathbf{T} \cdot \boldsymbol{\tau}$, or

$$\langle\cos\theta\rangle = \mathbf{p}_0 \cdot (\mathbf{1} - \mathbf{A})^{-1} \cdot \mathbf{b} \cdot \boldsymbol{\tau} \tag{3–24}$$

Thus, $\langle\cos\theta\rangle$ can be found by inverting the matrix $(\mathbf{1} - \mathbf{A})$ and carrying out the indicated operations, as was done for example by Mullen.[5]

The accuracy of this method is limited by the size of the matrix $\mathbf{A}$ which can be used. Unless $\mathbf{A}$ is of infinite order, there will be some sites not represented in $\mathbf{A}$. Vacancies which reach these sites can actually still return, exchange with our atom, and contribute to $\langle \cos\theta \rangle$. In Eq. (3–24), however, these contributions are neglected if **A** is not of infinite order.

Combining equivalent and negatively equivalent sites increases the number of sites which can be represented in a matrix **A** of a given order. Even with the aid of high-speed electronic computers, however, it usually is not practical to invert very large matrices. Thus, in practice, finite **A** matrices including sites to perhaps the fifth coordination shell are usually used. This gives results that are accurate for impurity diffusion to approximately three significant figures. In the special case of self-diffusion, even better accuracy (to approximately five significant figures) can be obtained by centering the boundary on the original vacancy site rather than on the tracer site.[3,5,8]

Matrix methods allow other simplifications. For example, LeClaire and Lidiard,[2] who were the first to use a matrix approach, took advantage of the fact that the vector $\boldsymbol{\tau}$ in the face-centered cubic structure is an eigenvector of the matrix **A**. Tharmalingam and Lidiard[9] later showed that this is true for both **A** and $(\mathbf{1} - \mathbf{A})^{-1}$ in all crystals where each jump lies along an axis of at least two- or threefold rotational symmetry. Also, Franklin[8] by use of crystal group theory was able to express $\langle \cos\theta \rangle$ in terms of the eigenvalues and eigenvectors of a matrix which is similar, but not identical, to **A**. Solution of the eigenvalue equation for this matrix leads directly to an expression for $\langle \cos\theta \rangle$.

(3) Electrical Analog: Compaan and Haven[3,10,11] noted that the crystal lattice could be likened to an electrical network, with the flow of vacancies or interstitialcies between lattice sites being analogous to the flow of electric charge in a network of resistors. By making extensive use of symmetry properties, they were able to simplify their networks. In some instances, they solved the electrical equations for the networks exactly. In other instances, they built model networks extending as far as the ninth coordination shell and experimentally determined the important parameters. This method shows great versatility and yields very accurate values of f

TABLE 3–1. CORRELATION FACTORS FOR SELF-DIFFUSION[a]

Crystal Structure	*Correlation Factor*
Vacancy Mechanism, two-dimensional lattices	
Honeycomb lattice	$\frac{1}{3}$
Square lattice	0.46694
Hexagonal lattice	0.56006
Vacancy Mechanism, three-dimensional crystal structures	
Diamond	$\frac{1}{2}$
Simple cubic	0.65311
Body-centered cubic	0.72722
Face-centered cubic	0.78146
Hexagonal close-packed (with all jump frequencies equal)	0.78121 normal to c-axis 0.78146 parallel to c-axis
Interstitialcy Mechanism (θ = angle between the displacement vectors of the two atoms participating in the jump)	
NaCl, collinear jumps ($\theta = 0$)	$\frac{2}{3}$
NaCl, noncollinear jumps with $\cos\theta = \frac{1}{3}$	$\frac{32}{33} \approx 0.9697$
NaCl, noncollinear jumps with $\cos\theta = -\frac{1}{3}$	0.9643
Ca in CaF_2, collinear jumps ($\theta = 0$)	$\frac{4}{5}$
Ca in CaF_2, noncollinear jumps with $\theta = 90°$	1

[a] According to Compaan and Haven.[11] Many additional values can be found in references 3 and 11. For noncubic crystals, also see reference 5; and, for diffusion via vacancy pairs, see reference 4. The values above all assume that only nearest neighbor jumps are allowed.

for self-diffusion. A partial list of the results for self-diffusion is given in Table 3–1.

(4) Combinatorial Methods: Schoen and Lowen[12] used combinatorial methods to follow the vacancy paths and sum all contributions to $\langle\cos\theta\rangle$. They were able to obtain exact

analytical expressions for $\langle\cos\theta\rangle$ in a number of simple pure lattices.

3–6. GENERAL MATRIX EXPRESSION FOR THE CORRELATION FACTOR

Although (3–16) and (3–17) are very useful equations, they are not valid in all situations. The requirement of two- or threefold rotational symmetry around each jump vector restricts their application to structures having high symmetry, such as cubic, simple orthorhombic, and simple tetragonal structures. If diffusion occurs by divacancies or the symmetry is destroyed by neighboring impurity atoms, the equations are not valid, even for cubic structures. To cover these situations, a more general matrix expression has been developed by Howard,[4,13] who based his treatment on an approach first used by Mullen.[5]

Equivalent Jumps

As before, the correlation factor is found by calculating $\langle X^2\rangle$. The terms in (3–5) which contribute to $\langle X^2\rangle$ involve a summation over γ of sets of terms $\langle x_\gamma{}^2\rangle + 2\sum_{m=1}^{\infty}\langle x_\gamma x_{\gamma+m}\rangle$. Even in anisotropic structures, many of the sets are equivalent. For example, let us consider the planar lattice in Fig. 3–3. Here jump p from site A to site B and jump q from site C to site D

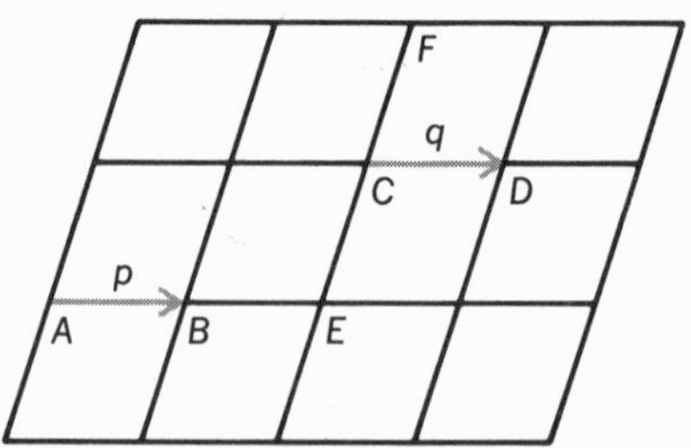

3–3 Jump p from site A to site B is equivalent crystallographically to jump q from site C to site D. Other jumps, such as those from E to C and from C to F, belong to a second set of equivalent jumps.

are of equal distance and in parallel directions. It follows immediately that $x_p = x_q$. Also sites B and D are separated by an integral number of unit cells, and thus, in a pure crystal, the average subsequent atom displacement will be the same from each of these sites. Therefore, $\langle x_p x_{p+m} \rangle = \langle x_q x_{q+m} \rangle$, and

$$\langle x_p^2 \rangle + 2 \sum_{m=1}^{\infty} \langle x_p x_{p+m} \rangle = \langle x_q^2 \rangle + 2 \sum_{m=1}^{\infty} \langle x_q x_{q+m} \rangle \qquad (3\text{–}25)$$

In any regular structure, there will be only a finite number of jumps which are not equivalent to some other jump in the sense of (3–25). Thus

$$\langle X^2 \rangle = \sum_{\alpha=1}^{R} n_\alpha [\langle x_\alpha^2 \rangle + 2 \sum_{m=1}^{\infty} \langle x_\alpha x_{\alpha+m} \rangle] \qquad (3\text{–}26)$$

where n_α is the average number of jumps of type α and R is the number of independent sets α. Then

$$\langle X^2 \rangle = \sum_{\alpha=1}^{R} n_\alpha x_\alpha^2 [1 + 2k_\alpha] \qquad (3\text{–}27)$$

where k_α equals zero if x_α equals zero, but otherwise,

$$k_\alpha = \sum_{m=1}^{\infty} \xi_m^{\alpha} \qquad (3\text{–}28)$$

with

$$\xi_m^{\alpha} = \langle x_\alpha x_{\alpha+m} \rangle / x_\alpha^2 \qquad (3\text{–}29)$$

In a random walk, $\langle X^2 \rangle = \sum_{\alpha=1}^{R} n_\alpha x_\alpha^2$ so

$$f_x = 1 + \frac{2 \sum_{\alpha=1}^{R} n_\alpha k_\alpha x_\alpha^2}{\sum_{\alpha=1}^{R} n_\alpha x_\alpha^2} \qquad (3\text{–}30)$$

Here, f_x is the correlation factor for planar diffusion in the x-direction.

The summations in (3–30) quite often reduce to only one or two terms. For example, in Fig. 3–3, the set of all jumps having jump vectors which could take an atom from site A to site B *or* in the reverse direction from site B to site A form a single set α_1. The remaining possible jumps which have vectors parallel or antiparallel to the line E–C–F form a second set α_2. In the simple case of cubic crystals, there often needs to be only one set with $x_\alpha \neq 0$.

Matrix Expressions for f_x

The x_α and n_α in (3–30) can be found directly from the lattice geometry and jump probabilities. However, k_α is unknown. We can let $p_{m\pm}{}^{\alpha\beta}$ be the probability that, if the initial jump of the atom is of type α, the mth jump following is of type β and in the same or opposite direction as the initial jump if we take the subscript as $+$ or $-$, respectively. Then

$$\xi_m{}^\alpha = \sum_{\beta=1}^{R} (p_{m+}{}^{\alpha\beta} - p_{m-}{}^{\alpha\beta}) \frac{|x_\beta|}{|x_\alpha|} = \sum_{\beta=1}^{R} t_m{}^{\alpha\beta} \frac{|x_\beta|}{|x_\alpha|} \tag{3–31}$$

where

$$t_m{}^{\alpha\beta} = p_{m+}{}^{\alpha\beta} - p_{m-}{}^{\alpha\beta} \tag{3–32}$$

We may express $p^{\alpha\beta}_{(m+1)\pm}$ in terms of $p_{m\pm}{}^{\alpha\beta}$,

$$p^{\alpha\beta}_{(m+1)+} = \sum_{\epsilon=1}^{R} (p_{m+}{}^{\alpha\epsilon} p_{1+}{}^{\epsilon\beta} + p_{m-}{}^{\alpha\epsilon} p_{1-}{}^{\epsilon\beta}) \tag{3–33}$$

$$p^{\alpha\beta}_{(m+1)-} = \sum_{m=1}^{R} (p_{m+}{}^{\alpha\epsilon} p_{1-}{}^{\epsilon\beta} + p_{m-}{}^{\alpha\epsilon} p_{1+}{}^{\epsilon\beta}) \tag{3–34}$$

so that

$$t_{m+1}{}^{\alpha\beta} = \sum_{\epsilon=1}^{R} (p_{m+}{}^{\alpha\epsilon} - p_{m-}{}^{\alpha\epsilon})(p_{1+}{}^{\epsilon\beta} - p_{1-}{}^{\epsilon\beta}) = \sum_{\epsilon=1}^{R} t_m{}^{\alpha\epsilon} t_1{}^{\epsilon\beta} \tag{3–35}$$

If we define a square matrix $\mathbf{T}_m$ whose elements are $t_m^{\alpha\beta}$, Eq. (3–35) becomes $\mathbf{T}_{m+1} = \mathbf{T}_m\mathbf{T}_1$. By iteration, we obtain

$$\mathbf{T}_m = (\mathbf{T}_1)^m \tag{3–36}$$

This is a generalized form of the equation $\langle\cos\theta_m\rangle = (\langle\cos\theta\rangle)^m$, as in Eq. (3–13), and reduces the correlation problem to one of calculating correlations between only two successive atom jumps, rather than between all possible pairs of jumps.

It is convenient to convert all quantities to matrix notation. We can define

$$\rho_\alpha = \frac{n_\alpha \mid x_\alpha \mid}{\sum_{\alpha=1}^{R} n_\alpha x_\alpha^2} \tag{3–37}$$

and

$$K_\alpha = \mid x_\alpha \mid k_\alpha = \sum_{m=1}^{\infty} \sum_{\beta=1}^{R} t_m^{\alpha\beta} \mid x_\beta \mid \tag{3–38}$$

where the right-hand equality follows from (3–28) and (3–31). If the vector $\mathbf{K}$ is defined as having components K_α and the vector $\boldsymbol{\rho}$ as having components ρ_α, Eq. (3–30) becomes

$$f_x = 1 + 2\boldsymbol{\rho} \cdot \mathbf{K} \tag{3–39}$$

A vector $\mathbf{d}$ can be defined with components $\mid x_\beta \mid$. Then Eq. (3–38) yields

$$\mathbf{K} = \sum_{m=1}^{\infty} \mathbf{T}_m \cdot \mathbf{d} = (\mathbf{T}_1 + \mathbf{T}_2 + \mathbf{T}_3 + \cdots) \cdot \mathbf{d} \tag{3–40}$$

When (3–36) is used to relate $\mathbf{T}_m$ and $\mathbf{T}_1$,

$$\mathbf{K} = \mathbf{T}_1 \cdot (\mathbf{1} + \mathbf{T}_1 + (\mathbf{T}_1)^2 + \cdots) \cdot \mathbf{d} = \frac{\mathbf{T}_1}{\mathbf{1} - \mathbf{T}_1} \cdot \mathbf{d} \tag{3–41}$$

and

$$f_x = 1 + 2\boldsymbol{\varrho} \cdot \frac{\mathbf{T}_1}{\mathbf{1} - \mathbf{T}_1} \cdot \mathbf{d} \tag{3–42}$$

which is Howard's general matrix equation applicable to any structure.

When all $|x_\alpha|$ are equal, (3–42) becomes

$$f_x = 1 + 2\boldsymbol{\sigma} \cdot \frac{\mathbf{T}_1}{\mathbf{1} - \mathbf{T}_1} \cdot \mathbf{1} \tag{3–43}$$

where $\mathbf{1}$ on the right is a unit column matrix and $\boldsymbol{\sigma}$ is a row matrix with components of σ_α

$$\sigma_\alpha = n_\alpha \Big(\sum_{\alpha=1}^{R} n_\alpha \Big)^{-1} \tag{3–44}$$

Physically, the σ_α are jump probabilities for the various jumps α.

Applications

The components of $\mathbf{T}_1$ can be calculated by the methods discussed to calculate $\mathbf{T}$ and $\langle \cos\theta \rangle$ in Section 3–5. Here the matrix approach described in Section 3–5 is especially useful.[4] In general, $\mathbf{p}_0$ is a square matrix. The elements $p_0^{\alpha\beta}$ of this matrix are the probabilities that the imperfection is at site β with respect to the atom after an α type jump.

For diffusion by a single vacancy mechanism in cubic crystals, only one set α is necessary. Then the quantities in (3–43) are scalars. Also $\boldsymbol{\sigma}$ equals unity, so (3–43) reduces directly to (3–16) as found earlier.

As a second simple example, let us consider a case where $R = 2$ and all jumps have equal x-components. Then, Eq.

(3–43) is valid with

$$\boldsymbol{\delta} = \left(\frac{n_1}{n_1 + n_2}, \frac{n_2}{n_1 + n_2}\right) \tag{3–45}$$

$$\mathbf{T}_1 = \begin{pmatrix} t^{11} & t^{12} \\ t^{21} & t^{22} \end{pmatrix} \tag{3–46}$$

and

$$\mathbf{1} = \begin{pmatrix} 1 \\ 1 \end{pmatrix} \tag{3–47}$$

Here the subscripts 1 on the $t^{\alpha\beta}$ in (3–46) are omitted to simplify the notation.

If the two types of jumps occur with equal frequency, n_1 equals n_2, and $\boldsymbol{\delta} = (\frac{1}{2}, \frac{1}{2})$. Then, after inverting the matrix $\mathbf{1} - \mathbf{T}_1$, we find

$$f_x = \frac{(1 + t^{12})(1 + t^{21}) - t^{11}t^{22}}{(1 - t^{11})(1 - t^{22}) - t^{12}t^{21}} \tag{3–48}$$

For diffusion by a single vacancy mechanism, the cross-terms t^{12} and t^{21} in the matrix $\mathbf{T}_1$ usually are small compared with t^{11} and t^{22}. This has been confirmed by Mullen in direct calculations for self-diffusion in the hexagonal-close-packed and body-centered tetragonal structures.[5] On the other hand, Howard has found that the cross-terms are quite important for diffusion by a divacancy mechanism or by bound vacancy-impurity pairs.[4,13]

In diffusion by an interstitialcy mechanism, the cross-terms are of extreme importance. Here the jumps from normal lattice site to interstitial sites can be called α_1 jumps and the interstitial to normal jumps α_2. Then $t^{21} = \langle \cos\theta' \rangle$ and $t^{12} = t^{11} = t^{22} = 0$. Also n_1 equals n_2; and, in cubic crystals, all jumps are equal in length. Then (3–48) applies, and $f = 1 + \langle \cos\theta' \rangle$, as found previously in (3–17). The entire deviation of f from unity is due to the cross-term t^{21}.

3–7. PARTIAL CORRELATION FACTORS AND THE S VECTORS

Directional Correlation Factors

In noncubic crystals, the correlation factor depends on crystallographic direction. Equation (3–4) gives the correlation factor for planar diffusion along the x-axis. This factor may be designated as f_x. Similar expressions in terms of $\langle Y^2 \rangle$ and $\langle Z^2 \rangle$ yield f_y and f_z for planar diffusion along the y-axis and z-axis. When the D tensors in (3–3) are both diagonalized and have identical principal axes, the quantities f_x, f_y, and f_z relate the corresponding diagonal elements of the D tensors.

Partial Correlation Factors

In addition to f_x, f_y, and f_z, it at times is useful to define partial correlation factors $f_{\alpha x}$, $f_{\alpha y}$, and $f_{\alpha z}$. Here $f_{\alpha x}$, $f_{\alpha y}$, and $f_{\alpha z}$ are the values of f_x, f_y, and f_z for α type jumps.

For diffusion along the x-axis, one can write

$$f_x = \sum_{\alpha=1}^{R} n_\alpha x_\alpha{}^2 f_{\alpha x} \Big/ \sum_{\alpha=1}^{R} n_\alpha x_\alpha{}^2 \tag{3–49}$$

where, according to Eq. (3–30),

$$f_{\alpha x} = 1 + 2 \sum_{m=1}^{\infty} \xi_m{}^\alpha \tag{3–50}$$

This equation defines $f_{\alpha x}$. Similar equations can be found for

$f_{\alpha y}$ and $f_{\alpha z}$. In general, with subscripts μ taking the place of x, y, or z,

$$f_{\alpha\mu} = 1 + 2 \sum_{m=1}^{\infty} \frac{\langle \lambda_{\alpha\mu}\hat{\mathbf{u}} \cdot \boldsymbol{\lambda}_{\alpha+m} \rangle}{\lambda_{\alpha\mu}^{2}} \tag{3–51}$$

where $\hat{\mathbf{u}}$ is a unit vector along the μ-axis, $\boldsymbol{\lambda}_{\alpha+m}$ is the jump vector for the mth jump of the atom after an α type jump, and $\lambda_{\alpha\mu}$ is the μ-component of the α jump.

Partial correlation factors can also be expressed in matrix notation. If we define a row matrix $\mathbf{f}_I(x)$ whose elements are the partial correlation factors $f_{\alpha x}$, comparison of (3–50) with the equations in Section 3–6 gives

$$\mathbf{f}_I(x) = \mathbf{1} + 2\mathbf{X} \cdot \frac{\mathbf{T}_1}{\mathbf{1} - \mathbf{T}_1} \cdot \mathbf{d} \tag{3–52}$$

where the square matrix $\mathbf{T}_1$ and the column matrix $\mathbf{d}$ are defined as in (3–41). Also $\mathbf{X}$ is a square matrix whose diagonal elements equal $| x_\alpha^{-1} |$ while all other elements in the matrix equal zero. In the simple but not uncommon case where the $| x_\alpha |$ all equal either zero or a constant distance d,

$$\mathbf{f}_I(x) = \frac{\mathbf{1} + \mathbf{T}_1}{\mathbf{1} - \mathbf{T}_1} \cdot \mathbf{1} \tag{3–53}$$

where the $\mathbf{1}$ on the far right is a unit column matrix and the $\mathbf{1}$'s in the built-up fraction are unit square matrices.

Use of partial correlation factors allows each type of jump and its effect on the diffusion coefficient to be considered separately. For example, one can compare the contributions of basal and nonbasal jumps to diffusion along the basal plane in hexagonal-close-packed crystals. Also, it at times is more convenient to calculate the partial correlation factors $f_{\alpha x}$ and then use (3–49) to find f_x than it is to calculate f_x directly from (3–42). For example, Huntington and Ghate[14] have used

Eq. (3–51) to derive expressions for the partial correlation factors in terms of the correlation vectors $\mathbf{S}_\alpha$. These expressions are particularly useful for calculating correlation factors for impurity diffusion in noncubic crystals.

The S Vectors

One can define a vector

$$\mathbf{S}_\alpha = \sum_{m=1}^{\infty} \langle \boldsymbol{\lambda}_{\alpha+m} \rangle \tag{3–54}$$

where $\boldsymbol{\lambda}_{\alpha+m}$ is defined as in Eq. (3–51). The vector $\mathbf{S}_\alpha$ equals the average displacement of the diffusing atom resulting from subsequent exchanges with the particular vacancy (or interstitialcy) which caused the α jump. Normally $\mathbf{S}_\alpha$ is very nearly antiparallel to the jump vector $\boldsymbol{\lambda}_\alpha$ of the α jump. It represents the extent to which subsequent correlated jumps tend to reduce the displacement $\boldsymbol{\lambda}_\alpha$. In terms of $\mathbf{S}_\alpha$, Eq. (3–51) becomes

$$f_{\alpha\mu} = 1 + \frac{2\mathbf{S}_\alpha \cdot \boldsymbol{\mu}}{\lambda_{\alpha\mu}} \tag{3–55}$$

Thus, if $\mathbf{S}_\alpha$ is known, all of the $f_{\alpha\mu}$ can be found.

The $\mathbf{S}_\alpha$ are related to one another by a set of equations,

$$\mathbf{S}_\alpha = \frac{-w_r(\boldsymbol{\lambda}_\alpha - \mathbf{S}_r) + \sum_s w_s \mathbf{S}_s}{w_r + \sum_s w_s} \tag{3–56}$$

where, after an original $\boldsymbol{\lambda}_\alpha$ jump, w_r is the vacancy or interstitialcy jump frequency for the return jump $-\boldsymbol{\lambda}_\alpha$, which involves a re-exchange with the diffusing atom; and the w_s are the jump frequencies for vacancy or interstitialcy jumps in other directions (to various sites s), not involving a re-exchange with the diffusing atom. The $\mathbf{S}_s$ are the average subsequent atom displacements after an imperfection has arrived at the various sites s (by w_s jumps, which do not displace the diffusing atom); while $\mathbf{S}_r$ equals the average subsequent displacement after correlated reverse jumps $-\boldsymbol{\lambda}_\alpha$. These equations can be solved for $\mathbf{S}_\alpha$.

Often, (3–54) can be simplified. For example, the configurations giving rise to $\mathbf{S}_\alpha$ and $\mathbf{S}_r$ differ only in that the diffusing atom and the vacancy have exchanged sites. When there is inversion symmetry through each site or mirror symmetry across a plane which is normal to the jump vector $\boldsymbol{\lambda}_\alpha$ and passes through $\boldsymbol{\lambda}_\alpha$'s midpoint, $\mathbf{S}_r = -\mathbf{S}_\alpha$. Then $\mathbf{S}_\alpha$ is completely determined by the $\mathbf{S}_s$ and the jump frequencies w_r and w_s.

For sites s which do not neighbor on the diffusing atom, it often is a reasonable approximation to take $\mathbf{S}_s$ equal to zero (or some other fixed value). Then the components of $\mathbf{S}_\alpha$ and the $f_{\alpha\mu}$ can be calculated solely in terms of the jump frequencies w_r and w_s. By this approach, Huntington and coworkers[14–16] have found expressions for impurity correlation factors in a number of anisotropic crystals.

Simple Applications. When there is two- or threefold rotational symmetry around the jump vector $\boldsymbol{\lambda}_\alpha$, as for example in cubic structures, the preceding equations simplify. Because of the symmetry, the vector $\mathbf{S}_\alpha$ necessarily lies along the same axis as $\boldsymbol{\lambda}_\alpha$. Thus, $f_{\alpha x} = f_{\alpha y} = f_{\alpha z} = f_\alpha$, and

$$f_\alpha = 1 + 2\frac{\mathbf{S}_\alpha}{\boldsymbol{\lambda}_\alpha} \tag{3–57}$$

This result leads naturally to the idea of effective jump frequencies discussed in Section 3–8.

As an application of (3–57), let us consider diffusion by an interstitialcy mechanism in a pure cubic crystal. After an interstitialcy has moved an atom into an interstitial site, future jumps of this interstitialcy give the atom zero average net displacement. If α_1 represents an interstitial-to-normal-site jump, $\mathbf{S}_{\alpha 1}$ therefore equals zero. For jumps from normal to interstitial sites, however, $\mathbf{S}_{\alpha 2}$ equals $\boldsymbol{\lambda}_\alpha\langle\cos\theta'\rangle$. Since these two types of jumps occur with equal frequency, (3–49) reduces to

$$f_x = \tfrac{1}{2}(1 + 0) + \tfrac{1}{2}(1 + 2\langle\cos\theta'\rangle) = 1 + \cos\theta' \quad (3\text{–}58)$$

in agreement with (3–17).

For a vacancy mechanism in cubic crystals, (3–54) yields $\mathbf{S}_\alpha = \boldsymbol{\lambda}_\alpha \sum_{m=1}^{\infty} (\langle\cos\theta\rangle)^m$. Then Eq. (3–57) reduces to (3–16).

3–8. EFFECTIVE JUMP FREQUENCIES AND CORRELATED SERIES OF JUMPS

Effective Jump Frequencies

When there is two- or threefold rotational symmetry around each jump vector $\boldsymbol{\lambda}_\alpha$, the vector $\mathbf{S}_\alpha$ necessarily lies along $\boldsymbol{\lambda}_\alpha$. Then, for any x-axis,

$$\langle X^2\rangle = \sum_{\alpha=1}^{R} \langle n_\alpha x_\alpha^2 f_\alpha\rangle = \sum_{\alpha=1}^{R} \langle n_\alpha^e x_\alpha^2\rangle \quad (3\text{–}59)$$

where for each individual α

$$n_\alpha^e = n_\alpha f_\alpha \quad (3\text{–}60)$$

Equations for $\langle Y^2\rangle$ or $\langle Z^2\rangle$ are found merely by replacing x_α^2 in (3–59) with y_α^2 or z_α^2, since in the present case $f_{\alpha x} = f_{\alpha y} = f_{\alpha z} = f_\alpha$. The resulting equations are those for a three-dimensional random walk with n_α^e playing the role of the average number of $\boldsymbol{\lambda}_\alpha$ jumps. Hence, n_α^e might be called the effective number of random jumps of type $\boldsymbol{\lambda}_\alpha$; and $\nu_\alpha^e = n_\alpha^e/\tau$ might be called the effective jump frequency for $\boldsymbol{\lambda}_\alpha$ jumps. This concept of effective jumps provides a useful physical interpretation of the correlation factor. The correlation factor from this view equals the fraction of actual jumps that are effective in causing random diffusion, as in Eq. (3–1).

Effective Jump Frequencies in a Driving Force

The idea of an effective three-dimensional random walk breaks down when a driving force is present, since the force in general changes the direction of $\mathbf{S}_\alpha$ and makes it nonparallel to $\boldsymbol{\lambda}_\alpha$. However, if attention is restricted to planar diffusion in certain directions, (3–59) still is valid. In many of these cases, it can also be shown that

$$\langle X \rangle = \sum_{\alpha=1}^{R} \langle n_{\alpha o}{}^{e} x_\alpha \varepsilon_\alpha \rangle = \sum_{\alpha=1}^{R} \langle n_{\alpha o} f_\alpha x_\alpha \varepsilon_\alpha \rangle \qquad (3\text{–}61)$$

where $\varepsilon_\alpha = x_\alpha F/2kT$, while $n_{\alpha o}{}^{e}$ and $n_{\alpha o}$ are values of $n_\alpha{}^{e}$ and n_α in the absence of a force. Then, even in a driving force, both $\langle X^2 \rangle$ and $\langle X \rangle$ for a correlated walk can be described in terms of one-dimensional random-walk equations, such as those in Chapter 2, but with the actual jump frequency ν_α being replaced by an effective jump frequency $\nu_\alpha{}^{e} = \nu_\alpha f$. This is discussed in detail in the remainder of this section and also in Chapter 4.

This approach is valid whether or not the $\mathbf{S}_\alpha$ and $\boldsymbol{\lambda}_\alpha$ lie along the same axes; therefore, it applies to diffusion in noncubic structures and also to diffusion in a driving force. The restriction on diffusion direction is unimportant in cubic structures. For these structures, diffusion is isotropic, and equations found valid for diffusion along one axis are also valid for diffusion along any axis. In noncubic structures, this restriction is significant. Still, equations for diffusion along several different axes can be calculated separately to give a description of diffusion in these structures.

Diffusion Normal to Close-Packed Planes

A correlated walk containing n jumps caused by M different vacancies is equivalent to a random walk containing M displacements of various lengths. An even simpler description of a correlated walk can be obtained by considering planar diffusion in a direction normal to a set of planes which obey the following conditions: (1) they are equally spaced and (2) vacancies cannot pass through a given plane in the set without stopping at least for a short while at a lattice site on this plane. These conditions are often satisfied by close-packed planes and even by other planes in simple structures. For example, the (100) planes in simple cubic, face-centered cubic, body-centered cubic, and diamond structures all satisfy these conditions if diffusion occurs by a nearest neighbor vacancy mechanism. Similar planes can be found in noncubic crystals. The plane containing the diffusing (tracer) atom is an important symmetry plane which we shall call plane b. By definition, plane b moves with the tracer. In the absence of driving forces, a vacancy which arrives on plane b is equally likely to cause positive and negative x-displacements in its subsequent exchanges with the tracer. The tracer displacement caused by the ith vacancy then can be divided into m_i segments random in direction. Each segment contains at least one tracer displacement, and the series of jumps forming a given segment is terminated when the vacancy arrives at a site on plane b (by exchanging with some atom other than the tracer). One then can talk in terms of N random displacements where

$$N = \sum_{i=1}^{M} m_i \tag{3–62}$$

It is useful for discussion to define each independent segment m_i as being caused by a separate "fresh vacancy". Then, N is the number of fresh vacancies which exchange with the tracer. A fresh vacancy by definition is one which either has not exchanged with the tracer previously, or else has arrived at a site on plane b since its last such exchange. The correlated walk reduces to a random walk containing N random displacements caused by N fresh vacancies. In contrast to the wide variation in the x-displacements caused by the M really distinct vacancies, the x-displacements from the N fresh vacancies are restricted to 0 or $\pm d$, where d is the distance between neighboring planes.

Let us consider the x-displacement caused by a given fresh vacancy. In particular, let us consider a case where the first exchange with the tracer is from the $+x$-direction, and the initial tracer displacement is $+d$. If the vacancy then moves (by exchange with other atoms) to plane b, the series of jumps resulting from this fresh vacancy is terminated after only one tracer jump. The net displacement due to this fresh vacancy then is just the initial displacement $+d$.

In general, however, there can be more than one tracer jump per series. The vacancy after the initial exchange is on the $-x$ side of the tracer. Also, the vacancy cannot pass through plane b without stopping at some site on plane b and being converted into a second fresh vacancy. Therefore, if our fresh vacancy re-exchanges with the tracer (before arriving at plane b), this second exchange must be from the -x-direction and give the tracer an x-displacement $-d$, just the reverse of that from the original jump. Since the x-displacements from these two jumps merely cancel, the net x-displacement of the tracer from a two-jump series will be zero.

The sequence of exchanges with this particular fresh vacancy could of course be prolonged by a third, fourth, or an infinite number of jumps before the vacancy moves to a plane containing the tracer. However, for any odd number of exchanges the net x-displacement will be $+d$, and for any even number of exchanges the net x-displacement will be zero. Similarly, if the original exchange had caused a tracer displacement $-d$, any odd number of exchanges would lead to $-d$ net x-displacement, and any even number of exchanges to zero net x-displacement.

Vacancies which give no net x-displacement do not contribute to either $\langle X^2 \rangle$ or $\langle X \rangle$. Therefore only N^e random displacements, all of magnitude $+d$ or $-d$, need to be considered in calculating $\langle X^2 \rangle$ or $\langle X \rangle$. Applying the random-walk equations gives $\langle X^2 \rangle = N^e d^2$. If N^e is separated into sets of jumps $N_\alpha{}^e$, where the first jump in set α is of type α, one finds in general

$$\langle X^2 \rangle = \sum_{\alpha=1}^{R} N_\alpha{}^e x_\alpha{}^2 = \sum_{\alpha=1}^{R} n_\alpha f_{\alpha x} x_\alpha{}^2 \qquad (3\text{–}63)$$

as in (3–59). Here, for all α with $x_\alpha \neq 0$, $x_\alpha{}^2$ equals d^2. Also,

$$N_\alpha{}^e = n_\alpha f_{\alpha x} \qquad (3\text{–}64)$$

and n_α is the number of jumps of type α.

For a true random walk,

$$\langle X^2 \rangle = \sum_{\alpha=1}^{R} n_\alpha x_\alpha{}^2 \qquad (3\text{–}65)$$

Since the correlation factor f_x equals $\langle X^2 \rangle_{\text{actual}} / \langle X^2 \rangle_{\text{random}}$, Eqs. (3–63) and (3–65) yield

$$f_x = \frac{\sum_{\alpha=1}^{R} n_\alpha x_\alpha{}^2 f_{\alpha x}}{\sum_{\alpha=1}^{R} n_\alpha x_\alpha{}^2} \qquad (3\text{–}66)$$

in agreement with (3–49). Therefore, the $f_{\alpha x}$ in (3–64) are the partial correlation factors discussed previously.

In the discussion above, the N^e displacements are random displacements having x-components equal to x_α. A driving force makes the number of $+x$-displacements differ from the number of $-x$-displacements. Still, as is shown below Eq. (3–73), the relation between $N_\alpha{}^e$ and n_α to first order is not changed by a driving force. Therefore, as in Eq. (1–12), the effect of a force F on $N_\alpha{}^e$ is given by

$$N_\alpha{}^e = N_{\alpha o}{}^e(1 + \varepsilon_\alpha) = n_{\alpha o} f_{\alpha x}(1 + \varepsilon_\alpha) \qquad (3\text{–}67)$$

Here $N_{\alpha o}{}^e$ and $n_{\alpha o}$ are the values of $N_\alpha{}^e$ and n_α in the absence of the force, and

$$\varepsilon_\alpha = x_\alpha F_\alpha / 2kT \tag{3–68}$$

In defining sets α, we now must distinguish between $+x$-displacements where $x_\alpha > 0$ and $-x$-displacements where $x_\alpha < 0$. Then by definition,

$$\langle X \rangle = \sum_{\alpha=1}^{R} N_\alpha{}^e x_\alpha \tag{3–69}$$

In the absence of a force, $\langle X \rangle = 0$. It follows that $\sum n_{\alpha o} f_{\alpha x} x_\alpha$ equals zero, and

$$\langle X \rangle = \sum_{\alpha=1}^{R} n_{\alpha o} f_{\alpha x} x_\alpha \varepsilon_\alpha \tag{3–70}$$

as in (3–61).

Equations (3–63) and (3–70) are equivalent to the random-walk equations found in Chapter 2 for $\langle X^2 \rangle$ and $\langle X \rangle$, the only difference being that $n_{\alpha o} f_{\alpha x}$ replaces the actual number of jumps. Thus, one can speak of an effective frequency of random jumps $\nu_\alpha{}^e$ which is related to the actual jump frequency $\nu_\alpha{}^a$ by the equation

$$\nu_\alpha{}^e = f_{\alpha x} \nu_\alpha{}^a \tag{3–71}$$

In cubic crystals, the dependence on α and on diffusion direction disappears. Thus $\nu^e = f\nu^a$, as in Eq. (3–1).

Correlation Factors and Matrices from Effective Jump Frequencies

Explicit expressions for the correlation factor f_x and the partial correlation factors $f_{\alpha x}$ can be found by relating $N_\alpha{}^e$ to n_α. For each α, $N_\alpha{}^e / n_\alpha$ equals the fraction of α jumps that satisfy the following conditions: (1) they originate a series of exchanges with a fresh vacancy, and (2) the series contains an odd number of exchanges so that the net x-displacement is $+d$ or $-d$. The probability that a series contains an odd number of exchanges is

$$1 - P_- + P_-P_+ - P_-^2P_+ + \cdots = \frac{1 - P_-}{1 - P_-P_+} \qquad (3\text{–}72)$$

where P_- is the probability that the initial jump will be followed by a reverse jump taking the atom back to its original plane, and P_+ is the probability that there will then be a second forward jump. The first, second, and succeeding terms in Eq. (3–72) give the probabilities that there will be 1, 2, or more jumps in a given series.

Often, only one set α needs to be considered, as for self-diffusion or diffusion of dilute impurities along a $\langle 100 \rangle$-axis in an otherwise pure cubic crystal by a single vacancy mechanism. Then P_+ and P_- are scalar probabilities. In general, however, there will be several sets α with different values of n_α. The n_α can be considered to be components of a vector (written in the form of a row matrix). Then both P_- and P_+ can be written as square matrices with the gjth element being the probability that an α_g jump will be followed by an α_j reverse jump.

Not every n_α jump is the *first* jump in a series of exchanges. The probability that a given n_α tracer jump originates a series equals $(1 - P_b)$, where P_b is the probability that the n_α jump was preceded by an exchange of the tracer with the same fresh vacancy. In the absence of driving forces and diffusion coefficient gradients, the probability that an atom jump in the $(+)$-direction is *preceded* by a correlated exchange (in the $(-)$-direction) is exactly the same as the probability that a jump in the $(-)$-direction is *followed* by a correlated exchange (in the $(+)$-direction). This latter probability is just P_+. When there is only one set α of equivalent sites, P_b equals the scalar probability P_+. In crystals with two or more sets α, a corresponding square matrix $\mathbf{P}_+$ is obtained. Combining this with (3–72) yields

$$N_\alpha{}^e = n_\alpha \frac{(1 - P_-)(1 - P_+)}{1 - P_-P_+} \tag{3–73}$$

The ratio $N_\alpha{}^e/n_\alpha = (1 - P_-)(1 - P_+)/(1 - P_+P_-)$ equals the correlation factor $f_{\alpha x}$. This same expression for $f_{\alpha x}$ is found when there is a driving force or diffusion coefficient gradient, as is derived for example in Chapter 4. [Equations (4–6) to (4–8) in Chapter 4 reduce to (3–73) if one lets $\nu_\alpha{}^e$ equal $N_\alpha{}^e/\tau$ and $\nu_\alpha{}^b G_\alpha$ equal n_α/τ.]

A driving force F changes both P_+ and P_-. However, since P_+ and P_- refer to jumps of equal magnitude but opposite direction, the change in P_+ is equal in magnitude but opposite in sign to the change in P_-. Therefore, to first order, the relation between $N_\alpha{}^e$ and n_α is not changed by the force.

In matrix notation, (3–73) becomes

$$\mathbf{N}^e = \mathbf{n} \cdot \frac{(\mathbf{1} - \mathbf{P})^2}{\mathbf{1} - \mathbf{P}^2} = \mathbf{n} \cdot \frac{\mathbf{1} - \mathbf{P}}{\mathbf{1} + \mathbf{P}} = \mathbf{n} \cdot \mathbf{f}_{\mathrm{II}} \tag{3–74}$$

where $\mathbf{N}^e$ and $\mathbf{n}$ are vectors having the components $N_\alpha{}^e$ and n_α, $\mathbf{P}$ equals the matrix $\mathbf{P}_+$ or $\mathbf{P}_-$ in the absence of a force, and $\mathbf{f}_{\mathrm{II}}$ is a square matrix equal to $(\mathbf{1} - \mathbf{P})/(\mathbf{1} + \mathbf{P})$.

By definition, if all $x_\alpha{}^2$ are equal,

$$f = \sum_{\alpha=1}^{R} N_\alpha{}^e / \sum_{\alpha=1}^{R} n_\alpha \tag{3–75}$$

In matrix notation, this becomes

$$f = \boldsymbol{\sigma} \cdot \mathbf{f}_{\mathrm{II}} \cdot \mathbf{1} \tag{3–76}$$

where $\mathbf{1}$ is the unit column vector, and $\boldsymbol{\sigma}$ is a row vector having components $\sigma_\alpha = n_\alpha / \sum_{\alpha=1}^{R} n_\alpha$. Since $\boldsymbol{\sigma} \cdot \mathbf{1}$ equals unity, (3–76) can also be expressed as

$$f = 1 - \boldsymbol{\sigma} \cdot \frac{2\mathbf{P}}{1 + \mathbf{P}} \cdot \mathbf{1} \tag{3–77}$$

which is exactly (3–43) with $\mathbf{P} = -\mathbf{T}_1$. One can also define

$$\mathbf{f}_{\text{I}} = \mathbf{f}_{\text{II}} \cdot \mathbf{1} \tag{3–78}$$

so that

$$f = \boldsymbol{\sigma} \cdot \mathbf{f}_{\text{I}} \tag{3–79}$$

When this is compared to (3–49), it is found that the components of the vector $\mathbf{f}_{\text{I}}$ are the partial correlation factors $f_{\alpha x}$ in the case where all $x_\alpha{}^2$ are equal. Finally in cubic crystals, $\mathbf{P}$ is a scalar and $\boldsymbol{\sigma} = 1$, so

$$f = \frac{1 - P}{1 + P} \tag{3–80}$$

This equals (3–16) with $P = -\langle\cos\theta\rangle$.

Values of f, $\mathbf{f}_{\text{I}}$, and $\mathbf{f}_{\text{II}}$ found above by relating $N_\alpha{}^e$ to n_α agree with previous values for correlation factor. The present discussion in terms of effective jumps, however, has the advantage that it applies directly to calculation of $\langle X \rangle$ in a driving force and not just to $\langle X^2 \rangle$ as do the discussions in Sections 3–3 to 3–7. As a result, the equations from Chapter 2 for a random walk in a driving force can be applied directly to a correlated walk for planar diffusion along certain axes. This is done merely by substituting an effective jump frequency $\nu_\alpha{}^e = \nu_\alpha{}^a f_{\alpha x}$ for the actual frequency $\nu_\alpha{}^a$.

Correlated Pairs

Physically, correlation effects occur because successive atom jumps involving a given vacancy (or interstitialcy) tend to cancel one another. One can think of the jumps in a correlated series, such as that leading to (3–72), canceling in pairs. The second jump in the series cancels the effect of the first jump so that neither jump is effective in promoting random diffusion. Similarly, the third and fourth jumps cancel, and so on. The correlation factor is just the fraction of jumps which are neither the initial nor the reverse jump in a canceling pair.

This idea of correlated pairs is particularly applicable to diffusion by an interstitialcy mechanism in a pure crystal. In this case, only alternate atom jumps are correlated to previous jumps, and thus the correlated jumps can obviously be separated into pairs.

The result that the correlation factor is not affected by a driving force arises naturally from the idea of correlated pairs. To first order, the probability of occurrence of such a pair is not affected by a driving force. Each pair involves one jump in the direction of the force and another jump in the opposite direction; thus, if the force aids one jump, it will hinder the other jump by an equal amount.[17]

3–9. CORRELATION FACTORS FOR IMPURITY DIFFUSION

In the present section, correlation effects for diffusion of isolated impurity atoms are considered.

When diffusion proceeds by a vacancy mechanism, $\langle \cos\theta \rangle$ and P depend on the probability of an atom exchanging places with a given vacancy more than once. For self-diffusion, this probability always can be expressed as a numerical constant, as in Table 3–1. For impurity diffusion, however, the probability depends on the ratio of the impurity jump frequency to that of the neighboring solvent atoms. Similar results are found for other mechanisms. This dependence on jump frequencies provides a significant difference between correlation effects for impurity diffusion and for self-diffusion.

Vacancy Mechanism

After an impurity-vacancy interchange, the vacancy may either re-exchange with the atom or exchange with a neighboring solvent atom. The re-exchange with the impurity occurs with probability

$$r = \frac{w_i}{w_i + \sum_s w_s} \tag{3–81}$$

where w_i is the jump frequency for exchange with the impurity, the w_s are frequencies for exchange with the solvent atoms, and the summation is over all solvent atoms which neighbor on the vacancy. Re-exchange with the impurity contributes to P, $\langle \cos\theta \rangle$, $\mathbf{S}_\alpha$, etc., and hence to the correlation factor. Therefore, the correlation factor depends on r and the ratios w_s/w_i.

Even after making a w_s jump from a site j, the vacancy may eventually return and exchange with the impurity. If the vacancy returns to site j for this exchange, the effect on $\mathbf{S}_\alpha$ (or P or $\langle \cos\theta \rangle$) is exactly the same as if the vacancy had immediately exchanged with the impurity and never made a w_s jump at all. Therefore, the fraction Y_{sa} of w_s jumps which are followed by an actual return of the vacancy to site j can be treated as if these jumps had not occurred at all.

A similar argument often can be applied to vacancies which return and exchange with the impurity from sites k other than site j. In cubic and a few other structures, there is two- or threefold rotational symmetry around all jump vectors $\boldsymbol{\lambda}_\alpha$. Then the contributions to $\mathbf{S}_\alpha$ from vacancies which return and exchange with the impurity from sites k will, when summed over all k, have zero average component normal to $\boldsymbol{\lambda}_\alpha$. The net contribution to $\mathbf{S}_\alpha$ or $\langle \cos\theta \rangle$ is the same as if a certain fraction Y_{se} of the w_s jumps had been followed by an effective return of the vacancy to site j. These vacancies also can be treated as though they had not left site j at all. In effect, the vacancy either exchanges with the impurity from site j (with

TABLE 3–2. CORRELATION FACTORS FOR IMPURITY DIFFUSION BY A VACANCY MECHANISM[a]

Crystal Structure	*Correlation Factor* $= H/(2w_2 + H)$
Diamond	$3Fw_3/(2w_2 + 3Fw_3)$
Simple cubic	$5Fw_3/(2w_2 + 5Fw_3)$
Body-centered cubic	$7Fw_3/(2w_2 + 7Fw_3)$
Face-centered cubic	$(2w_1 + 7Fw_3)/(2w_2 + 2w_1 + 7Fw_3)$

[a] These values are for a model which allows nearest neighbor jumps only and the following distinction between the various vacancy jump frequencies near an impurity: w_2 is the vacancy jump frequency for exchange with the impurity, w_1 is the vacancy jump frequency from one site neighboring on the impurity to another such site (this occurs only in face-centered cubic or hexagonal crystals), w_3 is the vacancy jump frequency from a site neighboring on the impurity to one not neighboring on the impurity, w_4 is the vacancy jump frequency for the reverse of a w_3 jump, and w_o is the vacancy jump frequency for any other jump. Jump frequencies near an impurity in a face-centered cubic crystal are illustrated in Fig. 3–4. Other illustrations appear in Reference 7. When $w_4 = w_o$, the following values of F are found: in the diamond structure, $3F = 2$; in the simple cubic structure, $5F = 3.77$; in the body-centered cubic structure, $7F = 5.33$; and in the face-centered cubic structure $7F = 5.15$. Values of F as a function of w_4/w_o are given in Fig. 3–5 for the diamond, body-centered cubic and face-centered cubic structures.

jump frequency w_i) or it moves off through the lattice and never returns [jump frequency $\sum_s w_s(1 - Y_{sa} - Y_{se})$]. The value of $\cos\theta$ for a return jump from site j is -1. Therefore, $\langle\cos\theta\rangle$ can be obtained from r by replacing $\sum_s w_s$ by the effective escape frequency $\sum_s w_s(1 - Y_{sa} - Y_{se})$ and multiplying by -1.

$$\langle\cos\theta\rangle = \frac{-w_i}{w_i + \sum_s w_s F_s} \tag{3–82}$$

with

$$F_s = 1 - Y_{sa} - Y_{se} \tag{3–83}$$

Values of F_s can be calculated by the methods described in Section 3–5. Results for several simple structures[7,18] are given in Table 3–2 and Fig. 3–5.

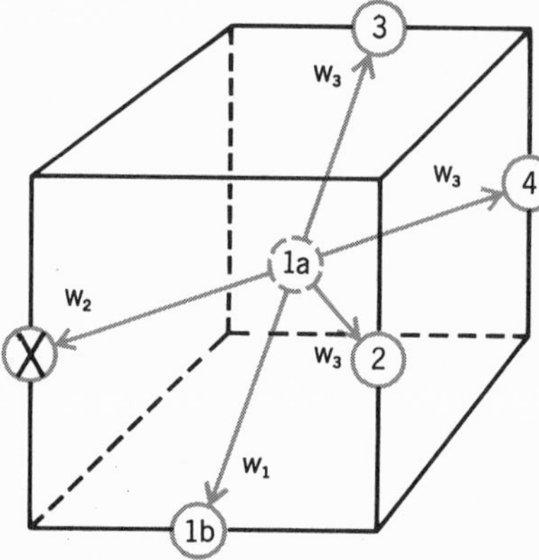

3–4 Vacancy jump frequencies for a vacancy neighboring on an impurity in a face-centered cubic crystal. The impurity is marked ×, while the sites marked 1, 2, 3, and 4 are first, second, third, and fourth nearest neighbors of the impurity. A w_4 jump is just the reverse of a w_3 jump.

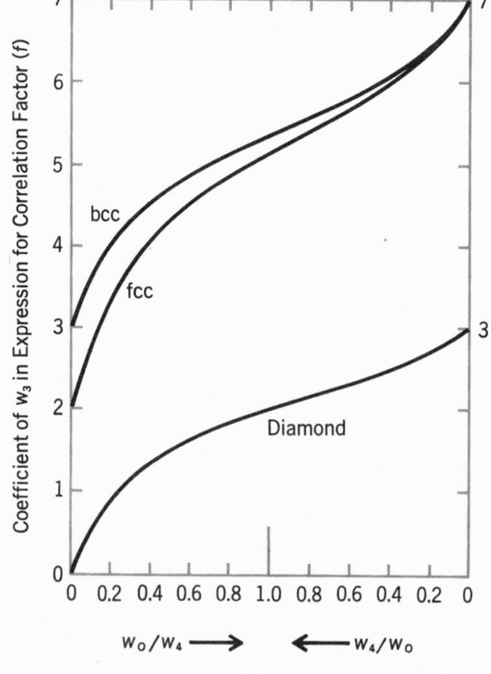

3–5 Values of F as a function of w_o/w_4 and w_4/w_o in diamond, body-centered cubic and face-centered cubic structures.

Effective Escape Frequency

The quantity $1 - F_s$ equals the fraction of w_s jumps following which the vacancy either actually returns to site j or arrives at some site k and "effectively" returns to site j. After an original atom-vacancy exchange, the vacancy does not occupy a random position with respect to the atom. Instead it is in a position such that a second jump would merely take the atom back to its original position and cancel the effect of the first jump. The quantity $\sum_s w_s F_s$ is an effective frequency for escape of the vacancy for its nonrandom position with respect to the impurity. Thus it may be called the effective escape frequency.

Substituting (3–82) into (3–16) yields

$$f = H/(2w_i + H) \qquad (3\text{–}84)$$

where the effective escape frequency H is given by

$$H = \sum_s w_s F_s \qquad (3\text{–}85)$$

The correlation factor for impurity diffusion is approximately unity if $H \gg 2w_i$ and approaches zero if $H \ll 2w_i$. The former case corresponds to a slow diffusing impurity and the latter to a fast diffusing impurity. In an intermediate case, the impurity correlation factor decreases as the frequency w_i increases. Thus, an increase in w_i does not cause a proportionate increase in the tracer diffusion coefficient D_i.

Since D_i is proportional to $w_i f$, we find in the limit where $H \ll 2w_i$ that the w_i dependence of D_i disappears. Instead H is the rate-limiting frequency. The frequency H involves jumps of the solvent atoms and does not involve jumps of the impurity. Thus, D_i for a fast diffusing impurity is rather insensitive to the impurity jump frequency. The diffusion coefficient for an impurity still can be much greater than the solvent diffusion coefficient, however, since the vacancy concentrations and solvent jump frequencies may be considerably enhanced near an impurity.

In (3–84), f is the impurity correlation factor for diffusion by a vacancy mechanism in cubic structures. In a simpler form, this can be written as

$$f = (1 + \alpha)^{-1} \tag{3–86}$$

where $\alpha = 2w_i/H$. An equation such as this also is valid for diffusion along [100]-axes in simple orthorhombic and simple tetragonal structures. However, the F_s, w_s, and w_i depend on the diffusion axes in these cases.

Interstitialcy Mechanism

For diffusion by an interstitialcy mechanism in cubic crystals

$$\langle \cos\theta' \rangle = \frac{\langle \cos\tau \rangle w_i}{w_i + H} \tag{3–87}$$

Here w_i and H refer to jump frequencies for an interstitialcy which is at an interstitial site neighboring on atom i. Also τ is the angle between the direction of an initial impurity jump from an interstitial to normal site and the direction a second impurity jump (from the normal site to an interstitial site) caused by this same interstitialcy. For collinear jumps, where the two atoms participating in the jump move in the same direction, $\cos\tau = -1$. In general, $\langle \cos\tau \rangle = -(\langle \cos\gamma \rangle)^2$, where γ is the angle between the directions of motion of the two atoms participating in the interstitialcy jump. The correlation factor from (3–17), including noncollinear jumps, is given by

$$f = \frac{w_i(1 - \langle \cos\gamma \rangle^2) + H}{w_i + H} \tag{3–88}$$

For collinear jumps $\cos\gamma = 1$, and (3–88) reduces to

$$f = (1 + \alpha')^{-1} \tag{3–89}$$

where $\alpha' = w_i/H$.

Planar Diffusion

If one takes the approach of Section 3–8 and considers planar diffusion normal to sets of close-packed planes, the concept of effective escape or randomization frequencies can be applied to calculations of P for planar diffusion. Here a vacancy upon reaching plane b will have randomized its position with respect to the impurity. If there is only one set of equivalent sites α neighboring the tracer, a vacancy which jumps from an α site to a neighboring site s has a probability Y_s of returning to a site in set α before it reaches plane b and a probability $F_s = 1 - Y_s$ of not returning without first reaching plane b. Then if w_s is the jump frequency from α to s, an effective escape frequency H can again be defined, as in (3–85).

After a particular w_s jump, the probability of return to set α may differ from the value of F_s for effective return to site j, defined in (3–83). However, in cubic crystals, $P = -\langle\cos\theta\rangle$, so that it is necessarily true that the sum $H = \sum_s w_s F_s$ is the same whether F_s is defined by (3–83) or by the equation

$$F_s = 1 - Y_s \tag{3–90}$$

in the manner described above. The individual values of F_s from (3–90) usually will differ from those given by (3–83). However, they obviously are closely related.

3–10. CORRELATION FACTORS IN ALLOYS

Equations (3–84) and (3–88) apply exactly to diffusion of dilute impurities in otherwise pure cubic crystals. If the effect of the impurity on the jump frequencies of the neighboring solvent atoms is specified, the F_s and H in principle can be calculated to as great an accuracy as desired. These equations also apply to diffusion of a tracer atom in a nondilute alloy. Here, however, the calculation of H is more difficult.

The average vacancy jump frequency from site g to site h is given by

$$w_{gh} = \sum_M w_{ghM} N_M \tag{3–91}$$

where w_{ghM} is the jump frequency for exchange with an atom of species M and N_M is the average fractional concentration of M atoms on the plane containing site h. In a homogeneous alloy, N_M does not depend on the position of site h. The jump frequency w_{ghM} normally will depend on the identities of the atoms which help form the barrier for the jump between sites g and h. To simplify the problem, however, we shall assume that the frequency w_{ghM} depends only on the identity of the atom that is jumping and not on the identities of any neighboring atoms. This implies that there is no binding energy between the vacancy and any particular atom. In a binary alloy, the average vacancy jump frequency W then is given by

$$W = w_A N_A + w_B N_B \tag{3–92}$$

where w_A is the frequency for exchange with a neighboring A atom and w_B that for exchange with a neighboring B atom. For simplicity, we assume that a vacancy jump to any average neighboring site occurs with a jump frequency W. Then the frequency H in (3–84) is given by

$$H = W \sum_s F_s \tag{3–93}$$

and simple expressions for correlation factors can be found in terms of the three "average" frequencies w_A, w_B, and W.

In an alloy, the successive jumps of the vacancies themselves will be related to one another. After exchange with an A atom, the vacancy still neighbors on this A atom. If w_A is larger than W, the vacancy after exchange with an A atom has a greater than random probability of making a reverse jump, by re-exchanging with the A atom. Similarly there is a smaller than random probability of re-exchange with a slow-diffusing B atom (with $w_B < W$). According to Eq. (3–49), the correlation factor for diffusion of vacancies in a binary alloy is given by

$$f_v = \frac{w_A N_A f_v^A + w_B N_B f_v^B}{w_A N_A + w_B N_B} \tag{3–94}$$

where f_v^A and f_v^B are the partial correlation factors for exchange with A and B atoms, respectively. In the present case, the x_α^2 in (3–49) are the same for both A and B type jumps and hence cancel out.

The correlation of vacancy jumps alters the effective escape frequency H. In the present model, the escape frequency is proportional to the vacancy diffusion coefficient D_v. If correlation effects are ignored, both D_v and H are directly proportional to W. When correlation effects are included, however, W should be replaced by the somewhat smaller frequency Wf_v, where Wf_v represents an effective frequency of random jumps. In the correlated case, (3–93) becomes

$$H = Wf_v \sum_s F_s = Wf_v M_o \tag{3–95}$$

Here M_o is the value of $\sum_s F_s$ in the absence of vacancy correlations with all nontracer atoms treated as having the same jump frequency. In face-centered cubic crystals, M_o equals 7.15; in body-centered cubic crystals, 5.33; in simple cubic crystals, 3.77; and in diamond, 2.

Then, with H given by (3–95), f_v by (3–94) and W by (3–92), one finds from (3–84) that the correlation factor f_A

for diffusion of A atoms in a random cubic binary alloy is

$$f_A = \frac{M_o(N_A w_A f_v{}^A + N_B w_B f_v{}^B)}{2w_A + M_o(N_A w_A f_v{}^A + N_B w_B f_v{}^B)} \tag{3–96}$$

In general, the partial vacancy correlation factor $f_v{}^i$ (for diffusion of vacancies by exchange with atoms of species i) does not equal the atom correlation factor f_i (for diffusion of species i). In the present model, vacancies jump at random whenever $w_A = w_B$, making $f_v{}^A = f_v{}^B = 1$ in this case. On the other hand, when $w_A = w_B$, the correlation factors for atom diffusion are given by $f_A = f_B = f_o$, where f_o is the correlation factor for diffusion of atoms in a pure crystal of the given crystal structure. (For face-centered cubic crystals, f_o equals 0.78.)

Even when $w_A \neq w_B$, the general relation

$$f_v{}^i = f_o{}^{-1} f_i \tag{3–97}$$

is always valid in the random alloy model used here.[19] This result is obtained by comparing atom and vacancy fluxes in a driving force. When diffusion is by a vacancy mechanism, the net vacancy flux is equal in magnitude (but opposite in direction) to the net atom flux. The vacancy flux resulting from exchanges with species i is proportional to $f_v{}^i$. The atom flux of species i is proportional to f_i. All other terms in the expressions for the two fluxes are identical except for the vacancy flow term discussed in Chapter 4. This term increases the atom flux in a random alloy by a factor $f_o{}^{-1}$, thus yielding (3–97).

In cubic crystals,

$$f_o = M_o/(M_o + 2) \tag{3–98}$$

and for both A and B atoms,

$$D_i^* = \tfrac{1}{6}\lambda^2 N_v z w_i f_i \tag{3–99}$$

With (3–97) to (3–99), one can re-write (3–96) in the form,

$$f_A = \frac{(M_o + 2)(N_A D_A^* + N_B D_B^*) - 2D_A^*}{(M_o + 2)(N_A D_A^* + N_B D_B^*)} \quad (3\text{–}100)$$

Similarly,

$$f_B = \frac{(M_o + 2)(N_A D_A^* + N_B D_B^*) - 2D_B^*}{(M_o + 2)(N_A D_A^* + N_B D_B^*)} \quad (3\text{–}101)$$

When D_A^*/D_B^* is greater than unity, f_A is less than f_o and f_B is greater than f_o. When $D_A^* = D_B^*$, $f_A = f_B = f_o$. Because of correlations, the ratio D_A^*/D_B^* (when $D_A^* > D_B^*$) will be smaller than w_A/w_B. According to (3–99),

$$\frac{D_A^*}{D_B^*} = \frac{f_A w_A}{f_B w_B} \quad (3\text{–}102)$$

Resulting values of D_A^*/D_B^* in a face-centered cubic crystal are plotted in Fig. 3–6 as a function of w_A/w_B for several values of $N_A (= 1 - N_B)$, with (3–100) and (3–101) used for f_A and f_B. In this model, D_A^*/D_B^* will not necessarily go to infinity when w_A/w_B goes to infinity. When $N_B > M_o/(M_o + 2)$, the maximum value of D_A^*/D_B^* is given by

$$\left(\frac{D_A^*}{D_B^*}\right)_{\text{max}} = \frac{(M_o + 2)N_B}{(M_o + 2)N_B - M_o} \quad (3\text{–}103)$$

In other cases, D_A^*/D_B^* will go to infinity, but more slowly than w_A/w_B goes to infinity.

The model above is that of a random alloy with no binding of a vacancy to any particular atom. For exchange with tracer atoms A and B, the vacancy jump frequencies are assumed to be w_A and w_B, regardless of surrounding atoms; whereas, for exchange with nontracer atoms, a single frequency W is assumed. This is a very simplified model. It probably does not apply to diffusion in dilute alloys, where binding may be im-

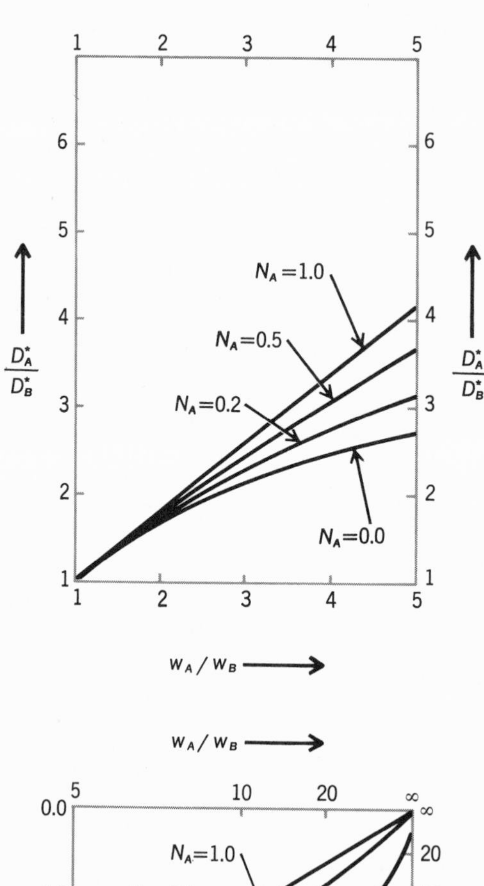

3–6 $D_A{}^*/D_B{}^*$ as a function of w_A/w_B in a face-centered cubic binary alloy. See Eq. (3–102).
(**a**) For the range $1 \leq w_A/w_B \leq 5$.

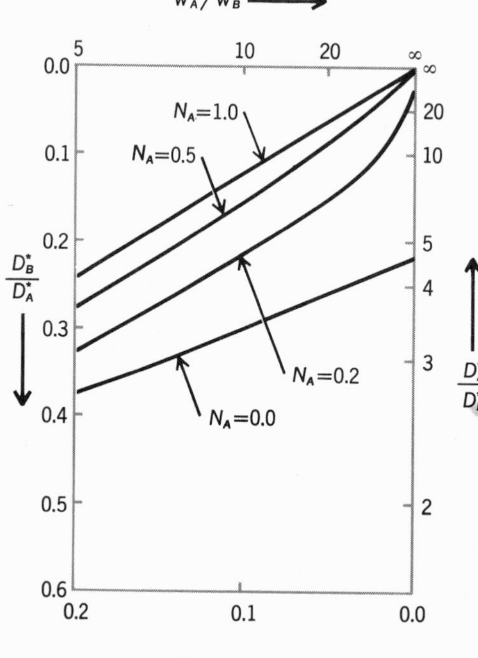

(**b**) For the range $5 \leq w_A/w_B \leq \infty$.

portant; and, even in nondilute alloys, it does not clearly provide an accurate average over all possible atom configurations. Nevertheless, this model does yield simple equations which include the major effects to be expected in alloys.

3–11. APPLICATIONS TO EXPERIMENT

Drift Mobility

Experimentally, there are two rather direct methods of measuring the correlation factor. The first method applies only to self-diffusion in ionic crystals and involves measurement of the drift mobility u in an electric field and the diffusion coefficient D. As described in Chapter 4, $u/D = q/kTf$ for self-diffusion by a vacancy mechanism, and $u/D = 2q/kTf$ for self-diffusion by a collinear interstitialcy mechanism. Since the charge q of the ion and Boltzmann's constant k are known, measurement of u, D, and the temperature T allows the correlation factor f to be calculated (if the diffusion mechanism is known).

For self-diffusion, the correlation factor is a numerical constant dependent only on the lattice geometry and the diffusion mechanism. Therefore, in many cases, it already is known. As a result, measurements of u (or the ionic conductivity σ) are used mostly to determine which diffusion mechanisms are operating[6,20–29] and almost never to measure an unknown correlation factor for a given mechanism. (See Section 7–3.)

Isotope Effect

A second method of measuring the correlation factor depends on the isotope effect in diffusion.[30] Two isotopes of a given element, because of their difference in mass, will not have exactly the same diffusion coefficient. The mass difference causes their vibrational frequencies to differ. According to classical rate theory, the vibrational frequencies, and hence the jump frequencies, should be inversely proportional to the square root of the masses.[31] For two isotopes ρ and σ of the same element, this gives

$$\frac{w_\rho}{w_\sigma} = \left(\frac{m_\sigma}{m_\rho}\right)^{1/2} \tag{3–104}$$

This difference in jump frequency causes the correlation factors, f_ρ and f_σ, and the diffusion coefficients, D_ρ and D_σ, to differ also.

For both isotopes, $D_i = kw_i f_i$, where k depends on geometric factors and defect concentrations. Since k is the same for any two isotopes,

$$\frac{D_\sigma - D_\rho}{D_\rho} = \frac{w_\sigma f_\sigma - w_\rho f_\rho}{w_\rho f_\rho} \tag{3–105a}$$

One can define $\Delta D = D_\sigma - D_\rho$, $\Delta w = w_\sigma - w_\rho$, and $\Delta f = f_\sigma - f_\rho$. Then (3–105a) can be rewritten as

$$\frac{\Delta D}{D_\rho} = \frac{\Delta w}{w_\rho}\left(1 + \frac{w_\rho}{f_\rho}\frac{\Delta f}{\Delta w} + \frac{\Delta f}{f_\rho}\right) = \Omega\frac{\Delta w}{w_\rho} \tag{3–105b}$$

This expression also serves to define the quantity Ω. The expression for Ω reduces to

$$\Omega = 1 + \frac{w_\sigma}{f_\rho}\frac{\Delta f}{\Delta w} \tag{3–106a}$$

When $\Delta w/w$ and $\Delta f/f$ are small (as is usually the case), this can be rewritten to first order in small quantities as[32]

$$\Omega = 1 + \frac{\partial \ln f}{\partial \ln w} \tag{3–106b}$$

In the special case where each jump vector lies along an axis of at least two- or threefold symmetry (as in cubic crystals),

$$f_\rho = \frac{H}{2w_\rho + H} \quad \text{and} \quad f_\sigma = \frac{H}{2w_\sigma + H} \tag{3–107}$$

If H is the same for both ρ and σ, (3–106a) reduces to $\Omega = f_\sigma$ and (3–105b) becomes

$$\frac{\Delta D}{D_\rho} = f_\sigma \frac{\Delta w}{w_\rho} \tag{3–108}$$

In certain extreme circumstances, H for isotope ρ may differ by a nonnegligible amount from H for isotope σ, making (3–108) only approximately correct.[33] In most cases, however, (3–108) provides a very useful relation between the measured quantities $\Delta D/D_\rho$ and the atomic quantities f_σ and $\Delta w/w_\rho$.

From Eq. (3–104), one finds

$$\frac{\Delta w}{w_\rho} = \left(\frac{m_\rho}{m_\sigma}\right)^{1/2} - 1 \tag{3–109a}$$

According to this equation, $\Delta w/w_\rho$ can be calculated directly from knowledge of the masses m_ρ and m_σ. For diffusion of substitutional atoms, the masses in (3–104) and (3–109a) probably should not be the actual masses of the diffusing isotopes, but instead should be "reduced masses" which include effects from the masses of neighboring atoms.[34–37] These neighboring atoms must move to allow a diffusing atom to pass through the saddle point in its jump. Also, after the jump is completed, these atoms may have moved to a slightly different location from that occupied before the jump. (For example, a net motion of the neighboring atoms occurs if there is relaxation around the site occupied by the vacancy which caused the atom jump.) In a ring or interstitialcy mechanism, motion by atoms other than the diffusing atom is even more pronounced. The introduction of the reduced mass reduces the predicted $\Delta w/w_\rho$. In place of (3–109a), one may write

$$\frac{\Delta w}{w_\rho} = \Delta K[(m_\rho/m_\sigma)^{1/2} - 1] \tag{3–109b}$$

where m_ρ and m_σ in (3–109b) are the actual masses of the diffusing isotopes and ΔK is smaller than unity. If T_g is the total kinetic energy in the normal mode ν_g, where ν_g is the unstable mode which if excited leads to the decomposition of the saddle point configuration and the passage of the diffusing atom to the new lattice site, ΔK can be interpreted as the fraction of T_g which is possessed by the diffusing atom at the saddle point.[33]

Then

$$\frac{\Delta D}{D_\rho} = \Omega\Delta K\left[\left(\frac{m_\rho}{m_\sigma}\right)^{1/2} - 1\right] \tag{3–110a}$$

and, when (1–108) is valid,

$$\frac{\Delta D}{D_\rho} = f\Delta K\left[\left(\frac{m_\rho}{m_\sigma}\right)^{1/2} - 1\right] \tag{3–110b}$$

Here the subscript on f is omitted since in all cases $f_\rho \approx f_\sigma$.

Since the masses m_ρ and m_σ for two isotopes of the same element usually do not differ greatly, the values of $\Delta D/D$ usually are less than 0.05. This small variation can be quite difficult to measure accurately even when the two isotopes diffuse simultaneously in the same crystal. Application of a driving force (such as an electric field) enchances the separation of the isotopes[38,39] and may allow a more convenient determination of $\Delta D/D_\rho$.

Some measured values of $\Omega \Delta K$ are listed in Table 3–3. In all of these cases, we expect $\Omega \approx f$, where f is the correlation factor of the diffusing isotope. In most instances of self-diffusion or interstitial diffusion in Table 3–3, $\Omega \Delta K \approx f$. Thus, in most instances, ΔK is approximately unity. Since physically the maximum allowed value of ΔK is unity and in cubic crystals $\Omega = f$ to a good approximation, the measured value of $\Omega \Delta K = (\Delta D/D_p)/[(m_p/m_\sigma)^{1/2} - 1]$ provides a lower limit for the value of f of the tracer being studied. For self-diffusion, the value of f depends only on the diffusion mechanism. Thus, if a large value of $\Omega \Delta K$ is measured for self-diffusion, this automatically excludes as a possible diffusion mechanism any mechanism where f is smaller than the measured $\Omega \Delta K$. If the diffusion mechanism is known, a measurement of $\Omega \Delta K$ allows ΔK to be determined experimentally. On the other hand, if the diffusion mechanism is not known, theoretical values of $\Omega \Delta K$ for various possible mechanisms can be compared with the experimental value of $\Omega \Delta K$ to distinguish the most probable diffusion mechanisms.[32,37]

Activation Energies

In impurity diffusion, the variation of the correlation factor with temperature can change the measured activation energy Q and make it differ from the true activation energy $E = E_m + E_f$. Experimentally it is found that the equation $D = D_o \exp(-Q/kT)$ is obeyed over a rather wide temperature range. The measured activation energy Q is found from the slope of a $\ln D$ vs $(1/T)$ plot, assuming that D_o is a constant independent of temperature. In terms of atomic quantities,

$$D = \tfrac{1}{6}\lambda^2 \nu f \qquad (3\text{–}111\text{a})$$

where

$$\nu = \nu_o \exp(-E/kT) \qquad (3\text{–}111\text{b})$$

The jump distance is always taken to be that at room tem-

TABLE 3–3. ISOTOPE EFFECT MEASUREMENTS

Isotopes	*Solvent*	$\Omega\Delta K$	*Ref.*
DIFFUSION OF SMALL INTERSTITIAL ATOMS ($f = 1$)[a]			
H^1, H^2	Pd	$0.85 \pm \Delta$ with $\Delta > 0.15$	*d*
H^1, H^2	Steel	0.89 ± 0.05	*e*
He^3, He^4	Fused Quartz	1.08 ± 0.03	*f*
Li^6, Li^7	Si	0.9 ± 0.25	*g*
Li^6, Li^7	W	0.9 ± 0.25	*h*
C^{12}, C^{13}	Fe	1.0 ± 0.25	*i*
Ne^{20}, Ne^{22}	Fused Quartz	1.0 ± 0.2	*j*
SELF-DIFFUSION IN FCC LATTICE OR SUBLATTICE ($f = 0.78$)[b]			
Na^{22}, Na^{24}	NaCl	0.73 ± 0.07	*k*
Pd^{103}, Pd^{112}	Pd	0.81 ± 0.04	*m*
Ag^{105}, Ag^{111}	Ag	0.8 ± 0.04	*n*
OTHER CASES (f UNCERTAIN)[c]			
Li^6, Li^7	Na	0.91 ± 0.08	*p*
Na^{22}, Na^{24}	Na	0.36 ± 0.04	*q*
Na^{22}, Na^{24}	AgCl	0.99 ± 0.02	*r*
Cr^{50}, Cr^{54}	NiCr(0–20% Cr)	0.5 ± 0.2	*s*
Fe^{55}, Fe^{59}	Ti at 1082°C	0.02 ± 0.02	*t*
Fe^{55}, Fe^{59}	Ti at 1369°C	0.09 ± 0.02	*t*
Fe^{55}, Fe^{59}	Cu at 716°C	0.59 ± 0.05	*u*
Fe^{55}, Fe^{59}	Cu at 1056°C	0.74 ± 0.05	*u*
Fe^{55}, Fe^{59}	Ag at 725°C	0.76 ± 0.08	*u*
Fe^{55}, Fe^{59}	Ag at 880°C	0.49 ± 0.07	*u*
Ni^{58}, Ni^{60}, Ni^{62}	NiCu(0–100% Ni)	1.0 ± 0.3	*v*
Zn^{65}, Zn^{69}	Ag	0.50 ± 0.05	*w*
Cd^{109}, Cd^{115m}	Cu	-0.05 ± 0.05	*x*
Cd^{109}, Cd^{115m}	Ag	0.0 ± 0.1	*x*

[a] Diffusion assumed to be by an interstitial mechanism with correlation factor $f = 1$.

[b] Diffusion assumed to be by a single vacancy mechanism with correlation factor $f = 0.78$.

[c] For impurity diffusion, f depends on the vacancy jump frequencies near

perature and hence is constant. Also ν_o should be reasonably constant as a function of temperature. For impurity diffusion and diffusion involving multiple mechanisms with different activation energies, however, f does depend on temperature. Thus,

$$Q = E - k[\partial \ln f/\partial(1/T)] \qquad (3\text{–}112)$$

For impurity diffusion by a vacancy mechanism, the correlation factor depends on the ratio of the impurity jump frequency to the various solvent jump frequencies in the vicinity of the impurity. These frequencies each depend on temperature, and in general have different energies of motion. Thus, f will depend on temperature and make Q differ from E. If Q_i for a dilute substitutional impurity is appreciably smaller

---

the impurity and hence is unknown (but should be between 0 and 1). For a discussion of the Na^{22}, Na^{24} in Na results (bcc structure), see reference *q* and reference 33.

[d] W. Jost and A. Widmann, *Z. physik. Chem.* **B29**, 247 (1935).

[e] R. C. Frank, W. L. Lee and R. L. Williams, *J. Appl. Phys.* **29**, 898 (1958).

[f] W. M. Jones, *J. Amer. Chem. Soc.* **75**, 3093 (1953).

[g] E. M. Pell, *Phys. Rev.* **119**, 1014 (1960).

[h] G. M. McCracken and H. M. Love, *Phys. Rev. Letters* **5**, 201 (1960).

[i] A. J. Bosman, P. E. Brommer, and G. W. Rathman, *J. Physique Radium* **20**, 241 (1959).

[j] R. C. Frank, D. E. Swets, and R. W. Lee, *J. Chem. Phys.* **35**, 1451 (1961).

[k] L. W. Barr and A. D. LeClaire, *Proc. Brit. Ceram. Soc.* **1**, 109 (1964).

[m] N. L. Peterson, *Phys. Rev.* **136**, A568 (1964).

[n] N. L. Peterson, quoted in reference *q*.

[p] A. N. Naumov and G. Ya. Ryskin, *Fiz. Tverd. Tela* **7**, 695 (1965); translated in *Soviet Physics—Solid State* **7**, 558 (1965).

[q] L. W. Barr and J. N. Mundy, "Diffusion in Body-Centered Cubic Metals" (American Society for Metals, Metals Park, Ohio, 1965), p. 171.

[r] P. Süptitz, *Phys. Stat. Sol.* **12**, 555 (1965).

[s] Th. Heumann and W. Reerink, *Acta Met.* **14**, 201 (1966).

[t] G. B. Gibbs, D. Graham, and D. H. Tomlin, *Phil. Mag.* **8**, 1269 (1963).

[u] J. G. Mullen, *Phys. Rev.* **121**, 1649 (1961).

[v] W. A. Johnson, *Trans. A.I.M.E.* **166**, 144 (1946).

[w] S. J. Rothman, N. L. Peterson, J. J. Hines, and R. Bastar, *Abstract Bulletin*, Inst. of Metals Div., Met. Soc., A.I.M.E. **1**, 8 (1966).

[x] A. H. Schoen, *Phys. Rev. Letters* **1**, 138 (1958).

than Q_s for self-diffusion of the solvent, the term $\partial \ln f/\partial(1/T)$ can be quite large.[40,41] Usually this term will cause $|E_i - E_s|$ to be smaller than the difference $|Q_i - Q_s|$. This effect is greatest for dilute impurities. It becomes smaller as the impurity concentration is increased, since then some of the competing "solvent" jumps involve impurity atoms also.

For self-diffusion in pure cubic crystals all jump frequencies are identical. Then f is a numerical constant independent of temperature and $Q = E$. On the other hand, whenever more than one energy of motion enters into the determination of the correlation factor, there necessarily is a nonzero correction to the activation energy. This can occur when diffusion in alloys, diffusion in noncubic crystals, or diffusion of impurities in otherwise pure crystals takes place by a vacancy or interstitialcy mechanism.

Solvent Diffusion Enhancement

An application where use of partial correlation factors is necessary occurs in the case of solvent diffusion enhancement. This is concerned with the increase in the average solvent diffusion coefficient when a mole fraction N_i of some impurity is added to the crystal.

Experimentally it is found for low values of N_i that[42]

$$D_s(N_i) = D_s(0)(1 + bN_i) \tag{3–113}$$

where $D_s(N_i)$ and $D_s(0)$ are the average solvent diffusion coefficients when the mole fraction of impurities equals N_i and zero, respectively. Also b is a numerical coefficient whose value depends on the type of impurity.

Theoretically, this enhancement can be explained as arising from the increased vacancy jump frequencies in the vicinity of an impurity. An expression is obtained below for b in a face-centered cubic crystal with vacancy jump frequencies w_o, w_1, w_3, and w_4 for exchange with solvent atoms and w_2 for exchange with an impurity, as defined in Section 3–9. The concept of effective jump frequencies ($\nu^e = f\nu^a$) discussed in Section 3–8 is used in this derivation.

First let us define f_o, f_1, f_3, and f_4 as the average partial correlation factors for w_o, w_1, w_3, and w_4 jumps. Every vacancy which neighbors on an impurity has four possible jumps which move the vacancy to another site neighboring on the impurity (jump frequency w_1) and seven possible jumps which move the vacancy to a site not neighboring on the impurity (jump frequency w_3). The contribution of these jumps to the average effective jump frequency ν_s^e of the solvent atoms equals the probability that a vacancy is located next to an impurity multiplied by the effective jump frequency ($w^e = fw^a$) from such a site. The resulting contribution to ν_s^e is

$$12N_{v\beta}N_i(4w_1 f_1 + 7w_3 f_3).$$

Here $N_{v\beta}$ is the probability that a site neighboring on an impurity contains a vacancy and the factor 12 arises because there are twelve sites which are nearest neighbors of the impurity. Also $N_{v\beta} = N_{vo}\exp(g/kT)$, where g is the vacancy-impurity binding energy and N_{vo} is the probability that a site far from any impurity is occupied by a vacancy. If the impurity did not change $N_{v\beta}$, w_1, and w_3 from their values in the absence of the impurity, the contribution of the w_1 and w_3 jumps to the average effective jump frequency would be $12N_{vo}N_i(11w_o f_o)$. Thus, the change in $N_{v\beta}$, w_1, and w_3 changes the average effective jump frequency for solvent atoms by

$$12N_{vo}N_i[-11w_o f_o + (4w_1 f_1 + 7w_3 f_3)\exp(g/kT)].$$

There also are contributions to ν_s^e from the w_4 jumps. These jumps are just the reverse of the w_3 jumps. For every site neighboring on an impurity, there are seven possible w_3 jumps and also seven possible w_4 jumps. If the presence of the impurity makes w_4 differ from w_o, the resulting change in ν_s^e is

$12N_{vo}N_i(-7w_of_o + 7w_4f_4)$ making a total change in ν_s^e of

$$\Delta\nu_s^e = 12N_{vo}w_of_oN_i\left[-18 + \left(\frac{4w_1f_1}{w_of_o} + \frac{7w_3f_3}{w_of_o}\right) \times \exp(g/kT) + \frac{7w_4f_4}{w_of_o}\right] \quad (3\text{–}114)$$

Now

$$\frac{D_s(N_i)}{D_s(0)} = \frac{\nu_s^e(0) + \Delta\nu_s^e}{\nu_s^e(0)} \quad (3\text{–}115)$$

where $\nu_s^e(0)$ is the average effective jump frequency at zero impurity concentration. In face-centered cubic crystals,

$$\nu_s^e(0) = 12N_{vo}w_of_o \quad (3\text{–}116)$$

Combining these equations with (3–113) then yields

$$b = -18 + \left\{\frac{4w_1f_1}{w_of_o} + \frac{7w_3f_3}{w_of_o}\right\}\exp(g/kT) + \frac{7w_4f_4}{w_of_o} \quad (3\text{–}117)$$

Here, it is assumed that divacancies do not form and each impurity remains isolated from other impurities.

The total number of associative (w_4) jumps, which bring the vacancy to a site neighboring on the impurity, must equal the number of dissociative (w_3) jumps which move the vacancy away from the impurity. Thus

$$w_3N_{v\beta} = w_4N_{vo} \quad (3\text{–}118)$$

and

$$w_3\exp(g/kT) = w_4 \quad (3\text{–}119)$$

and if we let $f_{34} = \frac{1}{2}(f_3 + f_4)$, we find

$$b = -18 + 4\frac{w_1}{w_3}\frac{w_4f_1}{w_of_o} + 14\frac{w_4f_{34}}{w_of_o} \quad (3\text{–}120)$$

In general, both f_1 and f_{34} depend on the ratios w_1/w_3, w_1/w_2, and w_4/w_o. Thus, b depends on all three of these ratios.[43]

REFERENCES

1. J. Bardeen and C. Herring, "Atom Movements," edited by J. H. Holloman (American Society for Metals, Cleveland, 1951), p. 87; also "Imperfections in Nearly Perfect Crystals," edited by W. Shockley (John Wiley and Sons, Inc., New York, 1952), p. 261.
2. A. D. LeClaire and A. B. Lidiard, *Phil. Mag.* **1,** 518 (1956).
3. K. Compaan and Y. Haven, *Trans. Faraday Soc.* **52,** 786 (1956).
4. R. E. Howard, *Phys. Rev.* **144,** 650 (1966).
5. J. G. Mullen, *Phys. Rev.* **124,** 1723 (1961).
6. R. J. Friauf, *Phys. Rev.* **105,** 843 (1957).
7. J. R. Manning, *Phys. Rev.* **116,** 819 (1959).
8. A. D. Franklin, *J. Res. Nat. Bur. Standards* **69A,** (Phys. and Chem.), 301 (1965).
9. K. Tharmalingam and A. B. Lidiard, *Phil. Mag.* **4,** 899 (1959).
10. K. Compaan and Y. Haven, "La Diffusion dans les Metaux," edited by J. D. Fast (Bibliotheque Technique Philips, Eindhoven, 1957), p. 19.
11. K. Compaan and Y. Haven, *Trans. Faraday Soc.* **54,** 1498 (1958).
12. A. H. Schoen and R. W. Lowen, *Bull. Amer. Phys. Soc. Series* II, **5,** 280 (1960).
13. R. E. Howard, "Reactivity of Solids," Fifth International Symposium, Munich, 1964 (Elsevier Publishing Co., Amsterdam, 1965), p. 249.
14. H. B. Huntington and P. B. Ghate, *Phys. Rev. Letters* **8,** 421 (1962).
15. H. B. Huntington, P. B. Ghate, and J. H. Rosolowski, *J. Appl. Phys.* **35,** 3027 (1964).
16. P. B. Ghate, *Phys. Rev.* **133,** A1167 (1964).
17. J. R. Manning, *Phys. Rev.* **124,** 470 (1961); **139,** A126 (1965).
18. J. R. Manning, *Phys. Rev.* **136,** A1758 (1964).
19. J. R. Manning, "Lattice Defects and Their Interactions," edited by R. R. Hasiguti (Gordon and Breach, New York, 1967).
20. W. D. Compton, *Phys. Rev.* **101,** 1209 (1956).
21. C. W. McCombie and A. B. Lidiard, *Phys. Rev.* **101,** 1210 (1956).

22. W. D. Compton and R. J. Maurer, *J. Phys. Chem. Solids* **1,** 191 (1956).
23. A. S. Miller and R. J. Maurer, *J. Phys. Chem. Solids* **4,** 196 (1958).
24. K. Compaan and Y. Haven, *Proc. Third Int. Symp. on the Reactivity of Solids,* Madrid 1956 (C. Bermejo, Madrid, 1957), p. 155; *Discussions Faraday Soc.* **23,** 105 (1957).
25. A. B. Lidiard, *Proc. Third Int. Symp. on the Reactivity of Solids,* Madrid 1956. (C. Bermejo, Madrid, 1957), p. 481; *Nuovo Cimento* **7,** Suppl. No. 2, 620 (1958).
26. D. W. Lynch, *Phys. Rev.* **118,** 468 (1960).
27. R. J. Friauf, *J. Phys. Chem. Solids* **18,** 203 (1961).
28. R. J. Friauf, *J. Appl. Phys. Suppl.* **33,** 494 (1962).
29. R. J. Friauf, *J. Phys. Chem.* **66,** 2380 (1962).
30. A. H. Schoen, *Phys. Rev. Letters* **1,** 138 (1958).
31. See, e.g., S. Glasstone, K. J. Laidler, and H. Eyring, "The Theory of Rate Processes" (McGraw-Hill Book Co., New York, 1961).
32. L. W. Barr and A. D. LeClaire, *Proc. Brit. Ceram. Soc.* **1,** 109 (1964).
33. A. D. LeClaire, *Phil. Mag.* **14,** 1271(1966).
34. G. H. Vineyard, *J. Phys. Chem. Solids* **3,** 121 (1957).
35. S. A. Rice, *Phys. Rev.* **112,** 804 (1958); A. W. Lawson, S. A. Rice, R. D. Corneliussen, and N. H. Nachtrieb, *J. Chem. Phys.* **32,** 447 (1960).
36. J. G. Mullen, *Phys. Rev.* **121,** 1649 (1961).
37. L. W. Barr and J. N. Mundy, "Diffusion in Body-Centered Cubic Metals" (American Society for Metals, Metals Park, Ohio, 1965), p. 171.
38. M. Chemla, *Ann. Physik* **1,** 959 (1956).
39. J. R. Manning, *J. Appl. Phys.* **33,** 2145 (1962).
40. J. R. Manning, *Phys. Rev. Letters* **1,** 365 (1958).
41. A. D. LeClaire, *Phil. Mag.* **7,** 141 (1962).
42. See, e.g., A. B. Lidiard, *Phil. Mag.* **5,** 1171 (1960).
43. R. E. Howard and J. R. Manning, *Phys. Rev.* **154,** 561 (1967).

4. CORRELATED WALK IN A DRIVING FORCE

4–1. VACANCY FLOW EFFECTS

A driving force makes atoms jump more frequently in one direction than another. As a result, there is a direct contribution from the force to the atom drift velocity $\langle v \rangle$. In addition, when diffusion proceeds by a vacancy mechanism, each atom jump is accompanied by a vacancy jump in the opposite direction. This creates a flow of vacancies equal in magnitude but opposite in direction to the flow of atoms. The vacancy flow influences the diffusion process and provides a second, more indirect, contribution from the force to the atom drift velocity. This indirect effect from a driving force is considered in the present chapter. The resulting equations are applied to diffusion of ions in an electric field. The indirect effect from the vacancy flow at times is larger than the direct effect of the field on the charged ions. Equations (4–24) and (4–45) are general equations for $\langle X \rangle$. Specific applications are discussed in Section 4–5.

An effect from a flow of vacancies (or interstitialcies) is physically reasonable. When diffusion occurs by a vacancy mechanism, a given atom cannot jump until a vacancy has moved into a neighboring site. In Fig. 4–1, the vacancy flow is from right to left. A vacancy in this case is more likely to approach a given (tracer) atom from the right, cause a jump, and then move away to the left than it is to approach from the left, cause a jump, and move away to the right. Consequently,

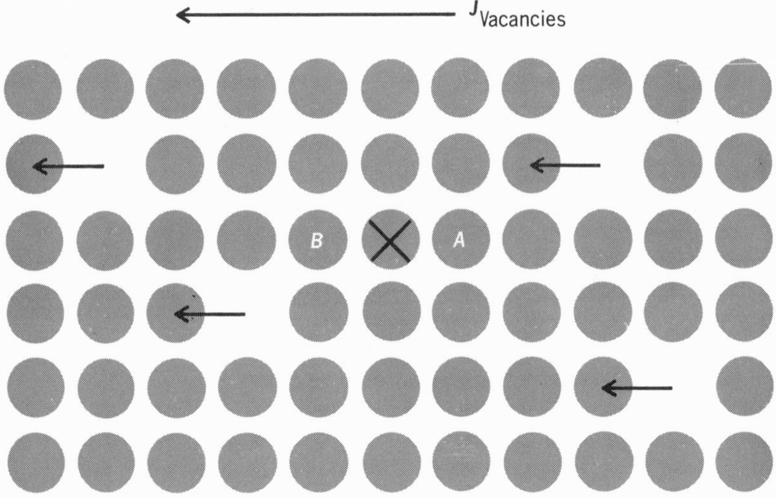

4–1 The effect of a flow of vacancies. The tracer atom is marked ×. Arrows show the motion of individual vacancies. When the vacancy flow is from right to left as shown in the figure, the individual vacancies are more likely to approach the tracer from the right (at site A) than from the left (at site B).

the tracer tends to jump more frequently to the right than to the left. This effect depends on the frequency with which vacancies approach a given atom from the various directions. Thus, it depends on the jump frequencies of atoms *other* than the tracer. Similar reasoning applies when there is a flow of interstitialcies.

It may be noted that the vacancy flow effect differs from the correlation effects discussed in Chapter 3. The correlation factor arises because jumps of the tracer itself affect the distribution of vacancies or interstitialcies in the tracer's vicinity. This factor is not changed by a driving force. In contrast, vacancy flow effects depend on changes in the vacancy distribution near the tracer resulting from the motion of atoms other than the tracer. These effects are proportional to the driving force and go to zero when the net flow of vacancies goes to zero.

4–2. J, $\langle X^2 \rangle$, AND $\langle X \rangle$ FOR A CORRELATED WALK IN A DRIVING FORCE

Quantitative expressions for a correlated walk in a driving force can be found by following the approach in Section 3–8. There it was shown that for planar diffusion in certain directions the correlated walk equations can be expressed in terms of effective jump frequencies. Even in a driving force, the resulting equations reduce to modified "random walk" equations, such as those presented in Chapter 2, but with the frequencies ν from Chapter 2 replaced by effective jump frequencies $\nu_\alpha{}^e = N_\alpha{}^e/\tau$. The atom flux J then can be found from the random-walk equations, with $\langle X^2 \rangle$ and $\langle X \rangle$ given by (2–38) and (2–47).

Symmetry Plane

When the conditions in Section 3–8 are satisfied, plane b passing through the tracer normal to the diffusion direction is a symmetry plane. In the absence of forces, a vacancy on this plane is equally likely to cause positive or negative tracer jumps. In a force field, this is no longer true; however, plane b is still distinct, since it then is the only plane where the average concentration of vacancies remains unaffected by the presence of a constant driving force.

For self-diffusion, a constant force causes a uniform flow of vacancies through the crystal. This uniform flow creates no variations in average vacancy concentrations. On the other hand, impurities in the crystal usually disrupt the uniform vacancy flow, allowing a more or less easy flow than in the rest of the crystal. Then vacancy concentrations both to the left and right of the impurity differ from those when the force is absent, being greater on one side and less on the other. Only on plane b is the vacancy concentration unaffected.

To illustrate this effect, let us consider an impurity which sits immobile while a current of vacancies flows past it. One can make an analogy to nonturbulent flow of water in a river around an immobile rock. The flow from the upstream side is impeded by the barrier to its flow. This leads to a pile up of water on the upstream side. The downstream side, which is protected from the flow, experiences an equal deficit of water (or vacancies), while the concentration on plane b is unaffected. For a fast diffusing impurity, one might imagine the rock as being replaced by a pump which expedites the flow in the region of the impurity, thus decreasing the pressure on the upstream side and increasing the pressure on the downstream side but leaving the pressure on plane b unaffected.

Because of this antisymmetry around plane b, the idea that a "fresh vacancy" forms whenever a vacancy reaches plane b is again useful. Also, the development of (3–63) and (3–70) in terms of effective jump frequencies can be used. In order to apply these equations, one needs only to calculate the effective jump frequencies $\nu_\alpha{}^e$.

Effective Jump Frequencies in a Driving Force

A fresh vacancy is one which either has never exchanged with the tracer or has arrived at a site on plane b since its last such exchange. We can define $\nu_{\pi\alpha}$ as the frequency with which fresh vacancies arrive at site α neighboring on the tracer. The sites at which fresh vacancies can be created will be called sites p. These sites include not only the actual vacancy sources in the crystal (dislocations, grain boundaries, etc.) but also all sites on plane b. The distortion of the vacancy flow by the tracer impurity does not affect the vacancy concentrations at these sites p. Thus $\nu_{\pi\alpha}$ can be calculated from the equilibrium vacancy concentrations at these sites and the frequency with which vacancies from these sites migrate to a particular site α. This migration frequency of course is influenced by the driving force.

Also we can define U_α as the probability that the vacancy after reaching site α will exchange with the tracer and begin a jump series which results in a net displacement of $+d$ or $-d$, the net result being one α-type jump. Then, if there are y_α equivalent sites of type α to which the tracer can jump,

$$\nu_\alpha{}^e = \nu_{\pi\alpha} U_\alpha y_\alpha \tag{4–1}$$

The probability that the vacancy on site α will not exchange with the tracer before arriving at a site p is $w_{\alpha\pi}/(w_{\alpha T} + w_{\alpha\pi})$, where $w_{\alpha T}$ is the frequency for exchange of the vacancy on site α with the tracer and $w_{\alpha\pi}$ is the frequency of jumps which begin the vacancy on a path from α to any site p *without* return to site α or exchange with the tracer. In counting jumps which contribute to $w_{\alpha\pi}$, possible jumps or series of jumps which take a vacancy from one equivalent α site to another can be neglected, since a vacancy on one α site has the same effect on diffusion along the x-axis as a vacancy at any other equivalent site. Then, to be consistent, $\nu_{\pi\alpha}$ must be redefined as the frequency with which fresh vacancies that have *not* first arrived at an equivalent site jump into our site α.

Let us consider a situation where there is only one class of equivalent sites α with $x_\alpha > 0$. Then

$$U_\alpha = \frac{w_{\alpha T}}{w_{\alpha T} + w_{\alpha\pi}} (1 - P_- + P_+P_- - P_-P_+P_- + \cdots) \tag{4–2}$$

where P_+, P_- are the probabilities of succeeding jumps in the series of jumps, as in Section 3–8.

When there is only one class α, a vacancy which jumps from a site α to a neighboring site s has a probability Y_s of returning to a site in set α before it reaches a site on plane b or at a vacancy sink, and a probability $F_s = 1 - Y_s$ of not returning without first reaching one of these p sites. Then, if w_s is the jump frequency from site α to s,

$$w_{\alpha\pi} = \sum_s w_s F_s \tag{4–3}$$

as in Section 3–8.

The frequency $w_{\alpha T} + w_{\alpha\pi}$ is the total effective jump frequency of a vacancy from site α. Also, $P_+ = w_{\alpha T}/(w_{\alpha T} + w_{\alpha\pi})$ and

$$\frac{w_{\alpha\pi}}{w_{\alpha T} + w_{\alpha\pi}} = 1 - P_+ \tag{4–4}$$

For convenience, one may define basic atom jump frequencies $\Gamma_\alpha{}^b$ and $\nu_\alpha{}^b$ which depend on the equilibrium vacancy concentration $N_{v\alpha e}$ at site α in the absence of a driving force. These are the atom jump frequencies one might expect in the absence of correlation or vacancy flow effects. For atom jumps to a given neighboring site α,

$$\Gamma_\alpha{}^b = w_{\alpha T} N_{v\alpha e} \tag{4–5a}$$

If there are y_α equivalent sites neighboring on the tracer to which jumps of type α can be made, the total basic jump frequency for α jumps is

$$\nu_\alpha{}^b = y_\alpha \Gamma_\alpha{}^b \tag{4–5b}$$

$$\nu_\alpha{}^b = w_{\alpha T} N_{v\alpha e} y_\alpha \tag{4–5c}$$

Equation (4–1) then can be written in the form

$$\nu_\alpha{}^e = \nu_\alpha{}^b G_\alpha f_\alpha \tag{4–6}$$

where

$$G_\alpha = \frac{\nu_{\pi\alpha}}{w_{\alpha\pi} N_{v\alpha e}} \tag{4–7}$$

and

$$f_\alpha = \frac{(1 - P_+)(1 - P_-)}{1 - P_+ P_-} \tag{4–8}$$

Here f_α is the correlation factor as found previously in (3–73) and G_α is the vacancy flow factor.

We have seen in Section 3–8 that $f_\alpha = (1 - P)/(1 + P)$, where P is the average value of P_+ and P_- in the absence of a driving force. Thus, the driving force does not affect f. An effect of the driving force on $\nu_\alpha{}^b$ arises from the factor $w_{\alpha T}$. The factor G_α also depends on the driving force and is related to the change in vacancy concentration at site α which results from the vacancy flow.

Applications to More Complex Structures

When there is more than one class of equivalent sites, jumps between different classes must be included in our equations. Then P is represented by a square matrix, and $w_{\alpha\pi}$ is replaced by $[w_{\alpha\pi} + \sum_\beta w_{\alpha\beta}]$ in Eqs. (4–2), (4–4), and (4–7). Here $w_{\alpha\beta}$ is the frequency of vacancy transitions from class α to class β, and element $P_{\alpha\beta}$ of the matrix $\mathbf{P}$ gives the probability of a correlated reverse jump of type β following an original jump of type α. The total effective atom jump frequency in the $+x$-direction is given by

$$\nu^e = \mathbf{G} \cdot \boldsymbol{\nu}^b \cdot \mathbf{f} \tag{4–9}$$

Here we let each α represent a class of sites having $x_\alpha > 0$, and ν^e is the total effective jump frequency summed over all α. Also, $\mathbf{G}$ is a row matrix having components G_α, $\mathbf{f}$ is a column matrix having components f_α as in (3–78), and $\boldsymbol{\nu}^b$ is a square matrix having diagonal terms equal to $\nu_\alpha{}^b$ and nondiagonal terms which are usually much smaller than $\nu_\alpha{}^b$. The nondiagonal element $\nu_{\alpha\beta}{}^b$ gives the contributions from vacancies which move from a site in class α to a site in a second class β neighboring on the tracer and then exchange with the tracer from a site β. A similar equation can be written for the effective atom jump frequency in the negative x-direction.

The nondiagonal terms in the matrix $\boldsymbol{\nu}^b$ give the effect of the possible vacancy jumps between nonequivalent sites α and β. When contributions from these terms are small, a good approximation to ν^e can be found from the equation

$$\nu^e \approx \sum_\alpha G_\alpha \nu_\alpha{}^b f_\alpha \tag{4–10}$$

In the following discussion, we shall be concerned mostly with cubic crystals and hence shall use Eq. (4–6). The results, however, can easily be generalized when the nondiagonal terms in the matrix $\boldsymbol{\nu}^b$ are small.

$\langle X^2 \rangle$, $\langle X \rangle$, and J

Let us consider a case where x_α for sites neighboring on the tracer is either $\pm d$ or zero and where the $+d$ jumps form one class of equivalent jumps while the $-d$ jumps form a second class of equivalent jumps. Since jumps where $x_\alpha = 0$ can be ignored, there are only two types of jumps which then need to be considered. A jump to a specific site with $x_\alpha = +d$ will have jump frequency Γ_R, while a jump to a given site with $x_\alpha = -d$ will have jump frequency Γ_L. The number of equivalent sites of each type can be designated as y_R and y_L. Equation (2–38), which applies in the limit where time τ goes to zero, then becomes

$$\langle X^2 \rangle = [y_R \Gamma_R{}^e d^2 + y_L \Gamma_L{}^e (-d)^2]\tau \tag{4–11}$$

where the superscript e indicates effective jump frequencies, as in Eq. (4–6). In the present case, the total effective jump frequency to the right $\nu_R{}^e$ equals $y_R \Gamma_R{}^e$ and that to the left $\nu_L{}^e$ equals $y_L \Gamma_L{}^e$. Thus, in the limit where τ goes to zero,

$$\langle X^2 \rangle = d^2(\nu_R{}^e + \nu_L{}^e)\tau \tag{4–12}$$

It may be noted that $\langle X^2 \rangle$ is proportional to the sum $\nu_R{}^e + \nu_L{}^e$.

By contrast, $\langle X \rangle$ depends on the difference between $\nu_R{}^e$ and

$\nu_L{}^e$. Equation (2–47) gives

$$\langle X \rangle = [y_R \Gamma_R{}^e d + y_L \Gamma_L{}^e(-d)]\tau \tag{4–13}$$

or

$$\langle X \rangle = d(\nu_R{}^e - \nu_L{}^e)\tau \tag{4–14}$$

To first order, a driving force does not change $\langle X^2 \rangle$ or the sum $\nu_R{}^e + \nu_L{}^e$, since any increase in $\nu_R{}^e$ is balanced by a corresponding decrease in $\nu_L{}^e$. In calculations of $\langle X \rangle$, however, the effect of the force is of foremost importance. In the absence of driving forces, $\nu_R{}^e$ equals $\nu_L{}^e$ on the average, making $\langle X \rangle$ then equal to zero; but in the presence of a driving force, $\nu_R{}^e \neq \nu_L{}^e$ and $\langle X \rangle$ is unequal to zero.

Of the terms on the right in Eq. (4–6), the basic jump frequency $\nu_\alpha{}^b$ depends on the force F through $w_{\alpha T}$,

$$w_{\alpha T} = w_{\alpha To}(1 + F_\alpha x_\alpha/2kT) \tag{4–15}$$

where $w_{\alpha To}$ is the value of $w_{\alpha T}$ in the absence of a force, and F_α is the x-component of the force on the tracer when it makes an α jump. Then

$$\nu_R{}^b = \nu_{Ro}{}^b(1 + A) \tag{4–16a}$$

$$\nu_L{}^b = \nu_{Lo}{}^b(1 - A) \tag{4–16b}$$

where $\nu_{Ro}{}^b$ and $\nu_{Lo}{}^b$ are the values of $\nu_R{}^b$ and $\nu_L{}^b$ in the absence of driving forces, and

$$A = F_\alpha d/2kT \tag{4–17}$$

It will be shown in Section 4–3 that in the absence of a force $G_\alpha = 1$, and in the presence of a force,

$$G_R = 1 + B \tag{4–18a}$$

$$G_L = 1 - B \tag{4–18b}$$

Finally, the correlation factor f_α is not affected by a driving force, and in cubic crystals f_α does not depend on α.

The above expressions for $\nu_\alpha{}^b$, G_α, and f_α along with Eq. (4–6) allow the expressions for $\langle X \rangle$ and $\langle X^2 \rangle$ to be evaluated. Often, y_L equals y_R and the subscripts on y can be omitted. For example, for diffusion normal to (100) planes in the face-centered cubic and body-centered cubic structures, $y_L = y_R = 4$; in the simple cubic, $y_L = y_R = 1$; and in the diamond structure, $y_L = y_R = 2$. In these cases,

$$\nu_{Ro}{}^b = \nu_{Lo}{}^b = y\Gamma^b \tag{4–19}$$

where Γ^b is the basic jump frequency to a given neighboring site. Then, (4–14) yields

$$\langle X \rangle = 2yd\Gamma^b f(A + B)\tau \tag{4–20}$$

and, in the limit where τ goes to zero, (4–12) yields

$$\langle X^2 \rangle = 2yd^2\Gamma^b f\tau \tag{4–21}$$

In more complex cases, these equations are still valid but proper average values of Γ^b, y, and d then must be calculated. By definition,

$$D = \lim_{\tau \to 0} \langle X^2 \rangle / 2\tau, \tag{4–22}$$

so

$$D = yd^2\Gamma^b f \tag{4–23}$$

and

$$\langle X \rangle = 2D\tau d^{-1}(A + B) \tag{4–24}$$

With (2–29) and the continuity relation $\partial c/\partial t = -\partial J/\partial x$, this yields

$$J = 2cDd^{-1}(A + B) - D(\partial c/\partial x) \tag{4–25}$$

where A is given by (4–17) and B can be calculated from (4–7) and (4–18). Here A gives the direct effect of the driving force while B gives the indirect effect from the vacancy flow term.[1] Upon substituting (4–17) into (4–25), one obtains an equation which is similar to the "random walk" equation (2–10). However, (4–25) also contains a vacancy flow term proportional to B and the expression for D from (4–23) includes a correlation factor. In the following section a general expression for B is obtained.

4–3. VACANCY FLOW TERM

Introduction

By definition, B is the deviation of the vacancy flow factor G_α from unity. When there is no vacancy flow, G_α is exactly unity and the deviation B is zero. This can be seen as follows:

The numerator $\nu_{\pi\alpha}$ in (4–7) equals the frequency of vacancy travel from an equilibrium site to site α. This equals the probability $N_{v\pi e}$ of a vacancy being at an equilibrium site multiplied by the frequency $w_{\pi\alpha}$ of it then traveling to site α. The denominator in (4–7) contains the equilibrium probability $N_{v\alpha e}$ of a vacancy being on site α multiplied by the frequency $w_{\alpha\pi}$ of it then traveling from site α to one of the equilibrium sites. When there is no vacancy flow, the total travel in one direction must be the same as that in the other direction. Thus, $N_{v\pi e}w_{\pi\alpha} = N_{v\alpha e}w_{\alpha\pi}$ in this case, making G_α equal to unity and B equal to zero.

When there is a driving force, the vacancy flow will no longer be zero. The equilibrium values $N_{v\pi e}$ and $N_{v\alpha e}$ are not affected by the force. However, the frequency (say $w_{\pi\alpha}$) for vacancies traveling in a direction aided by the force will be increased while the frequency ($w_{\alpha\pi}$) for travel in the opposite direction will be decreased. This makes G_α differ from unity and B unequal to zero.

Because B equals zero when there is no vacancy flow and differs from zero when there is a vacancy flow, the B term is called the vacancy flow term and G_α the vacancy flow factor.

A detailed mathematical evaluation of B is presented in the remainder of this section and in Section 4–4. It is found that B in a constant driving force is proportional to the average displacement $\langle n_p \rangle d$ which the vacancy undergoes in the direction of the force in moving from site α to an equilibrium site. In Section 4–4, explicit expressions for $\langle n_p \rangle$ are found. These expressions depend on the crystal structure and on the vacancy jump frequency ratios. When $\langle n_p \rangle$ is known, explicit expressions for B in a constant force can be calculated. These expressions for B then may be substituted into the basic equations (4–24) and (4–25) to obtain $\langle X \rangle$ and J in a driving force. Applications to diffusion in an electric field are given in Section 4–5.

Detailed Calculation of B

A fresh vacancy may arrive at site α by following a path from various sites p. At these sites, the vacancy concentration is not affected by the distortion of the vacancy flow around the tracer impurity. Therefore,

$$\nu_{\pi\alpha} = \sum_p N_{vpe} w_{p\alpha} \tag{4–26}$$

where N_{vpe} is the equilibrium vacancy concentration at site p and $w_{p\alpha}$ is the frequency with which a vacancy will make a series of jumps to move from site p to site α. Similarly

$$w_{\alpha\pi} = \sum_p w_{\alpha p} \tag{4–27}$$

where $w_{\alpha p}$ is the frequency for a series of jumps from site α to site p. Therefore, (4–7) can be rewritten as

$$G_\alpha = \frac{\sum_p N_{vpe} w_{p\alpha}}{N_{v\alpha e} \sum_p w_{\alpha p}} \tag{4–28}$$

In the absence of forces, there is no net flow of vacancies between sites α and p, so

$$N_{v\alpha e} w_{\alpha p o} = N_{vpe} w_{p\alpha o} \tag{4–29}$$

and $G_{\alpha o}$ equals unity. Here the subscript o on $w_{\alpha p}$, $w_{p\alpha}$, and G_α indicates the absence of driving forces.

Both $w_{p\alpha}$ and $w_{\alpha p}$ are changed by a driving force. A force along the x-axis changes the frequency of any given jump so that

$$w_\gamma = w_{\gamma o}(1 - \varepsilon_\gamma) = w_{\gamma o}(1 - x_\gamma F_\gamma / 2kT) \tag{4–30}$$

Here w_γ is the frequency for the γth jumps, $w_{\gamma o}$ is the frequency in the absence of a force, F_γ is the force on the atom making the γth jumps, and x_γ is the x-component of the vacancy displacement from this jump. The minus sign arises because the atom and vacancy move in opposite directions. The probability a_γ that a vacancy which is in position to make a γ jump will actually do so depends not only on w_γ but also on the frequencies w_d of other competing jumps,

$$a_\gamma = \frac{w_\gamma}{w_\gamma + \sum_d w_d} \tag{4–31}$$

The frequencies of these other jumps are changed by a force. As in (4–30),

$$w_d = w_{do}(1 - x_d F_d / 2kT) \tag{4–32}$$

so that

$$a_\gamma = \frac{w_{\gamma o}(1 - \varepsilon_\gamma)}{R_\gamma(1 - \Delta w(\gamma)/R_\gamma)} \tag{4–33}$$

where

$$R_\gamma = w_{\gamma o} + \sum_d w_{do}$$

and

$$\Delta w(\gamma) = (w_{\gamma o} x_\gamma F_\gamma + \sum_d w_{do} x_d F_d)(2kT)^{-1}$$

To first order,

$$a_\gamma = a_{\gamma o}(1 - \varepsilon_\gamma + \varepsilon_{\gamma\Delta}) \tag{4–34}$$

where $a_{\gamma o} = w_{\gamma o}/R_\gamma$ and $\varepsilon_{\gamma\Delta} = +\Delta w(\gamma)/R_\gamma$.

Let us consider a path which requires n jumps between sites g and h. The frequency w_{gh} with which a vacancy from site g follows this path equals the frequency w_1 of the first jump in the path multiplied by the probabilities $a_2 \cdots a_n$ of the $n - 1$ other jumps. Thus,

$$w_{gh} = w_1 \prod_{\gamma=2}^{n} a_\gamma \tag{4–35}$$

If w_{gho} is the value of w_{gh} in the absence of a force, (4–34) and (4–35) yield to first order

$$w_{gh} = w_{gho}(1 - \sum_{\gamma=1}^{n} \varepsilon_\gamma + \sum_{\gamma=2}^{n} \varepsilon_{\gamma\Delta}) \tag{4–36}$$

When the forces F_γ for all jumps along the path have the value F_1, the sum over ε_γ equals $(+F_1/2kT)$ multiplied by the x-displacement between the initial and final sites. The sum over $\varepsilon_{\gamma\Delta}$ equals a sum of $\Delta w/R$ for all sites in the path except the initial and final sites.

To find the total frequency with which a vacancy moves from site α to site p, one must sum over all paths connecting sites α and p. Thus,

$$w_{\alpha p} = \sum_q w^q_{\alpha po}\left(1 - \frac{x_{\alpha p}F_1}{2kT} + \varepsilon_q\right) \tag{4–37}$$

where index q denotes the distinct paths, $x_{\alpha p}$ is the x-component of the displacement from α to p, $w^q_{\alpha po}$ is the frequency with which the vacancy moves from α to p along path q in the absence of a field, and $\varepsilon_q = \sum_{\gamma=2}^{n} \varepsilon_{\gamma\Delta}$ for path q. For paths in the reverse direction,

$$w_{p\alpha} = \sum_q w^q_{p\alpha o}\left(1 + \frac{x_{\alpha p}F_1}{2kT} + \varepsilon_q\right) \qquad (4\text{–}38)$$

When the spacings between planes have a uniform value d, $x_{\alpha p}$ equals $n_p d$, where n_p is an integer equal to the number of planes that site p is to the right of site α. Then Eq. (4–28) yields

$$G_\alpha = \frac{\sum_p \sum_q N_{vpe} w^q_{p\alpha o}(1 + n_p\varepsilon_1 + \varepsilon_q)}{\sum_p \sum_q N_{v\alpha e} w^q_{\alpha po}(1 - n_p\varepsilon_1 + \varepsilon_q)} \qquad (4\text{–}39)$$

where

$$\varepsilon_1 = F_1 d/2kT \qquad (4\text{–}40)$$

Also

$$N_{vpe} w^q_{p\alpha o} = N_{v\alpha e} w^q_{\alpha po} \qquad (4\text{–}41)$$

since in the absence of forces the vacancy flow along any path must be the same in either direction. Thus, to first order,

$$G_\alpha = 1 + 2\varepsilon_1 \frac{\sum_p w_{\alpha po} n_p}{\sum_p w_{\alpha po}} \qquad (4\text{–}42)$$

where $w_{\alpha po}$ equals $\sum_q w^q_{\alpha po}$ and is the value of $w_{\alpha p}$ in the absence of a driving force. Also, $\sum_p w_{\alpha po}$ equals H from (3–85).

One can define

$$\langle n_p \rangle = \frac{\sum_p w_{\alpha po} n_p}{\sum_p w_{\alpha po}} \qquad (4\text{–}43)$$

with the convention that α is on the plane to the right of the tracer. Then, it follows that

$$B = 2\varepsilon_1 \langle n_p \rangle \tag{4–44}$$

When values of A and B from (4–17) and (4–44) with ε_1 given by (4–40) are substituted into (4–24) and (4–25), one finds

$$\langle X \rangle = \frac{D_T}{kT} [F_\alpha + 2F_1 \langle n_p \rangle] \tag{4–45}$$

and

$$J = \frac{cD}{kT} [F_\alpha + 2F_1 \langle n_p \rangle] - D(\partial c/\partial x) \tag{4–46}$$

It may be noted that $\langle n_p \rangle$ is independent of driving forces.

Throughout the preceding discussion, we have considered the effect of the driving forces F_α and F_1. These quantities enter the analysis in (4–15) and (4–30) through their effect on the frequencies $w_{\alpha T}$ for exchange of a vacancy with the tracer and w_γ, w_d for exchange with the other atoms.

Equations having the form of (4–45) and (4–46) can be obtained even when there is no actual external force, since these equations merely require that an atom have a preferred direction of jump. This could be provided by a chemical potential gradient in a nonideal solid solution or by heat of transport effects in a temperature gradient, as discussed in Chapter 5. In Section 4–5, we discuss effects from electric forces acting on charged ions in an ionic crystal.

For simplicity, it has been assumed above that F_1 has a single value for all jumps not involving the tracer. If this condition is not satisfied, the analysis must be modified. (See Section 5–7.) However, if the force undergoes only a small fractional change in the region near the tracer (say within 10 atom distances from the tracer, where the major contribution to $\langle n_p \rangle$ is normally obtained), the modification will be small. Consequently, (4–46) provides a very good approximation, even with a slowly varying driving force.

4–4. CALCULATION OF $\langle n_p \rangle$

Equations (4–45) and (4–46) give $\langle X \rangle$ and J in terms of $\langle n_p \rangle$, where $\langle n_p \rangle$ depends on the ratios of the various vacancy jump frequencies. In the present section, expressions for $\langle n_p \rangle$ are derived. A general expression is obtained in Eq. (4–63), and equations valid in special cases appear as (4–65), (4–66), and (4–78).

The average $\langle n_p \rangle$ equals d^{-1} times the average x-displacement of vacancies when they move from site α to the various equilibrium sites p. This average is evaluated in the absence of a driving force. The average x-displacement can be followed in a step-by-step manner. The contribution C_s to $\langle n_p \rangle$ resulting from a jump from site s is, on the average,

$$C_s = \frac{w_{s+} - w_{s-}}{R_s} \tag{4–47}$$

where w_{s+} is the frequency of jumps which change the x-displacement of the vacancy by $+d$; and w_{s-} is the frequency of jumps in the opposite direction, making a change $-d$. Also R_s is the total jump frequency from site s, so that w_{s+}/R_s is the probability of $+d$ displacement and w_{s-}/R_s is the probability of $-d$. Since we are interested here only in vacancies which arrive at a site p before exchanging with the tracer, jumps involving the tracer are excluded from the quantities $w_{s\pm}$ and R_s. Thus,

$$R_s = \sum_h w_{sh} \tag{4–48}$$

where w_{sh} is the vacancy jump frequency from site s to a neighboring site h and the summation is over all nontracer neighbors of site s. In terms of C_s,

$$\langle n_p \rangle = \sum_s C_s V_s \qquad (4\text{–}49)$$

where V_s is the average number of times a vacancy is at site s before it finally arrives at an equilibrium site.

The nonequilibrium sites on planes to the right of the tracer can be divided into classes of equivalent sites. For example, in the face-centered cubic structure, the four sites on plane a (to the right of the tracer) which are nearest neighbors of the tracer form one class of equivalent sites. Since a vacancy on any one of these sites has the same subsequent effect on the x-displacement of the tracer, jumps between equivalent sites can be ignored. Other classes of equivalent sites are formed by sites which (1) are equidistant from the tracer and (2) have the same x-displacement from the tracer. The classes can be numbered 1, 2, 3, $\cdots$ where class 1 is the class α of four nearest neighbors on plane a.

In moving along a path from site α to a site p, the vacancy must be at site α at least once (at the beginning of the path). It also can return to this site after it has reached one of the neighboring sites, so

$$V_1 = 1 + \sum_s \frac{w_{s1}}{R_s} V_s \qquad (4\text{–}50)$$

where w_{s1} is the sum of the jump frequencies from a given site in class s to the various sites in class 1. Here jumps w_{ss} from one site to another equivalent site are omitted. Therefore, they must also be omitted from the summation (4–48) giving R_s. For classes other than class 1,

$$V_s = \sum_h \frac{w_{hs}}{R_h} V_h \qquad (4\text{–}51)$$

where $s = 2, 3, 4, \cdots$.

Equations (4–50) and (4–51) form a set of linear equations which can be solved for V_1, V_2, V_3, $\cdots$ by use of determinants.

Thus,

$$V_s = \frac{M_s}{\varphi} \tag{4-52}$$

where

$$\varphi = \begin{vmatrix} 1 & -\dfrac{w_{21}}{R_2} & -\dfrac{w_{31}}{R_3} & \cdots \\ -\dfrac{w_{12}}{R_1} & 1 & -\dfrac{w_{32}}{R_3} & \cdots \\ -\dfrac{w_{13}}{R_1} & -\dfrac{w_{23}}{R_2} & 1 & \cdots \\ \vdots & \vdots & \vdots & \end{vmatrix} \tag{4-53}$$

and M_s equals φ with the sth column replaced by $\{1, 0, 0, 0, \cdots\}$. Since there are an infinite number of nonequilibrium sites, both φ and M_s contain an infinite number of terms.

The determinant M_s equals $M_{1s}(-1)^{s+1}$, where M_{1s} is the minor of the element in the first row and sth column of φ. Then, $\psi = \sum_s C_s M_s$ is given by

$$\psi = \begin{vmatrix} C_1 & C_2 & C_3 & \cdots \\ -\dfrac{w_{12}}{R_1} & 1 & -\dfrac{w_{32}}{R_3} & \cdots \\ -\dfrac{w_{13}}{R_1} & -\dfrac{w_{23}}{R_2} & 1 & \cdots \\ \vdots & \vdots & \vdots & \end{vmatrix} \tag{4-54}$$

where the first row of φ is merely replaced by $(C_1, C_2, C_3, \cdots)$. Finally,

$$\langle n_p \rangle = \sum_s C_s V_s = \varphi^{-1} \sum_s C_s M_s = \varphi^{-1}\psi \qquad (4\text{–}55)$$

Further detailed analysis[2] shows that

$$\varphi = \frac{M_1}{R_1} \sum_p w_{\alpha po} \qquad (4\text{–}56)$$

where, as in Eq. (4–3) or (3–85),

$$\sum_p w_{\alpha po} = \sum_{s=2}^{q} w_{1s} F_s + \sum_e w_{1e} \qquad (4\text{–}57)$$

Here w_{1s} and w_{1e} are the vacancy jump frequencies from α to a neighboring nonequilibrium site s or equilibrium site e (on plane b), respectively, and F_s is the fraction or w_{1s} jumps that contribute to the effective escape frequency. (The corresponding fraction for w_{1e} jumps is unity). When φ from (4–53) is expanded in terms of minors,

$$\varphi = M_1 - \sum_{s=2}^{q} \frac{w_{s1}}{R_s} M_s \qquad (4\text{–}58)$$

Here $q - 1$ is the number of nonequilibrium classes which can be reached in a single jump from class 1. The sum in (4–58) is finite since w_{s1} equals zero for $s > q$. From (4–56) and (4–58), it follows that

$$\sum_p w_{\alpha po} = R_1 - \sum_{s=2}^{q} \frac{R_1}{R_s} \frac{M_s}{M_1} w_{s1} \qquad (4\text{–}59)$$

Also

$$R_1 = \sum_{s=2}^{q} w_{1s} + \sum_e w_{1e} \qquad (4\text{–}60)$$

so that Eq. (4–59) can be rewritten as

$$\sum_p w_{\alpha po} = \sum_e w_{1e} + \sum_{s=2}^{q} w_{1s}\left(1 - \frac{w_{s1}}{w_{1s}}\frac{R_1}{R_s}\frac{M_s}{M_1}\right) \quad (4\text{–}61)$$

and from (4–57)

$$F_s = 1 - \frac{w_{s1}}{w_{1s}}\frac{R_1}{R_s}\frac{M_s}{M_1} \quad (4\text{–}62)$$

Returning to (4–55), we can find

$$\langle n_p \rangle = \frac{\Delta w_1 + \sum_{s=2}^{q} \Delta w_s \dfrac{w_{1s}}{w_{s1}}(1 - F_s) + \sum_{s=q+1}^{\infty} \Delta w_s \dfrac{R_1}{R_s}\dfrac{M_s}{M_1}}{\sum_{s=2}^{q} w_{1s}F_s + \sum_e w_{1e}} \quad (4\text{–}63)$$

where

$$\Delta w_s = w_{s+} - w_{s-} \quad (4\text{–}64)$$

and all quantities are evaluated in the absence of driving forces.

The F_s have been calculated for a number of cases, as in Chapter 3. Consequently (4–63) is an especially useful expression for $\langle n_p \rangle$. It should be remembered that $w_{\alpha po}$ is the frequency of paths from α to p that do not involve exchanges with the tracer. Therefore Δw_1 and R_1 do not include exchanges with the tracer.

The quantity $\langle n_p \rangle$ is a basic parameter in determining the vacancy flow effect from a driving force. Specific application will be discussed in Sections 4–5, 5–4, and 5–7. Equation (4–63) is the general expression for $\langle n_p \rangle$.

(1) If vacancy jump frequencies from sites which are three or more jumps from the tracer are unaffected by the presence

of the tracer, all Δw_s for $s > q$ equal zero. Then

$$\langle n_p \rangle = \frac{\Delta w_1 + \sum_{s=2}^{q} \Delta w_s \frac{w_{1s}}{w_{s1}} (1 - F_s)}{\sum_{s=2}^{q} w_{1s} F_s + \sum_{e} w_{1e}} \tag{4-65}$$

which depends only on the F_s and a limited number of jump frequencies involving jumps into or from sites 1.

(2) This expression simplifies still further if the frequencies for vacancy jumps from sites which are two jumps from the tracer (and nearest neighbor of site 1) are unaffected by the presence of the tracer. Then all Δw_s for $s > 1$ equal zero, and

$$\langle n_p \rangle = \frac{\Delta w_1}{2w_T} \frac{1 - f}{f} \tag{4-66a}$$

where w_T is the jump frequency for exchange of the vacancy with the tracer and f is the correlation factor for diffusion of the tracer. This follows since $f = (1 + 2w_T H^{-1})^{-1}$, where H is the denominator in (4–65).

(3) If all vacancy exchanges with nontracer atoms have the jump frequency w_o, one again finds $\Delta w_s = 0$ for $s > 1$, as above. However, Δw_1 does not reduce to zero since exchanges with the tracer are excluded in calculating Δw_1. If $w_{1+} = yw_o$, one finds $w_{1-} = (y - 1)w_o$ and $\Delta w_1 = w_o$. For self-diffusion, all nontracer jump frequencies equal w_o and also w_T equals w_o. In this special case,

$$\langle n_p \rangle = \tfrac{1}{2}(f^{-1} - 1) \tag{4-66b}$$

The relation between the vacancy flow term and correlation factor is discussed further in Section 4–5.

4–5. IONIC DRIFT MOBILITY IN AN ELECTRIC FIELD

The drift mobility u of an ion in an electric field E is given by

$$v_E = uE \tag{4-67}$$

where v_E is the average drift velocity resulting from the field. Thus, u is the average velocity in unit field, and

$$u = \frac{1}{E} \frac{\partial \langle X \rangle_E}{\partial \tau} \tag{4-68}$$

where $\langle X \rangle_E$ is the contribution to $\langle X \rangle$ which is proportional to E. The derivative of $\langle X \rangle_E$ with respect to time τ equals the average drift velocity from the field.

The ionic conductivity σ is given by

$$\sigma = \sum_i u_i q_i c_i \tag{4-69}$$

where q_i and c_i are the charge and concentration of species i. If the electric charge is transported almost entirely by one species, u_i for this species can be determined from a measurement of σ.

Also, u_i can be measured from a tracer diffusion experiment in an electric field. A layer of radioactive tracer ions originally at plane 0 will form a diffusion profile such as shown in Fig. 4–2 if allowed to diffuse under the influence of a uniform elec-

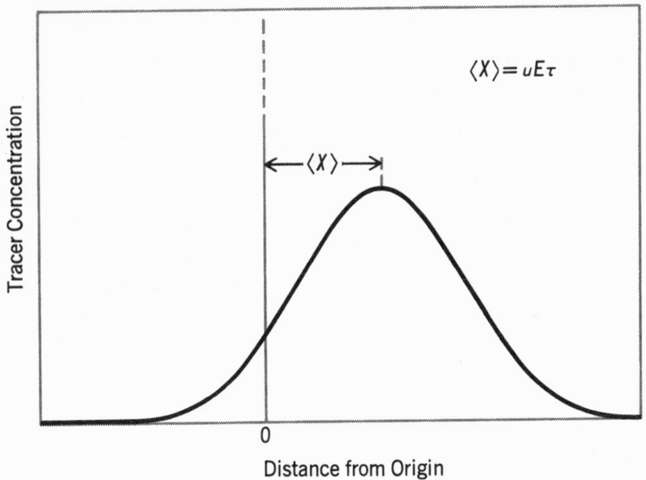

4–2 Concentration vs. position for a layer of tracer ions (originally at $x = 0$) after diffusion in a constant electric field (cf. Fig. 2–3).

tric field. Here the width and shape of the profile are the same as in the absence of a field. The only effect of the field is to shift the profile a distance $\langle X \rangle_E$. If $\langle X \rangle_E$, τ, and E are known, u for the tracer can be calculated from (4–68).

Vacancy Mechanism

In a field E, an isolated impurity of charge q_i experiences a force

$$F_\alpha = q_i E. \tag{4–70}$$

The solvent ions of charge q_s experience a force

$$F_1 = q_s E \tag{4–71}$$

When diffusion occurs by a vacancy mechanism, $\langle X \rangle$ for an impurity of charge q_i diffusing in a sublattice containing solvent ions of charge q_s is given by Eq. (4–45). Thus

$$\langle X \rangle = \frac{D_T}{kT}\left[q_i E + 2q_s E \langle n_p \rangle\right] \tag{4–72}$$

and, with (4–68), it follows that

$$\frac{u}{D} = \frac{q_i}{kT}\left[1 + \frac{2q_s}{q_i}\langle n_p \rangle\right] \tag{4–73}$$

This may be compared to the Nernst-Einstein relation[3] which states that $u/D = q_i/kT$. According to (4–73), the Nernst-Einstein is normally not obeyed. The reason for this is the contribution from the vacancy flow term, proportional to $q_s\langle n_p \rangle$.

Interstitialcy Mechanism

In an interstitialcy mechanism, two atoms participate in each jump. For a collinear interstitialcy mechanism, where the two atoms move in the same direction,

$$F_\alpha = (q_s + q_i)E \tag{4–74}$$

and

$$F_1 = 2q_sE \tag{4–75}$$

Equation (4–45) for $\langle X \rangle$ is valid for an interstitialcy mechanism if the factor 2 is removed from the second term on the right. The factor 2 is removed because only half of the jumps by a given atom require an imperfection at a neighboring site. Then for a collinear interstitialcy mechanism,

$$\frac{u}{D} = \frac{q_s + q_i}{kT}\left[1 + \frac{2q_s}{q_s + q_i}\langle n_p \rangle\right] \tag{4–76}$$

For this mechanism, one normally expects $q_s = q_i$, giving

$$\frac{u}{D} = \frac{2q_i}{kT}[1 + \langle n_p \rangle] \tag{4–77}$$

For each mechanism, $\langle n_p \rangle$ must be calculated separately in terms of the F_s and Δw_s in (4–63). In the interstitialcy mechanism, sites s refer to sites occupied by the interstitialcy.

Face-Centered Cubic Sublattice

For each structure, $\langle n_p \rangle$ must be calculated separately from (4–63). Let us consider a face-centered cubic sublattice (NaCl structure) with the following vacancy jump frequencies: w_1 between two sites neighboring on the tracer, w_3 from a nearest neighbor to a nonnearest neighbor site, w_4 for the reverse of a w_3 jump, and w_o for jumps not involving a nearest neighbor site. Then $w_{1s} = g_s w_3$, $w_{s1} = h_s w_4$, and $w_{1e} = 2w_1 + w_3$, where g_s and h_s are integers whose particular values depend on s. Also $\Delta w_1 = 3w_3 - 2w_1$ and for site $s = 2, \cdots, q$ on the second coordination shell $\Delta w_s = (w_o - w_4)k_s$, where k_s is an integer.

For all other s, Δw_s equals zero. This gives

$$\langle n_p \rangle = \frac{3w_3 - 2w_1 + (w_3/w_4)(w_o - w_4)7(1 - F)}{2w_1 + 7w_3F} \tag{4-78}$$

A detailed derivation of this equation (including values of g_s, h_s, and k_s) is given in Reference 2. In Fig. 3–5, $7F$ is plotted as a function of w_4/w_o.

When (4–78) is substituted into (4–73) one finds

$$\frac{u}{D} = \frac{q_i}{kT} \frac{2w_1\left\{1 - 2\frac{q_s}{q_i}\right\} + w_3\left\{7F + 6\frac{q_s}{q_i} - \frac{w_4 - w_o}{w_4}14(1 - F)\frac{q_s}{q_i}\right\}}{2w_1 + 7Fw_3} \tag{4-79}$$

When $q_s = q_i$, as for diffusion of a monovalent impurity in a monovalent sublattice,

$$\frac{u}{D} = \frac{q_i}{kT} \frac{-2w_1 + w_3[6 + 7F - 14(1 - F)(w_4 - w_o)/w_4]}{2w_1 + 7Fw_3} \tag{4-80}$$

For $w_4 = w_o$, $7F \approx 5.15$ and

$$\frac{u}{D} = \frac{q_i}{kT} \frac{-2w_1 + 11.15w_3}{2w_1 + 5.15w_3} \tag{4-81}$$

In the special case of self-diffusion, where the impurity is the same as the solvent ions, $w_o = w_1 = w_3 = w_4$ and

$$\frac{u}{D} = \frac{q_i}{kT} \frac{1}{f} \tag{4-82}$$

where $f = (2 + 7F)/(4 + 7F)$. This expression for f is just the expression for the correlation factor for self-diffusion in a face-centered cubic crystal. Thus f can be identified as the correlation factor. This also follows directly from (4–66) and (4–73), since for self-diffusion Δw_1 equals w_T and $\langle n_p \rangle = \frac{1}{2}(f^{-1} - 1)$.

For a divalent impurity diffusing in a monovalent sublattice, $q_i = 2q_s$. Then,

$$\frac{u}{D} = \frac{2q_s}{kT} \frac{\{7F + 3 - [(w_4 - w_o)/w_4]7(1 - F)\}w_3}{2w_1 + 7Fw_3} \tag{4–83}$$

When $w_4 \gg w_o$, Fig. 3–5 shows that $7F = 2$. Then u/D equals zero. This is as might be expected, since the vacancy in this case cannot escape more than one jump away from the divalent impurity. The resulting bound vacancy-impurity complex has zero effective charge relative to a pair of monovalent solvent ions. Thus, there is no net force on the complex and $\langle X \rangle$ and u equal zero. The only contributions to u for a divalent impurity occur when vacancies associate with the impurity and then dissociate after causing an impurity jump. According to (4–83), u/D also equals zero whenever $w_3 = 0$. Then the bound vacancy cannot move even one jump away from the impurity and there can be no dissociation.

The above relations for u/D are for an isolated impurity. When there is an uneven concentration of divalent impurities in a crystal, interaction between these charged impurities and the associated vacancies (introduced to maintain charge neutrality) may seriously affect D. Also both u and D may vary with concentration. These effects are probably best treated by the pair association method described in Chapter 7. In practice, these effects are negligible if there is a large uniform background concentration of vacancies, either thermal vacancies or those from a uniform concentration of other divalent ions. Whether this is the case can be determined from the shape of $W(X, \tau)$ as measured by tracer ions originally at plane 0. According to Howard and Lidiard,[4] $W(X, \tau)$ will be unsymmetric if u and D vary appreciably with concentration.

4-6. u/D FOR SELF-DIFFUSION

Vacancy Mechanism

Expressions for u/D can be calculated exactly in a very direct manner for the special case of self-diffusion in a pure crystal.[5] One starts with the equation,

$$J_i = u_i c_i E \tag{4-84}$$

which gives the flux J_i of species i resulting from a field E. A similar equation can be written for vacancies,

$$J_v = u_v c_v E \tag{4-85}$$

where the subscript v refers to vacancies. In a pure crystal, there is only one species of atoms on each sublattice. Also, when diffusion occurs by a vacancy mechanism, the flux of vacancies is equal and opposite to the flux of atoms. Thus,

$$u_i c_i = -u_v c_v \tag{4-86}$$

Since successive vacancy jumps in a pure crystal are not correlated, the equations from Chapter 2 apply directly to diffusion of the vacancies. In the absence of concentration gradients, we find

$$J_v = \frac{D_v c_v}{kT} F \tag{4-87}$$

where the driving force F is any influence which makes our diffusing entity (a vacancy in the present case) jump more frequently to the right than to the left. The electric field acts on the ions neighboring a given vacancy and hence serves this function. Thus, in (4-87), F equals $-q_i E$, where q_i is the ionic charge. Comparison of (4–85) and (4–87) gives

$$u_v = \frac{-q_i D_v}{kT} \tag{4–88}$$

Since the vacancy jumps are not correlated and do not require an imperfection at a neighboring site,

$$D_v = d^2 w \tag{4–89}$$

where w is the vacancy jump frequency for jumps giving displacements $\pm d$ along the x-axis. Thus, u_v is proportional to the actual vacancy jump frequency w. For atoms diffusing by a vacancy mechanism, the tracer diffusion coefficient is given by

$$D_i = d^2 w \left[\frac{c_v}{c_v + c_i}\right] f \tag{4–90}$$

and D_i is proportional to the effective jump frequency wf. With $c_v \ll c_i$, Eqs. (4–86) and (4–88) to (4–90) yield

$$\frac{u_i}{D_i} = \frac{q_i}{kT}\frac{1}{f} \tag{4–91}$$

in agreement with (4–82).

Interstitialcy Mechanism

For a collinear interstitialcy mechanism, the diffusion coefficient of the imperfection is given by

$$D_I = (2d)^2 w \tag{4–92}$$

The factor two enters here because the interstitialcy itself moves twice as far as either of the atoms participating in the interstitialcy jump. For the atoms,

$$D_i = d^2(2w)f\frac{c_I}{c_i} \tag{4-93}$$

Here the factor two enters because there are two separate atoms which move in each interstitialcy jump.

Equations (4–85) and (4–87) apply to interstitialcies as well as to vacancies, but with $F = +q_iE$ and $u_ic_i = +u_Ic_I$. Thus for diffusion by a collinear interstitialcy mechanism,

$$\frac{u_i}{D_i} = \frac{2q_i}{kTf} \tag{4-94}$$

The factor two, called the displacement factor, arises because the imperfection is displaced twice as far during a given jump as either atom. For noncollinear jumps, the displacement factor is smaller than two.[6,7] It can easily be calculated if the average displacement of the interstitialcy is known for use in Eq. (4–92).

Interstitial Mechanism

For diffusion of small impurities by the interstitial mechanism each impurity is an interstitial atom and follows a random walk. For these interstitials, $D_I = D_i$, $c_I = c_i$ and $J_I = J_i$. It follows from the method above that $u_I = u_i$ and

$$\frac{u_i}{D_i} = \frac{q_i}{kT} \tag{4-95}$$

This agrees with the Nernst-Einstein equation.

REFERENCES

1. J. R. Manning, *Phys. Rev.* **139,** A126 (1965).
2. J. R. Manning, *Phys. Rev.* **139,** A2027 (1965).
3. For a discussion of the Nernst-Einstein equation, see, e.g., A. B. Lidiard, "Handbuch der Physik" (Springer-Verlag, Berlin, 1957), Vol. 20, p. 324.
4. R. E. Howard and A. B. Lidiard, *Reports on Progress in Physics* **27,** 161 (1964).
5. C. W. McCombie and A. B. Lidiard, *Phys. Rev.* **101,** 1210 (1956).
6. R. J. Friauf, *Phys. Rev.* **105,** 843 (1957); *J. Appl. Phys. Suppl.* **33,** 494 (1962).
7. K. Compaan and Y. Haven, *Trans. Faraday Soc.* **54,** 1498 (1958).

5. DIFFUSION WHEN DIFFUSION COEFFICIENT DEPENDS ON POSITION

In Chapters 2 and 4, equations were derived for diffusion modified by a driving force but with constant diffusion coefficient. In the present chapter, effects arising when the diffusion coefficient and jump frequencies are a function of position are considered. A general expression for the atom flux, based on equations similar to those in Chapter 2, is derived and applied to specific driving forces, namely those from a chemical potential gradient and a temperature gradient. For simplicity, attention is centered on cubic crystals and binary alloys.

5–1. DIFFUSION EQUATIONS WITH VARIABLE DIFFUSION COEFFICIENT

Atom jump frequencies and diffusion coefficients in general are a function of alloy composition and depend exponentially on temperature. Therefore, a variation in diffusion coefficient with position can be expected when there is a chemical concentration gradient or temperature gradient. The atom flux J for planar diffusion in the x-direction can still be calculated in terms of $\langle X \rangle$ and $\langle X^2 \rangle$ in much the same manner as in Eq. (2–29). However, $\langle X \rangle$ and $\langle X^2 \rangle$ now depend on position. General equations can be developed as follows:

The concentration $c(x, \tau)$ of diffusing atoms at position x

and time τ is related to the concentration $c(x - \Delta, 0)$ at an earlier time 0 by the equation

$$c(x, \tau) = \sum_{\text{all } \Delta} c(x - \Delta, 0) W(\Delta, \tau, x_s) \tag{5-1}$$

Here Δ (equivalent to X in Chapter 2) is the net displacement of the atom from its starting point, and $W(\Delta, \tau, x_s)$ is the density function giving the probability of displacement Δ from starting position x_s after time τ. The symbol Δ is used here instead of X to emphasize that Δ represents an interval and does not represent a position as do x and x_s.

Since we let the diffusion coefficient vary with position, W depends not only on the displacement Δ but also on the starting point $x_s (= x - \Delta)$. Expanding $W(x_s)$ around the position x gives

$$W(\Delta, \tau, x_s) = W(\Delta, \tau, x) - \Delta(\partial W/\partial x) + \tfrac{1}{2}\Delta^2(\partial^2 W/\partial x^2) - \cdots \tag{5-2}$$

where the derivatives are evaluated at x. Also,

$$c(x - \Delta, 0) = c(x, 0) - \Delta(\partial c/\partial x) + \tfrac{1}{2}\Delta^2(\partial^2 c/\partial x^2) - \cdots \tag{5-3}$$

and

$$c(x, \tau) = c(x, 0) + \tau(\partial c/\partial t) + \cdots \tag{5-4}$$

When these are substituted into (5–1), one finds to first order in τ and second order in Δ,

$$c(x, 0) + \tau(\partial c/\partial t) = \sum_{\text{all } \Delta} c(x, 0) W(\Delta, \tau, x) - \sum_{\text{all } \Delta} [\partial(cW)/\partial x]\Delta + \tfrac{1}{2} \sum_{\text{all } \Delta} [\partial^2(cW)/\partial x^2]\Delta^2 \tag{5-5}$$

Here Δ and x can be chosen independent of one another with only x_s being a dependent variable. As a result, Δ and Δ^2 can be included under the partial derivatives and the derivative signs taken outside of the summations. Also c and its derivatives in (5–5) are those for a given x with no dependence on Δ. Therefore, c can be taken outside of the summation over Δ. The remaining summations are given by Eqs. (2–27) and (2–28), since the displacement Δ is equivalent to X. Consequently, (5–5) reduces to

$$\frac{\partial c}{\partial t} = -\frac{\partial}{\partial x}\left[\frac{c\langle X\rangle}{\tau} - \frac{\partial}{\partial x}\left(\frac{c\langle X^2\rangle}{2\tau}\right)\right] \tag{5-6}$$

where all quantities are evaluated at x.

To provide conservation of matter, the continuity relation

$$\partial c/\partial t = -\partial J/\partial x \tag{5-7}$$

must be satisfied. Equations (5–6) and (5–7) are valid for any x. Also J equals zero when $\langle X\rangle$ and $\langle X^2\rangle$ equal zero. Thus, the right-hand sides of (5–6) and (5–7) can be equated and the partial derivatives with respect to x omitted, giving

$$J = \frac{c\langle X\rangle}{\tau} - \frac{\partial}{\partial x}\left[\frac{c\langle X^2\rangle}{2\tau}\right] \tag{5-8}$$

The above derivation follows that given by Allnatt and Rice.[1] An earlier derivation of (5–8) was given by LeClaire,[2] who calculated J directly by considering the net transport of atoms across a plane at x.

The derivation of (5–8) assumes that τ is small. However, the requirement that τ must be small should be interpreted in the same manner as in Section 3–3. To include correlation effects in the distribution $W(\Delta, \tau, x_s)$, one must let each atom complete its full series of exchanges with a vacancy. Although the number N of vacancies which exchange with a given atom goes to unity, an infinite number of exchanges are allowed with this vacancy. In this limit $D = \langle X^2\rangle/2\tau$, where D is the tracer diffusion coefficient (in a homogeneous system in the absence of driving forces). One can also write in this limit $\langle X \rangle / \tau = \partial \langle X \rangle / \partial \tau = \langle v \rangle$, and

$$J = c\langle v \rangle - \partial (cD)/\partial x \tag{5–9}$$

or

$$J = c\langle v \rangle - D(\partial c/\partial x) - c(\partial D/\partial x) \tag{5–10}$$

When D does not depend on position, (5–10) is equivalent to Eqs. (4–25) and (2–10), which were derived under the assumption of constant D. Also, Eq. (5–6) reduces directly to (2–29) if both $\langle v \rangle$ and D are constant.

It is shown in Section 7–1 that $\langle v \rangle$ in general contains a term $\partial D/\partial x$. [Specific examples of this can be seen in Eqs. (5–57) and (5–110).] Thus, (5–9) and (5–10) always can be expressed as

$$J = c\langle v \rangle_F - D(\partial c/\partial x) \tag{5–11}$$

where $\langle v \rangle_F = \partial \langle X \rangle_F / \partial t$ is the drift velocity resulting from the driving forces alone. Thus, in spite of the $\partial D/\partial x$ term in (5–10), J to first order shows no net dependence on $\partial D/\partial x$.

The evaluation of $\langle X \rangle$ and $\langle v \rangle$ with chemical concentration or temperature gradients and resulting equations for J are discussed in the following sections.

5–2. BASIC JUMP FREQUENCIES IN A DIFFUSION COEFFICIENT GRADIENT

The mean displacement $\langle X \rangle$ in cubic crystals can be calculated directly from equations for the effective jump frequency, such as Eq. (4–6), by considering diffusion along a $\langle 100 \rangle$ direction. As discussed in Chapter 4, this approach using effective jump frequencies can be extended to diffusion along certain directions in anisotropic crystals, especially if matrix quantities are introduced. For simplicity, however, the following discussion is confined to cubic crystals. The factors $\nu_\alpha{}^b$, G_α, and f_α, which compose the effective jump frequency $\nu_\alpha{}^e$, then are scalar quantities given by Eqs. (4–5), (4–7), and (4–8).

To apply these equations, we need a general expression for the basic jump frequency, valid even when there is a diffusion coefficient gradient. This is derived in the present section in terms of "driving forces" and jump frequency gradients. In succeeding sections, the "driving forces" on the atoms in a chemical concentration gradient are described, and the effect of such a gradient on G_α and f_α is calculated. A general expression for $\langle v \rangle$ is given in (5–31). Detailed expressions for the atom flux in a chemical concentration gradient are calculated in Sections 5–5 and 5–6. Finally, in Section 5–7, "driving forces" and atom fluxes in a temperature gradient are discussed.

Vacancy Jump Frequencies

When the energy of motion is a function of position x, the vacancy jump frequency w_0 in plane 0 normal to the x-axis differs from the frequency w_α in plane +1, the next plane to the right. One may write

$$w_\alpha = w_0[1 + d(\partial \ln w/\partial x)] \tag{5–12}$$

If a driving force F_v acts on the vacancies, the jump frequency $w_{0\alpha}$ for a jump from site 0 on plane 0 to site α on plane +1 differs from $w_{\alpha 0}$ for the reverse jump from α to 0. We assume that any effect which makes $w_{0\alpha}$ greater than w_0 makes $w_{\alpha 0}$ correspondingly smaller than w_α. (See the discussion in Section 7–1.) Then, to first order,

$$w_{0\alpha} + w_{\alpha 0} = w_0 + w_\alpha = 2w_m \tag{5–13}$$

Here w_m is defined as the average of w_0 and w_α. Also, as in Eqs. (1–11) to (1–13),

$$w_{0\alpha} - w_{\alpha 0} = w_m F_v d/kT = 2w_m \varepsilon_v \tag{5–14}$$

where $\varepsilon_v = F_v d/2kT$. Equation (5–14) provides an atomistic definition of F_v and ε_v in terms of $w_{0\alpha}$, $w_{\alpha 0}$, and w_m.

Macroscopically, the composition and other properties of a crystal can be considered to vary continuously as a function of position. The composition (or other property) associated with a given plane is the value of the macroscopic composition of the plane. To first order, w_0 and w_α equal the vacancy jump frequencies in homogeneous crystals having the properties (composition, temperature, etc.) associated with plane 0 and +1, respectively; while w_m is that in a homogeneous alloy having the properties associated with plane m, midway between planes 0 and +1.

Combining Eqs. (5–12) to (5–14) gives to first order

$$w_{0\alpha} = w_0[1 + \varepsilon_v + \tfrac{1}{2}d(\partial \ln w/\partial x)] \qquad (5\text{–}15\text{a})$$

$$w_{\alpha 0} = w_0[1 - \varepsilon_v + \tfrac{1}{2}d(\partial \ln w/\partial x)] \qquad (5\text{–}15\text{b})$$

Here, ε_v arises from the driving force, and $\frac{1}{2}d(\partial \ln w/\partial x)$ arises from the diffusion coefficient gradient.

Atom Jump Frequencies

Equations similar to (5–12) to (5–15) can be written for the atom jump frequencies between sites 0 and α.

In analogy with (5–14), we can write

$$\Gamma_{0\alpha} - \Gamma_{\alpha 0} = \Gamma_m F_i d/kT = 2\Gamma_m \varepsilon_i \qquad (5\text{–}16)$$

where $\Gamma_{0\alpha}$ is the basic atom jump frequency from site 0 to site α, $\Gamma_{\alpha 0}$ is that from site α to site 0, Γ_m is that in a homogeneous crystal having the properties associated with plane m, midway between planes 0 and +1, and $\varepsilon_i = F_i d/2kT$. Here, the symbol Γ for the basic atom jump frequency replaces the symbol w in (5–14), while subscript i replaces the subscript v. Equation (5–16) defines ε_i and the driving force F_i in terms of the atomic quantities $\Gamma_{0\alpha}$ and $\Gamma_{\alpha 0}$. The atom jump frequencies $\Gamma_{0\alpha}$ and $\Gamma_{\alpha 0}$ are related to the vacancy jump frequencies $w_{\alpha 0}$ and $w_{0\alpha}$ by the equations

$$\Gamma_{0\alpha} = w_{\alpha 0} N_{v\alpha e} \tag{5-17}$$

$$\Gamma_{\alpha 0} = w_{0\alpha} N_{v0e} \tag{5-18}$$

where $N_{v\alpha e}$ and N_{v0e} are the equilibrium vacancy concentrations for sites on planes +1 and 0, respectively, neighboring on our atom. (Note that when an *atom* moves from 0 to α, a *vacancy* moves in the *opposite* direction from α to 0.)

As before, we assume to first order

$$\Gamma_{0\alpha} + \Gamma_{\alpha 0} = \Gamma_0 + \Gamma_\alpha = 2\Gamma_m \tag{5-19}$$

where Γ_0 and Γ_α are the basic atom jump frequencies in planes 0 and +1, respectively (to first order, equal to those in the corresponding homogeneous alloys). Also,

$$N_{v\alpha e} = N_{v0e}[1 + d(\partial \ln N_v/\partial x)] \tag{5-20}$$

Therefore,

$$\varepsilon_i = -\varepsilon_v + \tfrac{1}{2}d(\partial \ln N_v/\partial x) \tag{5-21}$$

and

$$\Gamma_{0\alpha} = \Gamma_0\{1 + \varepsilon_i + \tfrac{1}{2}d(\partial \ln N_v/\partial x) + \tfrac{1}{2}d(\partial \ln w/\partial x)\} \tag{5-22}$$

In the present equations, the superscript b has been omitted to simplify the notation. Also, the subscript 0 is included specifying the original atom site, since in the present chapter we allow the jump frequencies to depend not only on the direction of the jump but also on the original atom location. Otherwise the present equations are analogous to those in Section 4–2, with $\Gamma_{0\alpha} = \Gamma_R{}^b = \nu_R{}^b y_R{}^{-1}$ and $\Gamma_0 = \Gamma^b = \nu_o{}^b y_R{}^{-1}$. In the present notation, Eq. (4–16) becomes

$$\nu_{0\alpha} = y_\alpha \Gamma_{0\alpha} = y_\alpha \Gamma_0(1 + A) \tag{5-23}$$

Thus (5–22) yields

$$A = \varepsilon_i + \tfrac{1}{2}d(\partial \ln N_v/\partial x) + \tfrac{1}{2}d(\partial \ln w/\partial x) \qquad (5\text{–}24)$$

Here ε_i is the term arising from the driving force on the atom, as in (4–17); while the other terms on the right arise from the diffusion coefficient gradient.

In the present notation, Eq. (4–6) becomes

$$\nu_\alpha{}^e = \nu_{0\alpha} G_{0\alpha} f_{0\alpha} \qquad (5\text{–}25)$$

Correlation Factor in a Diffusion Coefficient Gradient

Since $w_{0\alpha}$ depends on position, P_+ and P_- in Eq. (4–8) will not be equal. Instead, to first order,

$$P_+ = P_m[1 + \zeta] \qquad (5\text{–}26a)$$

$$P_- = P_m[1 - \zeta] \qquad (5\text{–}26b)$$

where ζ is a small quantity and P_m is the value of P for jumps in plane m normal to the gradient and midway between planes 0 and +1. Equation (4–8) to first order then becomes

$$f_{0\alpha} = \frac{1 - P_m}{1 + P_m} = f_m \qquad (5\text{–}27)$$

where f_m is the correlation factor for jumps in plane m (or in a homogeneous system having the properties associated with plane m). Since the correlation factor depends equally on the frequency of jumps in the positive and negative directions, it is reasonable that $f_{0\alpha}$ should have a value associated with plane m. In general,

$$f_{0\alpha} = f_0[1 + \tfrac{1}{2}d(\partial \ln f/\partial x)] \qquad (5\text{–}28)$$

where f_0 is the value of the correlation factor in a homogeneous system having the properties associated with plane 0.

General Expression for the Drift Velocity $\langle v \rangle$

In general, as in Eq. (4–18),

$$G_{0\alpha} = 1 \pm B \tag{5–29}$$

where the + sign refers to jumps to plane +1 and the − sign to jumps to plane −1.

The mean displacement $\langle X \rangle$ can be expressed in terms of the effective jump frequencies given in Eq. (5–25). With $\nu_{0\alpha}$, $f_{0\alpha}$, and $G_{0\alpha}$ for jumps from site 0 to sites α given by Eqs. (5–23), (5–28), and (5–29) with $y_\alpha = y$ as in (4–19), one finds

$$\langle X \rangle = 2yd\tau \Gamma_0^b f_0[A + B + \tfrac{1}{2}d(\partial \ln f/\partial x)] \tag{5–30}$$

Except for the additional term $\frac{1}{2}d(\partial \ln f/\partial x)$, this equation is the same as (4–20). With A given by (5–24),

$$\langle v \rangle = D_i^*[(\partial \ln D_i^*/\partial x) + 2d^{-1}(\varepsilon_i + B)] \tag{5–31}$$

where $\langle v \rangle = \partial \langle X \rangle / \partial \tau$. Here and in the remainder of this chapter, an asterisk is used to distinguish the tracer diffusion coefficient D_i^* from other "diffusion coefficients" which will be discussed.

As previously,

$$D_i^* = d^2 y \Gamma_0^b f_0 = d^2 y w N_v f \tag{5–32}$$

In the right-hand expression, the subscripts 0 have been omitted since all quantities are those at plane 0.

Equation (5–31) gives the average drift velocity when driving forces and also a diffusion coefficient gradient are present. The atom flux J is found by substituting this expression into (5–10). The quantities ε_i and B depend on the driving forces acting in each particular case. In Sections 5–3 and 5–4, ε_i and B in a chemical concentration gradient are considered. Final expressions appear as Eqs. (5–42) and (5–71).

5–3. DRIVING FORCE FROM A CHEMICAL CONCENTRATION GRADIENT

For diffusion in an electric field, the value of the driving force $F(=qE)$ is obvious since the field exerts a force directly on charged ions. For diffusion in a chemical concentration gradient, however, F must be derived by a consideration of thermodynamic quantities, such as chemical potential gradients in nonideal solutions.

Atom Chemical Potential

The chemical potential μ_i for species i is defined by the equation

$$\mu_i = (\partial G/\partial N_i) \tag{5–33}$$

where G is the Gibbs free energy of the system, N_i is the concentration of i atoms, and the derivative is evaluated with all other state variables, such as pressure, temperature, and concentrations of other species, held constant.

In equilibrium, the chemical potential does not vary with position and there is zero net flux of i atoms. On the other hand, if μ_i does vary with position, an atom flux J_i occurs tending to reduce this variation. In a linear theory, the flux is proportional to the chemical potential gradient $\partial\mu_i/\partial x$. There also may be effects from the chemical potential gradients of the other atom species in the crystal. In a linear theory, the equation for diffusion of i atoms in a chemical concentration gradient is (see Section 6–1)

$$J_i = -\sum_i L_{ik}[\partial(\mu_k - \mu_v)/\partial x] \tag{5–34}$$

Here, μ_k and μ_v are the chemical potentials of atom species k and vacancies, respectively; the L_{ik} are unknown coefficients (which may be calculated from kinetic theories); and the summation is over all atom species, including species i.

If vacancies are maintained in equilibrium, $\partial\mu_v/\partial x$ equals zero, and these terms drop out of the equation. The vacancy flow effects discussed in Chapter 4 contribute nonzero cross-terms $L_{ik}(\partial\mu_k/\partial x)$ where $i \neq k$. However, these effects are included separately in the vacancy flow term B in our kinetic equations. Thus, they can be omitted from our present calculation of forces contributing to A. If vacancy flow terms are omitted and there are no other special interactions between differing atom species, the cross-terms vanish and (5–34) reduces to the single term

$$J_i^u = -L_{ii}^u(\partial\mu_i/\partial x) \tag{5–35}$$

where L_{ii}^u is an unknown coefficient and the superscripts u indicate that vacancy flow effects are omitted.

Driving Force

The corresponding driving force on the individual atoms may be calculated as follows: In general,

$$\mu_i = \mu_i' + kT \ln N_i \tag{5–36}$$

where μ_i' is the contribution from factors other than the entropy of mixing. Since the total concentration of all constituents $(\sum_i c_i)$ is a constant and $N_i = c_i/\sum_i c_i$, Eqs. (5–35) and (5–36) yield

$$J_i^u = -D_i^* \frac{\partial c_i}{\partial x} + \frac{c_i D_i^* F_i}{kT} \tag{5–37}$$

where

$$D_i^* = L_{ii}^u kT/c_i \tag{5–38}$$

and

$$F_i = -(\partial\mu_i'/\partial x) \tag{5–39}$$

Equation (5–37) has the same form as Eq. (2–10), which was obtained by considering a random walk modified by a constant driving force. One can interpret F_i as an effective force causing the individual atom to jump in a preferred direction along the gradient.

In terms of the activities a_i and activity coefficients γ_i,

$$\mu_i = kT \ln a_i = kT \ln \gamma_i N_i \tag{5–40}$$

Comparing this with (5–36) gives

$$\frac{\partial\mu_i'}{\partial x} = kT \frac{\partial \ln \gamma_i}{\partial x} \tag{5–41}$$

Then ε_i in (5–16) is given by

$$\varepsilon_i = -\tfrac{1}{2}d(kT)^{-1}(\partial\mu_i'/\partial x) = -\tfrac{1}{2}d \frac{\partial \ln \gamma_i}{\partial x} \tag{5–42}$$

The chemical potential has the units of an energy. In an energy barrier diagram, the effect of the gradient on μ_i' can be represented as in Fig. 1–9b with the slope of the base line equaling $(\partial\mu_i'/\partial x)$. A jump in the direction of the gradient adds to the system an energy $(\partial\mu_i'/\partial x)(d)$. Thus the force opposing this jump is $(\partial\mu_i'/\partial x)$. This may be compared with energies and forces from an electric field, as considered in Chapter 4. There the increase in energy is $-qEd$ and the force aiding the jump is qE.

In an ideal solution, there is no heat of mixing. Then $\partial\mu_i'/\partial x$ is zero, and the only contribution to $(\partial\mu_i/\partial x)$ comes from the entropy term $kT\partial \ln N_i/\partial x$. In this case, the driving force F_i is zero, and the atom flux is given by just the first term on the right in (5–37). A nonzero $\partial\mu_i'/\partial x$ arises when a mixing of the constituents brings about a change in enthalpy so that there is a heat of mixing (either positive or negative). In summary, a driving force F_i is obtained only in *nonideal* solid solutions. A positive heat of mixing creates a driving force tending to increase the mixing of constituents, whereas a negative heat of mixing tends to decrease the rate of mixing.

5–4. VACANCY FLOW TERM AND CORRELATION FACTOR IN A CHEMICAL CONCENTRATION GRADIENT

The factor $G_{0\alpha}$ in Eq. (5–25) gives the effect of the vacancy flow on the effective jump frequency. Equations for G in a driving force were developed in Chapter 4. In this section, it is shown that the variation of diffusion coefficient (and vacancy concentration) with position as the result of a chemical concentration gradient does not affect $G_{0\alpha}$. Consequently, the equations for G derived in Chapter 4 are still valid.

Average Vacancy Jump Frequencies

To calculate $G_{0\alpha}$ one must find the frequency with which vacancies move from sites j neighboring on an impurity to sites p where equilibrium concentrations are maintained. In a chemical concentration gradient, the net driving force for vacancy motion differs from the driving force on the individual atoms. Let us consider a binary alloy. The frequency $W_{0\beta}$ with which a vacancy jumps from site 0 to a given neighboring site β is

$$W_{0\beta} = N_{A\beta}w_{0\beta A} + N_{B\beta}w_{0\beta B} \qquad (5\text{–}43)$$

where $N_{A\beta}$ and $N_{B\beta}$ are the mole fractions of A and B species on the plane containing site β, and $w_{0\beta A}$ and $w_{0\beta B}$ are the frequencies of exchange with A and B atoms on site β. When site β is on the plane in the $+x$-direction from site 0,

$$w_{0\beta A} = w_{A0}[1 - \varepsilon_A + \tfrac{1}{2}d(\partial \ln w_A/\partial x) + \tfrac{1}{2}d(\partial \ln N_v/\partial x)] \tag{5–44a}$$

$$w_{0\beta B} = w_{B0}[1 - \varepsilon_B + \tfrac{1}{2}d(\partial \ln w_B/\partial x) + \tfrac{1}{2}d(\partial \ln N_v/\partial x)] \tag{5–44b}$$

as in (5–15) with (5–21). Subscripts A and B refer to jumps of A and B atoms, and w_{A0} and w_{B0} are the frequencies for jumps lying entirely in plane 0. A minus sign appears before the ε terms since the vacancy and atom move in the opposite directions. The mole fractions N_A and N_B depend on position, and in binary alloys the concentration gradients are related by $\partial N_A/\partial x = -\partial N_B/\partial x$. Thus,

$$N_{A\beta} = N_{A0}[1 + d(\partial N_A/\partial x)] \tag{5–45a}$$

$$N_{B\beta} = N_{B0}[1 - d(\partial N_A/\partial x)] \tag{5–45b}$$

In a binary alloy, the Gibbs-Duhem relation states

$$\frac{\partial \ln \gamma_A}{\partial \ln N_A} = \frac{\partial \ln \gamma_B}{\partial \ln N_B} \tag{5–46}$$

Thus, with ε_A and ε_B given by (5–42), one finds

$$W_{0\beta} = W_0[1 + (\delta_v + \xi_v + \rho_v + \sigma_v)] \tag{5–47}$$

where

$$W_0 = N_{A0}w_{A0} + N_{B0}w_{B0} \tag{5–48}$$

$$\delta_v = \tfrac{1}{2}dW_0^{-1}[w_{A0}N_{A0}(\partial \ln w_A/\partial x) + w_{B0}N_{B0}(\partial \ln w_B/\partial x)] \tag{5–49}$$

$$\xi_v = \tfrac{1}{2}dW_0^{-1}(w_{A0} - w_{B0})(\partial \ln \gamma_A/\partial \ln N_A)(\partial N_A/\partial x) \tag{5–50}$$

$$\rho_v = \tfrac{1}{2}d(\partial \ln N_v/\partial x) \tag{5–51}$$

$$\sigma_v = dW_0^{-1}(w_{A0} - w_{B0})(\partial N_A/\partial x) \tag{5–52}$$

For jumps from site β to site 0, a similar detailed analysis shows

$$W_{\beta 0} = W_0[1 + (\delta_v - \xi_v - \rho_v)] \tag{5–53}$$

Here δ_v arises from the diffusion coefficient gradient and has the same effect on $w_{0\beta}$ as on $w_{\beta 0}$ (see Fig. 1–9c), whereas ξ_v, ρ_v, and σ_v arise from "driving forces". Their contribution depends on the sense of the jump between sites 0 and β.

Vacancy Flow Term

Equations (5–20), (5–47), and (5–53) can be used with (4–28) to yield G. Here the average vacancy jump frequency W_0 takes the place of the jump frequencies $w_{\gamma o}$ from (4–30). In cubic crystals, the analysis follows the lines of Section 4–3 and gives to first order

$$G_{0\alpha} = 1 - (2\xi_v + \sigma_v)\langle n_p \rangle \tag{5–54}$$

where $\langle n_p \rangle$ is given by (4–43) and (4–63) evaluated in the absence of a concentration gradient.

Since the term δ_v appears with a plus sign in both the numerator and denominator of the expression (Eq. 4–28) for G, it cancels out to first order. The contribution from ρ_v just cancels the effect from the variation of the vacancy concentration N_{vpe} as a function of x. Thus neither the diffusion coefficient gradient nor vacancy concentration gradient appears in the final expression for $G_{0\alpha}$.

A given atom A or B in a nondilute alloy should not significantly affect vacancy jump frequencies in its vicinity. Then, all jump frequencies in Eq. (4–63) for $\langle n_p \rangle$ can be set equal to W_0. Also, $\Delta w_1 = W_0$ and all other Δw_γ equal zero. As in (5–29),

$$G_{0\alpha} = 1 \pm B \tag{5–55}$$

where the + sign refers to jumps to plane +1 and the − sign to jumps to plane −1. One finds for cubic binary alloys,

$$B = \frac{-d(w_A - w_B)}{H}\left(1 + \frac{\partial \ln \gamma_A}{\partial \ln N_A}\right)\frac{\partial N_A}{\partial x} \tag{5–56}$$

Here H is the effective escape frequency discussed in Sections 3–9 and 3–10. To first order, H equals $w_{\alpha\pi}$ from Eq. (4–3), being the value of $w_{\alpha\pi}$ in the absence of a driving force. H also equals $\sum_p w_{\alpha po}$ given in Eq. (4–57). The subscripts 0 have been omitted here to simplify the notation, since all quantities are those associated with plane 0.

Vacancy Supersaturations

As discussed in Chapter 4, the vacancy distribution near each impurity normally will have higher than equilibrium concentrations on one side and correspondingly lower than equilibrium concentrations on the other side whenever there is a net vacancy flow through the crystal. This leads to the factor $G_{0\alpha}$. In spite of the variations near individual impurities, average vacancy concentrations over a whole plane can be maintained very nearly at equilibrium. This average equilibrium on an entire plane is not affected by randomly placing impurities on the left and right of the plane. Thus, a factor

$G_{0\alpha}$ which differs from unity does not require long-range vacancy supersaturations over an entire plane.

In the present discussion, we have assumed zero vacancy supersaturations. This is completely correct if the over-all vacancy flow is uniform. A vacancy flow which depends on x would give a nonzero contribution to $\partial c_v/\partial t$ and tend to increase or decrease the local vacancy concentrations. Even in this case, however, vacancy concentrations on each plane can be maintained approximately at equilibrium by the creation and destruction of vacancies at dislocations or grain boundaries. According to Balluffi,[3] this should serve in most cases to keep vacancy supersaturations to less than 1%.

5-5. DRIFT VELOCITY, ATOM FLUX, AND INTRINSIC DIFFUSION COEFFICIENT

With ε_i for a chemical concentration gradient in a binary alloy given by (5–42), Eq. (5–31) becomes

$$\langle v \rangle = D_i^*[(\partial \ln D_i^*/\partial x) - (\partial \ln \gamma_i/\partial x) + 2Bd^{-1}] \quad (5\text{–}57)$$

Upon substituting (5–57) into (5–10), one finds

$$J_i = 2c_i D_i^* Bd^{-1} - D_i^*[1 + (\partial \ln \gamma_i/\partial \ln N_i)](\partial c_i/\partial x) \quad (5\text{–}58)$$

The diffusion coefficients D in (5–10) are tracer diffusion coefficients, and therefore in (5–58) they are specifically designated by the asterisk. Also, subscripts i are used to designate quantities referring to atom species i.

More Accurate Expression for B

Equation (5–56) is only an approximate expression for the vacancy flow term B since, in its derivation, it was assumed that each vacancy jump was independent of previous jumps. This assumption that vacancy jumps are not correlated to previous jumps is not valid for diffusion in an alloy (see Section 3–2, exchange mechanism). An improved expression for B can be found as follows:

The fact that successive vacancy jumps are correlated will reduce the net vacancy flux J_v. One may write

$$J_{vc} = KJ_{vu} \tag{5–59}$$

where subscripts c and u refer to correlated and uncorrelated vacancy motion. At this point, the quantity K is an unknown coefficient of proportionality.

The quantity B arises because of the flow of vacancies. When, as was assumed above, a vacancy experiences no binding to impurities and the impurity does not affect the vacancy jump frequencies in its vicinity, B is directly proportional to J_v. Thus, a reduction in J_v will reduce B by an equal factor. The corrected value B_c, including correlation effects, can be written as

$$B_c = KB_u \tag{5–60}$$

Here K is the same factor as in (5–59) and B_u is the value B given in (5–56). The quantity H which appears in (5–56) also is influenced by vacancy correlation. To include all correlation effects, a corrected expression for H, such as Eq. (3–95), should be used.

The flux J_{vc} in a binary alloy can be calculated in two separate ways: (1) from a direct calculation of J_{vu} and (2) from a calculation of the atom fluxes J_A and J_B, using Eq. (5–56) for B_u. These two equations for J_{vc} then can be solved for K.

(1) Equation (2–1) when applied to vacancies becomes

$$J_v = yd(N_{v0}W_{0\beta} - N_{v\beta}W_{\beta 0})S \tag{5–61}$$

Here S is the number of sites per unit volume, N_{v0} and $N_{v\beta}$ are the molar vacancy concentrations on two neighboring planes, 0 and β, $W_{0\beta}$ is the vacancy jump frequency from 0 to β, and $W_{\beta 0}$ is that from β to 0. Values of $W_{0\beta}$ and $W_{\beta 0}$ not taking correlation effects into account are given by (5–47) and (5–53), whereas $N_{v\beta}$ is related to N_{v0} by an equation similar to (5–20). To first order, this gives

$$J_{vu} = d^2 N_v y(w_A - w_B)[1 + (\partial \ln \gamma_A / \partial \ln N_A)](\partial c_A/\partial x) \tag{5–62}$$

where $\partial c_A/\partial x = S\ \partial N_A/\partial x$ and all quantities are those at plane 0. From Eq. (5–32),

$$D_A^* - D_B^* = d^2 y N_v (w_A f_A - w_B f_B) \tag{5–63}$$

The general relation

$$f_i = H/(2w_i + H) \tag{5–64}$$

for the correlation factor in cubic crystals then yields

$$D_A^* - D_B^* = d^2 y N_v \frac{w_A H^2 - w_B H^2}{(2w_A + H)(2w_B + H)} \tag{5–65}$$

$$D_A^* - D_B^* = d^2 y N_v (w_A - w_B) f_A f_B \tag{5–66}$$

Equations (5–59), (5–62), and (5–66) finally give

$$J_{vc} = K(f_A f_B)^{-1}(D_A^* - D_B^*)[1 + (\partial \ln \gamma_A/\partial \ln N_A)] \times (\partial c_A/\partial x) \tag{5–67}$$

(2) Since the vacancy flux is equal and opposite to the atom flux, J_{vc} can also be obtained from the equation,

$$J_{vc} = -(J_{Ac} + J_{Bc}) \tag{5–68}$$

where J_{Ac} and J_{Bc} are given by (5–58) with B set equal to B_c. From (5–60) and (5–68), one finds

$$J_{vc} = (D_A^* - D_B^*)[1 + (\partial \ln \gamma_A/\partial \ln N_A)](\partial c_A/\partial x) - 2(c_A D_A + c_B D_B^*)d^{-1}B_u K \quad (5\text{–}69)$$

Equating Eqs. (5–67) and (5–69) with B_u given by (5–56) and H by (3–95) yields for cubic crystals

$$K = f_A f_B f_o^{-1} \quad (5\text{–}70)$$

Here a random alloy model is assumed, with Eqs. (3–94), (3–97), and (3–98) giving values of f_v and f_o. Also, the relations $N_A D_A^* + N_B D_B^* = d^2 y N_v (N_A w_A f_A + N_B w_B f_B)$ and $W = N_A w_A + N_B w_B$ have been used. This expression for K can then be substituted into (5–67) to give J_{vc} and into (5–60) and (5–56) to give B_c. With H given by (3–95) and f_v^i by (3–97),

$$B_c = -\frac{d(D_A^* - D_B^*)}{M_o(N_A D_A^* + N_B D_B^*)}\left(1 + \frac{\partial \ln \gamma_A}{\partial \ln N_A}\right)\frac{\partial N_A}{\partial x} \quad (5\text{–}71)$$

Intrinsic Diffusion Coefficients

An intrinsic diffusion coefficient D_i^I for i atoms in a chemical concentration gradient can be defined by

$$J_i = -D_i^I(\partial c_i/\partial x) \quad (5\text{–}72)$$

When B has the value B_c, D_i^I for the constituents A and B in a binary alloy, according to (5–58), is given by

$$D_i^I = D_i^*[1 + (\partial \ln \gamma_i/\partial \ln N_i)]r_i \quad (5\text{–}73)$$

where

$$r_i = 1 + \frac{(\partial N_A/\partial x)}{(\partial N_i/\partial x)} \frac{2N_i(D_A^* - D_B^*)}{M_o(N_A D_A^* + N_B D_B^*)} \tag{5–74}$$

If i is species A, $\partial N_i/\partial x = \partial N_A/\partial x$; and if i is species B $\partial N_i/\partial x = -(\partial N_A/\partial x)$. When i is the faster diffusing of the two species, r_i is greater than unity; when i is the slower diffusing species, r_i is smaller than unity; and when D_A^* equals D_B^*, r_i equals unity.

The factor $[1 + (\partial \ln \gamma_i/\partial \ln N_i)]$ is called the thermodynamic factor and may be designated by the symbol α. It arises when the heat of mixing depends on composition (nonideal solid solution). When mixing of constituents A and B decreases the net enthalpy of the system, there is an increased tendency toward interdiffusion. Then the thermodynamic factor is greater than unity, and D_A^I and D_B^I are increased. A factor of 2 is not unusual. When mixing increases the net enthalpy, the thermodynamic factor is less than unity. This reduces the rate at which mixing occurs. In special cases, it is possible for the thermodynamic factor to become negative, giving "up-hill diffusion" with $D_i^I < 0$. Then an existing concentration gradient would tend to become more pronounced instead of gradually disappearing, as is normally the case.

When D_A^* is larger than D_B^*, it is convenient to rewrite Eq. (5–73) in the following form, where the expressions in parentheses are always positive,

$$D_A^I = D_A^*\alpha\left[1 + \frac{2}{M_o}\left(1 - \frac{D_B^*}{N_A D_A^* + N_B D_B^*}\right)\right] \tag{5–75}$$

$$D_B^I = D_B^*\alpha\left[1 - \frac{2}{M_o}\left(\frac{D_A^*}{N_A D_A^* + N_B D_B^*} - 1\right)\right] \tag{5–76}$$

The terms proportional to $2/M_o$ arise from the vacancy flow effect. In a binary alloy, the vacancy flow is in the same direction as that of the slower diffusing constituent (B) and opposite to that of the faster diffusing constituent (A). The vacancy flow term gives all constituents a tendency to flow in a direction opposite to the flow of vacancies. Hence, it increases the flux of A and increases the intrinsic diffusion coefficient $D_A{}^I$; while it decreases the flux of B and decreases the intrinsic diffusion coefficient $D_B{}^I$. When one of the constituents is present in only dilute concentration, the thermodynamic factor α goes to unity and also $D_i{}^I/D_i{}^*$ for the dilute constituent goes to unity. Thus, in the absence of other forces, intrinsic diffusion coefficients of dilute constituents always equal the tracer diffusion coefficient $D_i{}^*$ of that constituent. By contrast, for a nondilute constituent, $D_i{}^I$ does not equal $D_i{}^*$. For the faster constituent $D_A{}^I$ can be as large as $D_A{}^*\alpha(M_o + 2)M_o{}^{-1}$, and $D_B{}^I$ of the slower constituent can go to zero. When $N_A \leq 2/(M_o + 2)$, our random alloy model imposes a maximum value on $D_A{}^*/D_B{}^*$, given by (3–103). Thus, $D_B{}^I$ in this model never becomes negative.

5–6. KIRKENDALL SHIFT AND CHEMICAL INTERDIFFUSION COEFFICIENT

The preceding equations apply in general to diffusion in a chemical concentration gradient in binary alloys. In particular, they can be applied to interdiffusion between two specimens in a binary alloy diffusion couple. Here each specimen is originally homogeneous but there is a sharp concentration gradient at the interface between the two specimens. This gradient gradually smooths out because of diffusion. Since the concentration gradient at the interface gives rise to a net flow of atoms and vacancies, more atoms will be on one side of the interface after diffusion than before diffusion. If there is no change in lateral dimensions of the specimens, a marker wire introduced originally at the interface appears to move toward one end of the diffusion couple. This effect, which was first

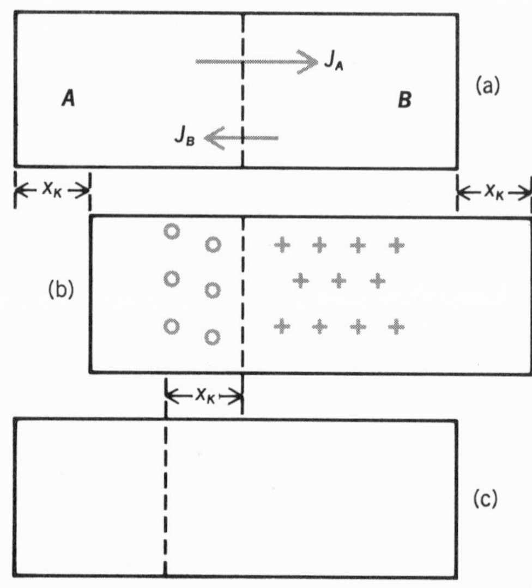

5–1 Kirkendall shift.
(a) During the diffusion, A atoms diffuse to the right across the marker plane (designated by the dashed line) while B atoms diffuse to the left.
(b) If A diffuses faster than B, more atoms are on the right of the markers after diffusion than before diffusion. Also fewer atoms are on the left. This expands the crystal volume on the right and shrinks that on the left. If the plane containing the markers is held in a fixed position, the crystal moves to the right a distance x_K. The hollow circles indicate the region with a surplus of vacancies, where porosity might be found. The plus signs indicate the region where extra planes are added.
(c) If the crystal is then moved into alignment with diagram (a) and compared with (a), it appears that the wires have moved to the left a distance x_K.

observed by Kirkendall,[4] is called the Kirkendall shift. (See Fig. 5–1.)

The marker wire is assumed to identify a given lattice plane. The flux of A or B atoms with respect to a given lattice plane can be expressed in terms of intrinsic diffusion coefficients D_i^I as in Eq. (5–72). If the plane is moving with velocity v_K with respect to the ends of the diffusion couple, the flux J_i' of species i with respect to the ends of the couple is

$$J_i' = -D_i^I(\partial c_i/\partial x) + v_K c_i \tag{5–77}$$

and the total atom flux J_t' with respect to the ends of the couple is

$$J_t' = J_A' + J_B' = v_K(c_A + c_B) - (D_A^I - D_B^I)(\partial c_A/\partial x) \tag{5–78}$$

If the ends of the diffusion couple are far enough away from the interface so that the concentration gradients equal zero and no diffusion occurs at these points, J_t' with distance measured in terms of lattice spacings equals zero, and

$$v_K = (D_A{}^I - D_B{}^I)(\partial N_A/\partial x) \tag{5–79}$$

where $N_A = c_A/(c_A + c_B)$. Now,

$$v_K = \partial x_K/\partial t \tag{5–80}$$

where x_K is the total Kirkendall shift. Experimentally x_K shows the typical parabolic dependence of diffusion processes on time,

$$x_K = It^{1/2} \tag{5–81}$$

where I is a constant. It follows that

$$x_K = 2v_{Kt}t \tag{5–82}$$

where v_{Kt} is the value of v_K at time t. Then, as originally found by Darken,[5]

$$x_K = 2t(D_A{}^I - D_B{}^I)(\partial N_A/\partial x)_t \tag{5–83}$$

where $(\partial N_A/\partial x)_t$ is the molar concentration gradient at time t. Since x_K is proportional to $t^{1/2}$, it follows that $\partial N_A/\partial x$ is proportional to $t^{-1/2}$. Values of $D_A{}^I$ and $D_B{}^I$ from (5–73) yield

$$x_K = 2f_o{}^{-1}t(D_A{}^* - D_B{}^*)[1 + (\partial \ln \gamma_i/\partial \ln N_i)](\partial N_A/\partial x)_t \tag{5–84}$$

where $f_o = M_o/(M_o + 2)$ and is the correlation factor for self-diffusion in the particular crystal structure (see Table 3–1). Thus, $f_o{}^{-1}$ ranges from approximately 1.28 for diffusion in a face-centered cubic crystal to 2 for diffusion in a crystal with a diamond structure.

If the vacancy flow term B in (5–58) were assumed to be zero (as was in effect assumed by Darken),[5] f_o^{-1} would not appear in (5–84). Thus, inclusion of the vacancy flow term increases the predicted Kirkendall by approximately 28% in face-centered cubic structures and by even more in other structures. The relation of (5–84) to the equations found by Darken is discussed further in Chapter 6.

From Eqs. (5–77) and (5–79), one also finds

$$J_A' = -J_B' = -(N_A D_B^I + N_B D_A^I)(\partial c_A/\partial x) \quad (5\text{–}85)$$

This equation defines the chemical interdiffusion coefficient $\tilde{D}$,

$$\tilde{D} = (N_A D_B^I + N_B D_A^I) \quad (5\text{–}86)$$

which gives the rate at which the concentration gradient tends to smooth itself out. From (5–73),

$$\tilde{D} = (N_A D_B^* + N_B D_A^*)[1 + (\partial \ln \gamma_i/\partial \ln N_i)]R \quad (5\text{–}87)$$

where

$$R = 1 + \frac{2N_A N_B (D_A^* - D_B^*)^2}{M_o(N_A D_B^* + N_B D_A^*)(N_A D_A^* + N_B D_B^*)} \quad (5\text{–}88)$$

Here R is unity when $N_A = 0$ or 1 and when $D_A^* = D_B^*$. Otherwise R is greater than unity. The second term on the right-hand side arises from the vacancy flow term B and is zero if B is zero. If D_A^* and D_B^* differ by a factor of 3 or less, R will be less than 1.07 for diffusion in a face-centered cubic crystal. Under the same conditions, $R \leq 1.25$ in the diamond structure. Thus, the effect of the vacancy flow term on the interdiffusion coefficient $\tilde{D}$ usually is smaller than on the Kirkendall shift x_K. R increases as N_A becomes more nearly equal to N_B and also as D_A^*/D_B^* increases.[6] The maximum value of R is f_o^{-1}.

Experimentally, x_K and $\tilde{D}$ can be determined from the concentration profile in a diffusion couple after diffusion.[7] If the thermodynamic factor is known from activity coefficient measurements, (5–84) and (5–87) allow the tracer diffusion coefficients to be calculated from the experimental $\tilde{D}$ and x_K. Conversely, if D_A^* and D_B^* have been measured in tracer experiments, (5–84) and (5–87) can be used to predict $\tilde{D}$ and x_K. Even if the thermodynamic factor is not known, (5–84) and (5–87) allow the ratio D_A^*/D_B^* to be calculated from an experimental $\tilde{D}$ and x_K.

Both $\tilde{D}$ and x_K are increased by the vacancy term. Serious errors can be made if f_o^{-1} is omitted from (5–84) and this equation then is used to calculate D_B^* from measured values of D_A^* and x_K. Also, large errors can be introduced if f_o^{-1} and R are omitted from (5–84) and (5–87) and these equations are used to calculate D_A^*/D_B^* from measured values of x_K and $\tilde{D}$.[8]

Vacancy Sources and Sinks, Porosity, and the Kirkendall Shift

The vacancy flux in a binary system is proportional to $(D_A^* - D_B^*)(\partial c_A/\partial x)$. Thus, the vacancies flow toward the region having the greater amount of the faster diffusing species and away from the region containing the slower diffusing species.

In a diffusion couple, the vacancy flux is nonuniform, going to zero at the ends of the couple where $\partial c_A/\partial x = 0$ and reaching a maximum near the middle of the diffusion zone. On the side of the couple originally containing the slower diffusing species, $\nabla \cdot J_v (= -\partial c_v/\partial t)$ is positive. This creates a deficit of vacancies in this region. In order to restore equilibrium, additional vacancies must be supplied by vacancy sources, such as dislocations, in this region. The production of vacancies at an edge dislocation causes the extra half plane associated with the dislocation to grow and expands the crystal volume on this side of the diffusion couple.

On the other side of the couple, $\nabla \cdot J_v$ is negative. Thus, $\partial c_v/\partial t$ is positive, and supersaturations of vacancies can arise. The additional vacancies often come together to form macroscopic pores in this region. Also they can disappear at vacancy sinks, such as dislocations. In the latter case, the crystal volume is decreased in this region. The decrease of crystal volume on the side containing the fast diffusing species and the increase of crystal volume on the side containing the slower diffusing species give rise to the Kirkendall shift. Because of porosity on the side containing the fast diffusing species, more accurate measurements of v_K as given in (5–79) can usually be obtained on the slow diffusing species side.

5–7. DIFFUSION IN A TEMPERATURE GRADIENT–VARIABLE DRIVING FORCE

Driving Force from a Temperature Gradient

The driving force arising from a temperature gradient is not immediately obvious. To determine the driving force, we consider the general thermodynamic equations discussed in Chapter 6.

In a temperature gradient, the thermodynamic equation for the atom flux J_i of i atoms can be written as

$$J_i = -\sum_k L_{ik}\left[\left(\frac{\partial \mu_k}{\partial x}\right)_T - \left(\frac{\partial \mu_v}{\partial x}\right)_T + \frac{Q_k^*}{T}\frac{\partial T}{\partial x}\right] \quad (5\text{–}89)$$

where the summation is over all species in the crystal, including species i. This equation is similar to (5–34), but in addition it contains terms involving the temperature gradient [see Eqs. (6–17) and (6–23)]. The coefficients Q_k^* are the reduced heats of transport for the various species k. In principle, Q_k^* can be determined from the flow of heat which results from a flux of species k in an isothermal system.

The vacancy chemical potential μ_v is given by

$$\mu_v = \mu_v' + kT \ln N_v \tag{5–90a}$$

where μ_v' is the contribution from terms other than the entropy of mixing. Thus,

$$\left(\frac{\partial \mu_v}{\partial x}\right)_T = \left(\frac{\partial \mu_v'}{\partial x}\right)_T + kT \frac{\partial \ln N_v}{\partial x} \tag{5–90b}$$

Here, N_v is an independent thermodynamic parameter, in general not dependent on T.

If we assume that there are sufficient vacancy sources and sinks to maintain the vacancy concentration at any plane at its equilibrium value, there is an auxiliary relation between N_v and T,

$$N_v = N_{vo} \exp(-E_f/kT) \tag{5–91a}$$

where N_{vo} is a constant. Then

$$\frac{\partial \ln N_v}{\partial x} = \frac{E_f}{kT^2}\frac{\partial T}{\partial x} - \frac{1}{kT}\frac{\partial E_f}{\partial x} \tag{5–91b}$$

Since

$$\left(\frac{\partial \mu_v'}{\partial x}\right)_T = \frac{\partial E_f}{\partial x} \tag{5–92}$$

substitution of (5–91b) into (5–90b) yields

$$\left(\frac{\partial \mu_v}{\partial x}\right)_T = \frac{E_f}{T}\frac{\partial T}{\partial x} \tag{5–93}$$

Equation (5–93) presents the apparent paradox that the derivative of μ_v with T held constant depends on $\partial T/\partial x$. However, the T dependence enters through the spacial dependence of N_v and the assumed relation (5–91a). In general, N_v and T

are independent thermodynamic parameters. The spacial dependence of N_v (i.e., its dependence on position) is not necessarily related to T.

The assumption that equilibrium vacancy concentrations are maintained leads in the present case to a nonzero $(\partial\mu_v/\partial x)_T$. This differs from the situation in (5–35), where the vacancy gradient arose because E_f was a function of x.

The coefficient L_{ii} contains a contribution L_{ii}^v from vacancy flow effects so we can write

$$L_{ii} = L_{ii}^u + L_{ii}^v \tag{5–94}$$

As in (5–38), the tracer diffusion coefficient is given by

$$D_i^* = L_{ii}^u kT/c_i \tag{5–95}$$

The L_{ik} also arise from vacancy flow effects. Thus (5–89) can be rewritten as

$$J_i = -D_i^* \frac{\partial c_i}{\partial x} + \frac{(F_Q + F_\mu' + F_B)D_i^* c_i}{kT} \tag{5–96}$$

where F_B is the effective force from all vacancy flow terms (i.e., L_{ii}^v and all L_{ik} with $i \neq k$), $F_\mu' = -(\partial\mu_i'/\partial x)$ is the effective force from the nonideal contribution to $\partial\mu_i/\partial x$, as in Eq. (5–39), and F_Q is the force from the temperature gradient itself,

$$F_Q = -(Q_i^* - E_f)T^{-1}(\partial T/\partial x) \tag{5–97}$$

Basic Jump Frequency

The effect of F_B is taken into account by considering vacancy flow effects separately and thus this does not contribute to the basic jump frequency. The force F_μ' was considered in Section

5-3. For an ideal solid solution or for a very dilute alloy, this force goes to zero. The force F_Q, however, has not been considered before.

In analogy with (5-97), we can define a force F_q which influences the individual atom jumps,

$$F_q = -(q_\alpha^* - E_{f\alpha})T^{-1}(\partial T/\partial x) \quad (5\text{-}98a)$$

where q_α^* is the atomic heat of transport for an α type jump and $E_{f\alpha}$ is the energy of vacancy formation on the site occupied by the vacancy before jump α.

If we let $\tilde{q}_\alpha = q_\alpha^* - E_{f\alpha}$, (5-98a) becomes

$$F_q = -\tilde{q}_\alpha T^{-1}(\partial T/\partial x) \quad (5\text{-}98b)$$

The resulting contribution to ε_i in (5-16) and (5-22) is

$$\varepsilon_i = F_q d/2kT \quad (5\text{-}99)$$

Equation (5-91) gives the value of $(\partial \ln N_v/\partial x)$ in a temperature gradient. Also, since $w \propto \exp(-E_{m\alpha}/kT)$, it follows that

$$\partial \ln w/\partial x = E_{m\alpha}(kT^2)^{-1}(\partial T/\partial x). \quad (5\text{-}100)$$

Thus (5-22) yields

$$\Gamma_{0\alpha} = \Gamma_0[1 + \tfrac{1}{2}d(E_{f\alpha} + E_{m\alpha} - \tilde{q}_\alpha)(kT^2)^{-1}(\partial T/\partial x)] \quad (5\text{-}101a)$$

where for simplicity $E_{f\alpha}$ is assumed to be independent of x. Then, A from (5-23) is given by

$$A = \tfrac{1}{2}d(E_{f\alpha} + E_{m\alpha} - \tilde{q}_\alpha)(kT^2)^{-1}(\partial T/\partial x) \quad (5\text{-}101b)$$

Here the terms $E_{f\alpha}$ and $E_{m\alpha}$ arise because of the diffusion coefficient gradient, and the term $-\tilde{q}_\alpha$ arises from the driving force. For vacancy jumps, Eqs. (5–15a) and (5–21) give

$$w_{0\alpha} = w_0[1 + \tfrac{1}{2}d(\tilde{q}_\alpha + E_{f\alpha} + E_{m\alpha})(kT^2)^{-1}(\partial T/\partial x)] \quad (5\text{–}102)$$

where again $E_{f\alpha}$ is assumed independent of x.

Kinetic Interpretation of F_q and q_α^*

Kinetically, the force F_q can be interpreted as follows: On an atomic basis, a driving force is any effect which makes a jump in one direction between two given sites occur more frequently than a jump in the opposite direction between these two sites. The atom jump frequency Γ equals wp, where p is the probability that a vacancy (or other necessary imperfection) is at a neighboring site and w is the jump frequency when the vacancy is present. In (5–98a), the term $E_{f\alpha}T^{-1} \times (\partial T/\partial x)$ arises because in a temperature gradient p for sites on plane 1 differs from p for sites on plane 2, the next plane to the right. On the other hand, the term $-q_\alpha^* T^{-1}(\partial T/\partial x)$ arises because of the effect of the temperature gradient on w.

It is shown in Section 6–1 that Q_i^* is the heat flow resulting from unit flow of i atoms. It follows on an atomic level that the flux $q_\alpha^*\lambda$ equals the amount of heat transported by a single atom jump (of length λ) multiplied by the average distance the heat is transported in the direction of the jump. Oriani[9] has emphasized that the average distance the heat is transported does not in general equal λ, and in fact may be significantly larger than λ. Thus, q_α^* bears no necessary relation to the activation energy for a jump.

If $q_\alpha^* > 0$, the jumping atom takes heat along with it. Then the jump will be biased toward the lower temperature side, where the excess heat can be more easily dissipated and will tend to reduce the existing temperature gradient. When $q_\alpha^* < 0$, a jump toward the high temperature side is favored.

According to (5–98), the force F_q for a jump in one direction can differ from that for a jump in the opposite direction. In practice, however, only the average value of F_q (for jumps in both directions between any two given sites) can be measured [see, for example, Eq. (5–108)].

Kinetic Expressions for the Reduced Heat of Transport

In a strictly thermodynamic theory, the L_{ik} and Q_i^* are unknown coefficients to be determined from experiment. In particular instances, however, useful kinetic expressions for L_{ik} and Q_i^* can be obtained. For example, the kinetic energy transported during a jump can be expressed in terms of phonon and electron energy distributions before and after the jump. This yields kinetic expressions for the reduced heat of transport.[9–14]

A somewhat different approach was used by Wirtz,[15] who calculated kinetic expressions similar to Eq. (5–102) for jumps with and against the temperature gradient. When the activation enthalpy was split into three parts, with h_1 regarded as being supplied at the position and temperature of the original atom site, h_2 at the midpoint of the jump, and h_3 at the final atom site, $q_\alpha^* = (\tilde{q}_\alpha + E_{f\alpha})$ in Eq. (5–102) was found to equal $h_1 - h_3$. In this model, one expects h_1, h_2, and h_3 all to be positive; and, consequently, one expects $| q_\alpha^* | \leq h$, where h is the total activation enthalpy. In several systems, however, the experimental results do not obey this inequality. Thus, it appears that Wirtz' approach should be modified.

Vacancy Flow Term, Nonconstant Driving Force

The vacancy flow term B depends on the vacancy-solvent jump frequencies. We have seen previously that an impurity can affect the vacancy jump frequencies in its vicinity. Thus, it was necessary to define frequencies w_1, w_2, w_3, and w_4 which differed from w_o, the vacancy jump frequency far from an impurity. Similarly, one should define heats of transport for the individual jumps, q_o^*, q_1^*, q_2^*, q_3^*, and q_4^*, which may differ considerably from one another. The driving force then is not the same for each solvent jump. This situation is considered below. It illustrates the considerations which are required to calculate B with a variable driving force.

An expression for B in the present case can be found from (4–18) and (4–28) by very much the same approach as that used in Chapter 4. The motion of the vacancies is the governing factor for B. From Eqs. (5–15a) and (5–100), it follows that, for a vacancy which moves by path q from site α to site p,

$$w_{\alpha p}{}^{q} = w^{q}_{\alpha po}[1 + \tfrac{1}{2}x_{\alpha s}E_{m\alpha s}(kT^{2})^{-1}(\partial T/\partial x) + \delta_{sp} + \epsilon_{q} + \sum \epsilon_{v}] \tag{5–103a}$$

where $x_{\alpha s}$ is the vacancy displacement in its first jump, which moves it from site α to a neighboring nonequivalent site s; $E_{m\alpha s}$ is the energy of motion for the vacancy jump from α to s; δ_{sp} is the sum of the contributions from the $(\partial \ln w/\partial x)$ terms for the remaining jumps which move the vacancy from s to p; the ϵ_q term arises from changes in R_γ, as in Eq. (4–37); and the ϵ_v terms arise from driving forces acting on the vacancies. The summation is over all jumps in the path between α and p. The subscript o indicates the value in the absence of a temperature gradient. Similarly, for vacancies moving along the path in the opposite direction,

$$w_{p\alpha}{}^{q} = w^{q}_{p\alpha o}[1 + \tfrac{1}{2}x_{\alpha s}E_{ms\alpha}(kT^{2})^{-1}(\partial T/\partial x) + \delta_{sp} + \epsilon_{q} - \sum \epsilon_{v}'] \tag{5–103b}$$

Here, we allow ϵ_v for the path from α to p to differ from $-\epsilon_v'$ for the reverse path. Also, $E_b = E_{m\alpha s} - E_{ms\alpha}$ does not necessarily equal zero. However δ_{sp} and ϵ_q are the same in (5–103a) and (5–103b).

Because of the temperature gradient, the average vacancy concentration on planes to the right or left of α differs from the concentration at the plane 0 containing α. If a linear variation of vacancy concentration with position is assumed,

$$N_{vpe}(x_{\alpha p}) = N_{vpe}(0)[1 + x_{\alpha p}E_{fp}(kT^2)^{-1}(\partial T/\partial x)] \quad (5\text{–}103c)$$

where $x_{\alpha p}$ is the x-displacement from site α to site p. With these changes, the method outlined in Section 4–3 yields, as in (4–42),

$$B = -\frac{\sum_p w_{\alpha po}[\sum \varepsilon_v + \sum \varepsilon_v' + (\frac{1}{2}x_{\alpha s}E_b - x_{\alpha p}E_{fp})(kT^2)^{-1}(\partial T/\partial x)]}{\sum_p w_{\alpha po}} \quad (5\text{–}104)$$

The ε_v and ε_v' can be found by comparing (5–102) with (5–15). For an individual jump w_{gh} from site g to site h,

$$\varepsilon_v = \tfrac{1}{2}d(E_{fg} + \tilde{q}_{gh})(kT^2)^{-1}(\partial T/\partial x) \quad (5\text{–}105a)$$

The energy of formation refers to that at the site occupied by the vacancy before the jump. We assume that this energy has a constant value of E_{fo} at all sites except those which are first nearest neighbors of the impurity. At these sites, the energy of formation is $E_{fo} - E_b$, where E_b is the binding energy between the vacancy and impurity. Comparison of (5–105a) with (5–98) and (5–99) shows that ε_v is proportional to q_{gh}^*. Also, in general,

$$\varepsilon_v = -\varepsilon_i + \tfrac{1}{2}d(\partial \ln N_v/\partial x). \quad (5\text{–}105b)$$

For a vacancy following a path from site α to s to p, the sum of ε_v over all jumps in this path is

$$\sum \varepsilon_v = \tfrac{1}{2}(kT^2)^{-1}(\partial T/\partial x)[x_{\alpha s}(E_{f\alpha} + \tilde{q}_{\alpha s}) + x_{sp}(E_{fo} + \tilde{q}_o)] \quad (5\text{–}106a)$$

The first term inside the square brackets arises from the initial jump which moves the vacancy away from site α to a neighboring nonequivalent site s. This differs from the contributions of other jumps in the path. Similarly,

$$\sum \varepsilon_v' = \tfrac{1}{2}(kT^2)^{-1}(\partial T/\partial x)[x_{\alpha s}(E_{fs} + \tilde{q}_{s\alpha}) + x_{sp}(E_{fo} + \tilde{q}_o)] \tag{5–106b}$$

Here, the first term inside the square brackets arises from jumps which move the vacancy into a site α.

Since $x_{\alpha p} = x_{\alpha s} + x_{sp}$,

$$\sum \varepsilon_v + \sum \varepsilon_v' = \tfrac{1}{2}(kT^2)^{-1}(\partial T/\partial x)\{x_{\alpha p}(2E_{fo} + 2\tilde{q}_o) + x_{\alpha s}[(E_{f\alpha} + E_{fs} - 2E_{fo}) + (\tilde{q}_{\alpha s} + \tilde{q}_{s\alpha} - 2\tilde{q}_o)]\} \tag{5–107}$$

It follows that

$$B = -\frac{d}{kT^2}\frac{\partial T}{\partial x} \times \left[\tilde{q}_o\langle n_p\rangle + \frac{\sum_{s=1}^{z-1} w_{\alpha so} d^{-1} x_{\alpha s}(\tfrac{1}{2}\tilde{q}_{\alpha s} + \tfrac{1}{2}\tilde{q}_{s\alpha} - \tilde{q}_o)}{\sum_{s=1}^{z-1} w_{\alpha so} F_{\alpha so}} \right] \tag{5–108}$$

where E_b equals $E_{fs} - E_{f\alpha}$ and is the increase in impurity-vacancy binding energy when the vacancy moves from site s to site α. In this derivation, it is assumed that $E_{fs} = E_{fo} = E_{fp}$ and $E_b = E_{fo} - E_{f\alpha}$. In face-centered cubic crystals, there are sites which neighbor both on site α and on the impurity, allowing E_{fs} and E_{fp} to equal $E_{f\alpha}$. Then details of the above derivation must be changed, but (5–108) is still valid. Each $\tilde{q}$ equals q^* minus the appropriate energy of formation, either E_{fo} or $E_{fo} - E_b$.

The first term on the right-hand side of (5–108) arises from the terms involving $x_{\alpha p}$ in (5–103) and (5–107). It is very similar to that in (4–44). The second term, involving the summations, in (5–108) arises because we have allowed a nonconstant driving force, i.e., the driving force between sites α and s differs from that for other solvent jumps. This term disappears if we do not distinguish between the possible solvent jumps. If in a face-centered cubic (or other cubic) crystal we assume $w_o = w_1 = w_3 = w_4 = w_{\alpha so}$ and $\tilde{q}_o = \tilde{q}_{\alpha s} = \tilde{q}_{s\alpha}$, it follows that

$$B = -\frac{d}{kT^2}\frac{\partial T}{\partial x}\frac{\tilde{q}_o}{M_o} \tag{5–109}$$

where $\langle n_p \rangle$ is given by (4–66b) and M_o is defined below Eq. (3–95). The $F_{\alpha so}$ in (5–108) are the same as the F_s in (3–93).

$\langle v \rangle$ and J in a Temperature Gradient for a Dilute Impurity

With $\langle v \rangle$ given by (5–31), ε_i by (5–99) and B by (5–109),

$$\langle v \rangle = \frac{\partial D_i^*}{\partial x} - \frac{Q_i^{**}D_i^*}{kT^2}\frac{\partial T}{\partial x} \tag{5–110}$$

where

$$Q_i^{**} = \tilde{q}_2 + 2\tilde{q}_o M_o^{-1} \tag{5–111}$$

and $\tilde{q}_2$ for the impurity jump differs from $\tilde{q}_o$ for solvent atom jumps. From Eq. (5–9), one finds

$$J_i = -D_i^*[(\partial c_i/\partial x) + c_i Q_i^{**}(kT^2)^{-1}(\partial T/\partial x)] \tag{5–112}$$

For a dilute impurity, equations having the form of (5–110) and (5–112) in general are found for $\langle v \rangle$ and J_i. Either of these equations then can be regarded as defining the parameter Q_i^{**}, the measured heat of transport. In (5–112), as in (5–89), J_i is the flux with respect to local lattice planes. These planes can be marked experimentally by inserting inert wires in the specimen. By measuring the coefficient of the $\partial T/\partial x$ term in the expression for J_i, one can experimentally determine Q_i^{**}.

Equation (5–111) relating Q_i^{**} to the $\tilde{q}_\alpha$ is valid only in the simple case where (5–109) can be assumed true. If a more complex expression, such as (5–108), is used for B, the resulting expression for Q_i^{**} is more complex than (5–111). Expressions relating Q_i^{**} to the $\tilde{q}_\alpha$ also can be found[16] from Lidiard's pair association model, which is described in Chapter 7.

Equations for Nondilute Atom Species

For a dilute impurity, F_μ' equals zero. For nondilute species, however, F_μ' often differs from zero. Then the term F_q in (5–99) is replaced by $F_q + F_\mu'$. Inclusion of the force F_μ' multiplies the $\partial c_i/\partial x$ term in (5–112) by the thermodynamic factor $[1 + (\partial \ln \gamma_i/\partial \ln N_i)]$. Also the vacancy flow effect which arises from a chemical concentration gradient multiplies the $\partial c_i/\partial x$ term by a factor r_i, such as given in (5–74) for a binary alloy. This gives for nondilute species i,

$$J_i = -D_i^*\left(1 + \frac{\partial \ln \gamma_i}{\partial \ln N_i}\right) r_i \frac{\partial c_i}{\partial x} - \frac{c_i D_i^* Q_i^{**}}{kT^2}\frac{\partial T}{\partial x} \qquad (5\text{–}113)$$

In dilute alloys, the thermodynamic factor goes to unity and can be neglected; and, for a dilute impurity, r_i goes to unity. However, for the solvent A in a dilute alloy, r_A does not go to unity.

The form of the $\partial T/\partial x$ term in (5–113) is the same as that in (5–112). However, Q_i^{**} (and D_i^*) can be expected to depend on composition and temperature. Thus, values of Q_i^{**} found from (5–113) in a nondilute alloy cannot be applied directly to dilute alloys.

Comparison of the Various Heats of Transport

At this point, it is good to emphasize that the term "heat of transport" can be used in several senses. The thermodynamic equation (5–89) contains a sum involving several thermodynamic heats of transport Q_k^*. By contrast, the "measured heat of transport" Q_i^{**} in (5–111) is a single experimental parameter. The kinetic equations relate Q_i^{**} to the $\tilde{q}_\alpha$ and q_α^* for the individual atom jumps. For self-diffusion, where $\tilde{q}_o = \tilde{q}_2$, Eq. (5–111) yields $Q_i^{**} = f^{-1}\tilde{q}_o$, where f is the correlation factor. In general, Q_i^{**} does not equal Q_i^*. Relations between Q_i^{**}, the Q_i^*, the $\tilde{q}_\alpha$, and the actual heat flow are discussed further in Section 6–1.

Soret Gradient

Since the Q^{**} for the different species in an alloy normally are not equal to one another, the effective driving forces exerted on these species in a temperature gradient also differ. As a result, a temperature gradient tends to create and maintain a chemical concentration gradient in any alloy. This gradient is called the Soret gradient. The creation of this gradient is called Soret effect.

The steady-state condition in a binary A-B alloy is that

$$J_A/J_B = c_A/c_B \tag{5–114}$$

Equation (5–113) gives values for J_A and J_B. For a binary alloy, (5–114) then gives

$$\frac{\partial \ln c_B}{\partial x} = \left[\frac{D_A^* Q_A^{**} - D_B^* Q_B^{**}}{r_B D_B^* + r_A D_A^*(c_B/c_A)}\right] \frac{(kT^2)^{-1}(\partial T/\partial x)}{[1 + (\partial \ln \gamma_i/\partial \ln N_i)]} \tag{5–115}$$

This equation is equivalent to the similar equation derived by Howard and Lidiard[17] in terms of Q_A^* and Q_B^*.

From (5–73) and (5–86), we see that the denominator in (5–115) equals N_A^{-1} times the chemical interdiffusion coefficient $\tilde{D}$. When species B is a tracer isotope of A, both $D_A^* = D_B^*$ and $Q_A^{**} = Q_B^{**}$; so there is no Soret gradient in this case.

Methods of Measuring Heats of Transport

For self-diffusion in a temperature gradient, no Soret gradient arises; however there is still a flow of atoms. According to (5–113), when there is no concentration gradient,

$$J_A = -\frac{c_A D_A{}^* Q_A{}^{**}}{kT^2}\frac{\partial T}{\partial x} \tag{5–116}$$

This flux can be measured by the motion of a set of marker wires, allowing $Q_A{}^{**}$ for self-diffusion to be measured. For Au, this method has yielded[18,19] $Q^{**} \approx -7$ kcal/mole. Marker motions in zinc[20] and α-iron[21], however, were so small that specific values of Q^{**} could not be determined. In the light of experimental uncertainties, it was concluded that $|Q^{**}| <$ 0.2 kcal/mole for zinc and $|Q^{**}| < 2$ kcal/mole for α-iron. Other experiments have shown conflicting positive and negative marker motions in zinc.[22,23] as have similar measurements on copper.[18,19] In some transition elements, large values of Q^{**} are found, such as $Q^{**} = 16$ kcal/mole for Pt[24] and $Q^{**} \approx 120$ kcal/mole for β-Zr.[25]

A second method of measuring Q^{**} is provided by the Soret gradient. In a binary alloy, this gradient depends on both $Q_A{}^{**}$ and $Q_B{}^{**}$, as in (5–115). If $D_A{}^*$ and $D_B{}^*$ differ greatly in magnitude, however, one of the terms $D_A{}^*Q_A{}^{**}$ or $D_B{}^*Q_B{}^{**}$ will be small compared to the other, allowing Q^{**} for the faster diffusing species to be determined. Also in a very dilute alloy where $c_B \ll c_A$, the term $r_A D_A{}^*(c_B/c_A)$ in the denominator of (5–115) should be negligible. Data[26] on the Soret gradient for slow-diffusing impurities in zinc give an estimate[17] of $Q_{\mathrm{Zn}}{}^{**} \approx$ 25 to 50 cal/mole; whereas for the fast diffusing impurity thallium diffusing in zinc,[16] $Q_{\mathrm{Tl}}{}^{**} \approx -0.5$ kcal/mole. Measurements also have been made for impurities diffusing in copper, silver, and gold.[19]

Since Q^{**} usually is not large, the marker shifts often are difficult to measure accurately. Soret gradient measurements can provide a much more sensitive method of determining heats of transport. Since $D_B{}^*$ for an interstitial impurity is usually much larger than $D_A{}^*$ for the solvent, the Soret gradient provides an especially good measurement for Q^{**} for interstitial impurities. For interstitial diffusion, there are several cases with large negative Soret effects where $|Q^{**}|$ is greater than the activation energy Q for diffusion.[9,27,28]

We note here that Q^{**} for self-diffusion and Q^{**} for diffusion of the solvent in a dilute alloy both equal $\tilde{q}_o f^{-1}$, where f is the correlation factor for self-diffusion. Thus, measured heats of transport in these cases are directly related to the atomic quantity $\tilde{q}_o$. For impurity diffusion, however, the relation between $Q_B{}^{**}$ and the atomic quantity $\tilde{q}_2$ is more complicated, as in (5–111) for example.

Vacancy Supersaturations

In Eq. (5–103c), a linear concentration gradient of vacancies was assumed over the distance $x_{\alpha p}$, whereas in Eqs. (5–106a) and (5–106b) a linear temperature gradient was assumed. Actually, with a linear temperature gradient, the equilibrium vacancy concentration will vary exponentially with x. Thus if $x_{\alpha p}$ is large, a correction must be made.

The exponential dependence on temperature will lead to a nonuniform flow of vacancies. Unless there are sufficient grain boundaries or dislocations to act as sources and sinks for vacancies, appreciable supersaturations or undersaturations may be obtained. Such an effect was neglected in the preceding equations. Brammer[21] and also Meechan and Lehman[18] have considered this problem. Brammer's results indicate that at moderate temperature gradients (100C deg/cm) this effect is small if the number of jumps in a vacancy lifetime is less than 10^{11} (with average x-displacement of 10^{-2} cm). These conditions probably are obeyed in most applications.

5–8. SUMMARY

Although the equations in this chapter became rather complex, the major results can be stated quite simply. First, general expressions for the atom flux J and drift velocity $\langle v \rangle = \partial \langle X \rangle / \partial \tau$ when there is a diffusion coefficient gradient were obtained in Eqs. (5–10) and (5–31). In order to apply these equations to diffusion in a chemical concentration gradient or temperature gradient, it was necessary to determine the driving forces resulting from these gradients. This was done in Section 5–3 and the first part of Section 5–7. In the case of the chemical concentration gradient, it was found that the intrinsic diffusion coefficient differed in two respects from the tracer diffusion coefficient: (1) the driving force from the nonideal part of the chemical potential contributed a "thermodynamic factor" α, and (2) the vacancy flow term contributed to D^I, increasing it for faster diffusing species in a binary alloy and decreasing it for the slower diffusing species, as in (5–73). These results were applied to chemical interdiffusion and the Kirkendall shift. The treatment of diffusion in a temperature gradient illustrated an approach which can be used when both the diffusion coefficient and the driving force vary with position. Applications to the Soret effect and measurements of heats of transport were then discussed.

Further general equations are given in Section 7–1.

REFERENCES

1. A. R. Allnatt and S. A. Rice, *J. Chem. Phys.* **33,** 573 (1960).
2. A. D. LeClaire, *Phil. Mag.* **3,** 921 (1958).
3. R. W. Balluffi, *Acta Met.* **2,** 194 (1954); H. Fara and R. W. Balluffi, *J. Appl. Phys.* **30,** 325 (1959).
4. E. O. Kirkendall, *Trans. A.I.M.E.* **147,** 104 (1942); A. D. Smigelskas and E. O. Kirkendall, *Trans. A.I.M.E.* **171,** 130 (1947).
5. L. S. Darken, *Trans. A.I.M.E.* **175,** 184 (1948).
6. J. R. Manning, *Acta Met.* **15,** 817 (1967).

7. C. Matano, *Japan. J. Phys.* **8,** 109 (1933); also see W. Jost, "Diffusion in Solids, Liquids, Gases" (Academic Press, New York, 1952), p. 31.
8. D. J. Schmatz, H. A. Domian, and H. I. Aaronson, *J. Appl. Phys.* **37,** 1741 (1966).
9. R. A. Oriani, *J. Chem. Phys.* **34,** 1773 (1961); O. D. Gonzalez and R. A. Oriani, *Trans. A.I.M.E.* **233,** 1878 (1965).
10. V. B. Fiks, *Fiz. Tverd. Tela* **3,** 3994 (1961) [English transl.: *Soviet-Physics—Solid State* **3,** 724 (1961).]
11. V. B. Fiks, *Fiz. Tverd. Tela.* **5,** 3473 (1963) [English transl.: *Soviet Physics—Solid State* **5,** 2549 (1964)].
12. G. Schottky, *Phys. Stat. Sol.* **8,** 357 (1965).
13. H. B. Huntington, *Bull. Amer. Phys. Soc. Series II,* **11,** 265 (1966).
14. L. A. Girifalco, *Phys. Rev.* **128,** 2630 (1962); **130,** 2599 (1963); *J. Chem. Phys.* **39,** 2377 (1963).
15. K. Wirtz, *Physik Z.* **44,** 221 (1943).
16. R. E. Howard and J. R. Manning, *J. Chem. Phys.* **36,** 910 (1962).
17. R. E. Howard and A. B. Lidiard, *Reports on Progress in Physics* **27,** 161 (1964).
18. C. J. Meechan and G. W. Lehman, *J. Appl. Phys.* **33,** 634 (1962).
19. D. Jaffe and P. G. Shewmon, *Acta Met.* **12,** 515 (1964).
20. P. G. Shewmon, *J. Chem. Phys.* **29,** 1032 (1958).
21. W. G. Brammer, *Acta Met.* **8,** 630 (1960).
22. R. A. Swalin, W. C. Olander, and P. Lin, *Acta Met.* **13,** 1063 (1963).
23. T. F. Archbold and P. G. McCormick, *Trans. Met. Soc. AIME* **236,** 713 (1966).
24. S. C. Ho, Th. Hehenkamp, and H. B. Huntington, *J. Phys. Chem. Solids* **26,** 251 (1965).
25. H. G. Feller and H. Wever, *J. Phys. Chem. Solids* **24,** 969 (1963).
26. F. R. Winter and H. G. Drickamer, *J. Chem. Phys.* **24,** 492 (1956).
27. L. S. Darken and R. A. Oriani, *Acta Met.* **2,** 841 (1954).
28. P. G. Shewmon, *Acta Met.* **8,** 605 (1960).

6. GENERAL THERMODYNAMIC EQUATIONS FOR DIFFUSION

6–1. NONEQUILIBRIUM THERMODYNAMIC EQUATIONS

In the preceding chapters, detailed atomic motions and the forces acting on individual atoms have been considered. This kinetic approach can successfully describe many diffusion phenomena. An alternate *thermodynamic* approach is possible, however, and can be usefully combined with kinetic models.

Basic Equations

The general theory of nonequilibrium thermodynamics as presented by Onsager, deGroot, and others[1–5] begins by defining fluxes J_i which are the time derivatives of appropriate state variables e_i. The state variables are not the thermodynamics parameters themselves but instead are the fluctuations of these parameters from their local equilibrium values in an adiabatically isolated system. Important thermodynamic parameters are local concentrations, temperature, and pressure. Then "thermodynamic forces" X_i conjugate to the fluxes are chosen. These forces are linear combinations of the state variables e_i and allow the equation for the rate of entropy production per unit volume σ to be expressed as

$$T\sigma = \sum_i J_i \cdot X_i \qquad (6\text{–}1)$$

where T is the absolute temperature. The forces X_i are not necessarily Newtonian forces, which exert an actual force on individual atoms. Instead they arise from the tendency of a system which has fluctuated away from equilibrium to return to equilibrium conditions. It is assumed that the regression of a fluctuation e_i follows the same laws as those for the return of a nonequilibrium system toward equilibrium. By using the concept of microscopic reversibility, Onsager showed that the fluxes can be expressed in the form

$$J_k = \sum_i L_{ki} X_i \tag{6–2}$$

where, in the absence of a magnetic field,

$$L_{ik} = L_{ki} \tag{6–3a}$$

The idea of microscopic reversibility in the present situation is related to the principle of time reversal symmetry in mechanics. Thus, in a magnetic field,

$$L_{ik}(B) = L_{ki}(-B) \tag{6–3b}$$

The coefficients L_{ki} depend on the thermodynamic parameters (concentrations, temperature, etc.) but are not influenced by the magnitudes of the forces X_i.

Equations (6–3) are known as the Onsager reciprocal relations. As a result of these relations, the flux of species i in a gradient of species k can be related to the flux of k in a gradient of i. These relations are difficult to test experimentally and have not been definitely verified for diffusion in solids. However, kinetic theories of diffusion also lead to these relations and we shall assume they are correct.

The summation in Eq. (6–2) is over all forces X_i which appear in Eq. (6–1). The condition that J_k depends not only on X_k but also on the X_i (with $i \neq k$) should not be neglected. In many cases, the $L_{ki}X_i$ cross-terms are quite significant.

We shall be concerned with fluxes of heat, vacancies, and n different atom species. The conjugate force X_k for atom species k can be written as

$$X_k = F_k - T\nabla\left(\frac{\mu_k}{T}\right) \tag{6–4}$$

where F_k is the actual external force on the atoms (Newtonian force), such as that provided by an electric field, and μ_k is the chemical potential of species k. For vacancies,

$$X_v = -T\nabla\left(\frac{\mu_v}{T}\right) \tag{6–5}$$

and for heat flow

$$X_q = -\frac{1}{T}\nabla T \tag{6–6}$$

Equations (6–2) then can be written as

$$J_k = \sum_{i=1}^{n} L_{ki}X_i + L_{kv}X_v + L_{kq}X_q \tag{6–7}$$

$$J_v = \sum_{i=1}^{n} L_{vi}X_i + L_{vv}X_v + L_{vq}X_q \tag{6–8}$$

$$J_q = \sum_{i=1}^{n} L_{qi}X_i + L_{qv}X_v + L_{qq}X_q \tag{6–9}$$

These equations can be simplified. In a crystal, it must be true that

$$\sum_{k=1}^{n} J_k + J_v = 0 \tag{6–10}$$

Since the forces X_i, X_v, and X_q are independent of one another, it follows that

$$\sum_k L_{ki} = -L_{vi} \tag{6–11}$$

Applying the Onsager relation and then interchanging the subscripts k and i yields

$$\sum_i L_{ki} = -L_{kv} \tag{6–12}$$

Similarly

$$\sum_i L_{qi} = -L_{qv} \tag{6–13}$$

Thus, (6–7) and (6–9) become

$$J_k = \sum_{i=1}^{n} L_{ki}(X_i - X_v) + L_{kq}X_q \tag{6–14}$$

$$J_q = \sum_{i=1}^{n} L_{qi}(X_i - X_v) + L_{qq}X_q \tag{6–15}$$

Heats of Transport

If we let

$$L_{kq} = \sum_{i=1}^{n} Q_i^* L_{ki} \tag{6–16}$$

where Q_i^* is called the heat of transport for species i, we find from (6–14),

$$J_k = \sum_{i=1}^{n} L_{ki}(X_i - X_v + Q_i^* X_q) \tag{6–17}$$

This is a simple expression for J_k in terms of the coefficients L_{ki} and Q_i^* for the n atom species.

The quantity Q_i^* can be given a physical interpretation.

Equation (6–15) can be rewritten as

$$J_q = \sum_{i=1}^{n} Q_i^* J_i + (L_{qq} - \sum_{i=1}^{n} L_{iq} Q_i^*) X_q \tag{6–18}$$

In an isothermal system, X_q equals zero. Thus Q_i^* gives the heat flow resulting from unit flux of species i in an isothermal system.

The forces as given by Eqs. (6–4) to (6–6) are at times somewhat inconvenient to use. As a result, alternative expressions,

$$X_k = F_k - (\nabla \mu_k)_T \tag{6–19}$$

$$X_v = -(\nabla \mu_v)_T \tag{6–20}$$

$$X_q = -T^{-1} \nabla T \tag{6–21}$$

are often used. Here the derivatives of μ_k and μ_v have their temperature dependence removed. When these new forces are used, Eqs. (6–1) through (6–18) still apply, but J_q then equals the "reduced heat flow". The reduced heat flow J_{qr} is related to the actual heat flow J_{qa} by the equation

$$J_{qr} = J_{qa} - \sum_{i=1}^{n} (h_i - E_f) J_i \tag{6–22}$$

where h_i is the partial specific enthalpy of species i and E_f is that for vacancies. The heats of transport used in Chapter 5 are obtained from the reduced heat flow. Thus, the Q_i^* in Chapter 5 are related to the heats of transport Q_{ia}^* derived from the actual heat flow by

$$Q_i^* = Q_{ia}^* - h_i + E_f \tag{6–23}$$

By analogy, q_α^* in Eq. (5–98a) gives the reduced heat flow resulting from a type α jump. Rewriting (6–23) in terms of atomic quantities then gives

$$q_\alpha^* = q_{\alpha a}^* - h_i + E_{f\alpha} \tag{6–24}$$

where $q_{\alpha a}^*$ is the actual heat flow resulting from the jump and h_i and $E_{f\alpha}$ are the partial specific enthalpies of the atom and the vacancy at their positions prior to the jump. We see that q_α^* is closely related to the heat flow resulting from a type α jump.

If a set of energy fluxes a_i can be found such that $\sum L_{ki}a_i = 0$ for all k, the measured atom fluxes J_k will be the same whether the heats of transport are Q_i^* or whether they are $Q_i^* + a_i$. Furthermore, heat fluxes J_q cannot be measured directly. Instead, only the temperature change, which is proportional to $\nabla \cdot J_q$, can be measured experimentally. Thus, if $\sum_i L_{ki}a_i = 0$ for all k and $\nabla \cdot a_i = 0$ for all i, heats of transport Q_i^* and $Q_i^* + a_i$ yield the same measurable values of J_k and $\nabla \cdot J_q$. When there is no linear relation among the fluxes, as in (6–14) and (6–15), there can be no set a_i such that $\sum_i L_{ki}a_i = 0$ for all k. Then the heats of transport are uniquely defined by (6–16). When there is a linear relation among the fluxes, however, relations $\sum_i L_{ki}a_i = 0$ for all k will exist. Then, the heats of transport are not uniquely defined unless an additional defining equation is introduced.[6]

When there is a linear relation among the fluxes J and among the forces X, the matrix of the Onsager coefficients L is not unique. The fluxes in (6–7) to (6–9) are related by Eq. (6–10). Thus, the L matrix in these equations is not unique. The fluxes (and forces) in (6–14) and (6–15) are independent of one another, however. Thus, the L matrix in these equations is unique.

Formally, species v in (6–7) to (6–9) might be regarded as being just another species i, with $i = n + 1$. If the summations in (6–16) and (6–18) then were allowed to include all species from 1 to $n + 1$, these equations would define heats of transport Q_i^* for $1 \leq i \leq n$ and Q_v^* (for $i = n + 1$). The J_i in this case are not independent, however, and the L matrix is not unique. Thus, the Q_i^* would not be uniquely defined unless an additional defining equation were introduced.

It is of interest to relate the measured heats of transport Q_A^{**} and Q_B^{**} to the actual heat flow resulting from an A or B atom jump. It follows in general from Eqs. (5–98) and (6–24) that $\tilde{q}_\alpha = q_\alpha^* - E_{f\alpha} = q_{a\alpha}^* - h_i$. For self-diffusion of A atoms, as noted below Eq. (5–112), $\tilde{q}_o = Q_A^{**}f$, where f is the correlation factor. Also, for self-diffusion, all jumps are of the same type. In this special case, the macroscopic quantities Q_i^* and E_f in (6–23), which represent average values over all types of jumps, equal the atomic jump quantities q_α^* and $E_{f\alpha}$ presented in (6–24). Consequently, for self-diffusion,

$$Q_A^{**} = f^{-1}(Q_A^* - E_f) = f^{-1}(Q_{Aa}^* - h_i) \qquad (6\text{–}25)$$

where Q_A^* is the reduced heat of transport, which appears in Eq. (5–89), and Q_{Aa}^* is the actual heat flow.

For an impurity, Q_B^{**} depends on at least two atomic heats of transport, $\tilde{q}_o$ and $\tilde{q}_2$, as in (5–111). In the case of (5–111), $\tilde{q}_o$ equals $Q_A^* - E_f$ and $\tilde{q}_2$ equals $Q_B^* - E_f$. If there is no vacancy-impurity binding energy, Q_i^{**} in general equals $(kT/D_i^*c_i)\sum_k L_{ki}(Q_k^* - E_f)$. Expressions for L_{ki} are discussed in Sections 6–2 and 6–3.

6–2. KINETIC EXPRESSIONS FOR THE L_{ki} IN BINARY ALLOYS

Nondilute Alloy

The L_{ki} can be related to kinetic expressions given in Chapters 4 and 5. In the present section, the L_{ki} for a nondilute two-component system are derived from kinetic equations in Chapter 5. It is found that the cross-terms (where $k \neq i$) can be quite important.

With the external forces F_A and F_B set equal to zero

$$X_A = -\left(\frac{\partial \mu_A}{\partial x}\right)_T = -kT\frac{\partial \ln \gamma_A c_A}{\partial x} = -kT\alpha c_A^{-1}\frac{\partial c_A}{\partial x} \qquad (6\text{–}26a)$$

and

$$X_B = -\left(\frac{\partial \mu_B}{\partial x}\right)_T = -kT\alpha c_B^{-1}(\partial c_B/\partial x) \qquad (6\text{–}26b)$$

Here, the thermodynamic factor α has the same value for both components A and B in the binary alloy,

$$\alpha = \left(1 + \frac{\partial \ln \gamma_A}{\partial \ln N_A}\right) = \left(1 + \frac{\partial \ln \gamma_B}{\partial \ln N_B}\right) \qquad (6\text{–}27)$$

Let us assume that vacancies are maintained at equilibrium concentrations (making $X_v = 0$) and that there is no temperature gradient (making $X_q = 0$). Then, since there are only two atom species (A and B), Eq. (6–17) reduces to

$$J_A = L_{AA}X_A + L_{AB}X_B \qquad (6\text{–}28)$$

$$J_B = L_{BA}X_A + L_{BB}X_B \qquad (6\text{–}29)$$

When the contributions to J_i in Eq. (5–72), with D_i^I given by (5–73), are separated into those arising from X_A and X_B, one finds equations having the form of (6–28) and (6–29), with

$$L_{AA} = \frac{c_A D_A^*}{kT}[1 + 2N_A D_A^* V] \qquad (6\text{–}30)$$

$$L_{BB} = \frac{c_B D_B^*}{kT}[(1 + 2N_B D_B^* V)] \qquad (6\text{–}31)$$

$$L_{AB} = L_{BA} = \frac{2c_A c_B D_A^* D_B^* V}{(c_A + c_B)kT} \qquad (6\text{–}32)$$

where

$$V = [M_o(N_A D_A^* + N_B D_B^*)]^{-1} \qquad (6\text{–}33)$$

It may be noted that the Onsager relation $L_{AB} = L_{BA}$ is obeyed. Also, it follows directly from Eqs. (6–28) and (6–29) and the expressions for X_A and X_B that

$$D_A{}^I = kT\alpha c_A{}^{-1}[L_{AA} - (c_A/c_B)L_{AB}] \qquad (6\text{–}34)$$

$$D_B{}^I = kT\alpha c_B{}^{-1}[L_{BB} - (c_B/c_A)L_{BA}] \qquad (6\text{–}35)$$

where $D_A{}^I$ and $D_B{}^I$ are intrinsic diffusion coefficients defined in (5–72). These expressions of course reduce to those given in Eq. (5–73).

The vacancy flow term in (5–58) contributes the entire value of the cross-term coefficients L_{AB} and L_{BA}. In addition, the second term in the expressions for L_{AA} and L_{BB} arises from the vacancy flow term. It is reasonable that the vacancy flow term should contribute to all four coefficients L_{AA}, L_{BB}, L_{BA}, and L_{BB}. The vacancy flow arises from forces on both A and B atoms. Then, through the vacancy flow term $2c_i D_i^* B d^{-1}$ in (5–58), the vacancy flow contributes to the fluxes of both constituents. A force X_A contributes a term proportional to $N_A D_A^*$ to the vacancy flow. Because of the vacancy flow term in (5–58), this in turn enhances the atom flux J_A and thus contributes to L_{AA}. Also it influences the flux J_B of B atoms and contributes to L_{BA}. Similar reasoning applies to the vacancy flow caused by the force X_B. In general, for any number of components, the forces X_i all contribute to the vacancy flow. The resulting vacancy flow term then increases all of the coefficients L_{ki} relating J_k to the various X_i.

The importance of the cross-terms L_{AB} and L_{BA} can be seen by considering Darken's equations for chemical interdiffusion and the Kirkendall shift.[7] In relating $D_A{}^I$ to D_A^*, Darken assumed that (1) the cross-terms L_{ki} in Eqs. (6–28) and (6–29) were zero and (2) the diagonal terms were given by $L_{ii} =$

$c_i D_i^*/kT$. It can be seen from (6–30) to (6–32) that neither of these assumptions is correct. Inclusion of the vacancy flow terms [proportional to V in (6–30) to (6–32)] appreciably affects the chemical interdiffusion coefficient and Kirkendall shift, as was discussed in Section 5–6. Thus, even in the simple case of a binary alloy, the cross-terms L_{ki} and the additional contributions to the diagonal terms can be important.

Special Cases

When B is merely a separate isotope (which can be called A^*) of species A, the expressions for the L_{ki} simplify. Then D_A^* equals D_B^* and the correlation factor f for each species is given by $f = M_o/(M_o + 2)$. Also, Eqs. (6–30) to (6–32) become

$$L_{AA} = \frac{c_A D_A^*}{kT}\left[1 + \frac{c_A}{c_A + c_A^*}\frac{(1-f)}{f}\right] \qquad (6\text{–}36)$$

$$L_{A^*A^*} = \frac{c_A^* D_A^*}{kT}\left[1 + \frac{c_A^*}{c_A + c_A^*}\frac{(1-f)}{f}\right] \qquad (6\text{–}37)$$

$$L_{AA^*} = L_{A^*A} = \frac{c_A c_A^* D_A^*}{(c_A + c_A^*)kT}\,\frac{1-f}{f} \qquad (6\text{–}38)$$

These equations agree with expressions found by Howard and Lidiard.[5] When substituted into (6–28) and (6–29), these values of L_{ki} give $J_A = -D_A^*(\partial c_A/\partial x)$ and

$$J_{A^*} = -D_A^*(\partial c_A^*/\partial x)$$

as expected. The vacancy flow terms in this special case are proportional to $(1-f)$. In general, however, these terms are not related to the correlation factor; see, for example, Eqs. (6–30) to (6–32) or (6–52).

Equations (6–30) to (6–32) also simplify when B is an impurity which is present in only trace amounts (i.e., $N_B \approx 0$ and $N_A \approx 1$). Then $f_A = M_o/(M_o + 2)$ and

$$L_{AA} \approx \frac{c_A D_A^*}{kT}\frac{1}{f_A} \tag{6–39}$$

$$L_{BB} \approx \frac{c_B D_B^*}{kT} \tag{6–40}$$

$$L_{AB} = L_{BA} \approx \frac{c_B D_B^*}{kT}\frac{1 - f_A}{f_A} \tag{6–41}$$

At this point, it is well to emphasize that Eqs. (6–30) to (6–32) for the L_{ki} were derived by explicitly assuming zero binding energy. Also, when a vacancy at a site next to a particular atom M is considered, it is assumed that all vacancy jumps except those with M have the same jump frequency, namely $w_A N_A + w_B N_B$. These assumptions often need to be modified, especially when diffusion in ionic crystals is considered. Dilute impurities with some vacancy-impurity binding are considered in Section 6–3. In addition, Howard and Lidiard,[5,8] using a "pair association" method, have calculated the L_{ki} for a face-centered cubic sublattice (NaCl structure). They included not only vacancy-impurity binding but also the variations in over-all vacancy concentration which arise when divalent impurities are introduced into a monovalent sublattice. These results are discussed in Chapter 7.

6–3. FURTHER APPLICATIONS INVOLVING THE L_{ki}

One important feature of the thermodynamic equations is that the L_{ki} coefficients are independent of the magnitude of the forces X_i. Thus, values of L_{ki} determined for particular values of the X_i also apply when certain of the X_i are altered or set equal to zero. In addition, the Onsager relations $L_{ki} = L_{ik}$ provide useful relations between experimental quantities.

The lack of dependence of L_{ki} on X_i is used below in describing diffusion of dilute impurities in an electric field. Then the Onsager relation is used to relate the Soret and Dufour effects. These examples are chosen since they relate directly to the kinetic equations in Chapters 4 and 5. Further examples (including equations for four components) are discussed by Howard and Lidiard[5] in their review article.

Modified Nernst-Einstein Relation

Let us consider diffusion of a dilute impurity B in an otherwise pure crystal of species A. For diffusion in an electric field E, the thermodynamic forces X_A and X_B are

$$X_A = F_A - (\nabla \mu_A)_T = q_A E - kTc_A^{-1}(\partial c_A/\partial x) \quad (6\text{–}42)$$

$$X_B = F_B - (\nabla \mu_B)_T = q_B E - kTc_B^{-1}(\partial c_B/\partial x) \quad (6\text{–}43)$$

where q_A and q_B are the charges of ions A and B. Since there are only small amounts of B, the activity coefficients γ_i and the factor α equal unity. Also, $\partial c_A/\partial x = -\partial c_B/\partial x$ in a binary system. Hence, Eqs. (6–28) and (6–29) become

$$J_A = -kT\left(\frac{L_{AA}}{c_A} - \frac{L_{AB}}{c_B}\right)\frac{\partial c_A}{\partial x} + (L_{AA}q_A + L_{AB}q_B)E \quad (6\text{–}44)$$

$$J_B = -kT\left(\frac{L_{BB}}{c_B} - \frac{L_{BA}}{c_A}\right)\frac{\partial c_B}{\partial x} + (L_{BB}q_B + L_{BA}q_A)E \quad (6\text{–}45)$$

When the field E is zero, (6–45) reduces to the equation for tracer diffusion with diffusion coefficient,

$$D_B^* = kT\left(\frac{L_{BB}}{c_B} - \frac{L_{BA}}{c_A}\right) \quad (6\text{–}46)$$

When $\partial c_B/\partial x$ is zero, (6–45) has the form $J_B = u_B c_B E$, where u_B is the drift mobility of B atoms in the field E. Thus,

$$u_B = c_B^{-1}(L_{BB}q_B + L_{BA}q_A) \tag{6–47}$$

Combining (6–46) and (6–47) gives

$$\frac{u_B}{D_B^*} = \frac{q_B}{kT}\left[1 + \frac{L_{BA}[(q_A/q_B) + (c_B/c_A)]}{L_{BB} - L_{BA}(c_B/c_A)}\right] \tag{6–48}$$

It follows that the Nernst-Einstein relation $(u_B/D_B = q_B/kT)$ is obeyed only when the cross-term coefficient L_{BA} equals zero.

Equation (6–48) can be simplified. Since B is present only in small quantities, one expects $c_B/c_A \ll 1$ and also $c_B/c_A \ll q_A/q_B$. Both experiments and the kinetic expressions for u/D, such as those in Chapter 4, indicate that the second term within the large brackets of (6–48) is of the order of or smaller than q_A/q_B. One concludes that L_{BA} cannot be appreciably greater than L_{BB}. Consequently, $(c_B/c_A)L_{BA} \ll L_{BB}$, and (6–48) reduces to

$$\frac{u_B}{D_B^*} \approx \frac{q_B}{kT}\left[1 + \frac{L_{BA}}{L_{BB}}\frac{q_A}{q_B}\right] \tag{6–49}$$

as given by Howard and Lidiard.[5] Also, Eq. (6–46) becomes

$$D_B^* \approx kTc_B^{-1}L_{BB} \tag{6–50}$$

in agreement with (6–40).

A kinetic expression for L_{BB} can be obtained by comparing Eqs. (6–50) and (3–2). For cubic crystals,

$$L_{BB} \approx \tfrac{1}{6}\lambda^2 N_v z w_B (kT)^{-1} f_B c_B \tag{6–51}$$

where f_B is the correlation factor for tracer impurity B. By comparing (6–49) and (4–73), one finds for a vacancy mechanism in cubic crystals,

$$L_{BA} \approx 2\langle n_p \rangle L_{BB} \tag{6–52}$$

From the equations for $\langle n_p \rangle$ in Chapter 4, we see explicitly how the vacancy jump frequencies enter into the expression for L_{BA}.

Although L_{BB} and L_{BA} do not depend on $\partial c_B/\partial x$ or the forces X_i, it should be emphasized that they do depend on c_B and on the vacancy jump frequencies. In the particular case at hand, it is assumed that $c_B \ll c_A$.

In terms of the experimental quantities $D_B{}^*$ and u_B,

$$L_{BB} \approx \frac{c_B D_B{}^*}{kT} \tag{6–53}$$

$$L_{BA} \approx \left(\frac{u_B}{D_B{}^*} - \frac{q_B}{kT}\right) c_B D_B{}^* q_A{}^{-1} \tag{6–54}$$

Here L_{BA} from (6–54) does not necessarily agree with that in (6–41) since the physical assumptions made to obtain (6–54) are not as restrictive as those made to derive (6–41).

Dufour Effect

As a final example, we shall consider a situation where the Onsager relation allows the result in one type of experiment to be predicted from the result of quite a different type of experiment.

The heat of transport $Q_{Aa}{}^*$ of a solvent species can be determined from the Soret gradient of a slow moving tracer impurity, as discussed in Chapter 5, along with (6–23) and (6–25). This heat of transport is not affected by the impurity and is the same as that which would be measured by marker motions in a crystal of pure A in a temperature gradient. Equations (6–16) and (6–39) give in the latter case

$$L_{A_q} = Q_{Aa}{}^* L_{AA} = Q_{Aa}{}^* c_A D_A{}^* / kTf \tag{6–55}$$

According to (6–15), the flux of heat J_q in a pure crystal (single-component system) is given by

$$J_q = L_{qA}(X_A - X_v) + L_{qq}X_q \tag{6–56}$$

Thus, if one imposes an external force F_A which makes $X_A - X_v$ unequal to zero, a flow of heat proportional to L_{qA} should occur. From the Onsager relation, $L_{qA} = L_{Aq}$. Then with (6–55), one finds $L_{qA} = Q_{Aa}{}^*c_AD_A{}^*/kTf$. Thus, the amount of heat flow in one experiment can be predicted from the amount of matter flow in a separate experiment.

This heat flow can give rise to the Dufour effect, i.e., the creation of a temperature gradient as a result of an atom flux. This effect has been measured in gases, but not in liquids or solids where the predicted effect is much smaller.

REFERENCES

1. L. Onsager, *Phys. Rev.* **37,** 405 (1931); **38,** 2265 (1932).
2. K. G. Denbigh, "The Thermodynamics of the Steady State" (Methuen and Co., London, 1951).
3. S. R. deGroot, "The Thermodynamics of Irreversible Processes" (North-Holland Publishing Co., Amsterdam, 1951).
4. S. R. deGroot and P. Mazur, "Non-Equilibrium Thermodynamics" (North-Holland Publishing Co., Amsterdam, 1962).
5. R. E. Howard and A. B. Lidiard, *Reports on Progress in Physics* **27,** 161 (1964).
6. R. E. Howard and A. B. Lidiard, *J. Chem. Phys.* **43,** 4158 (1965).
7. L. S. Darken, *Trans. A.I.M.E.* **175,** 184 (1948).
8. R. E. Howard and A. B. Lidiard, *J. Phys. Soc. Japan* (Suppl. II) **18,** 197 (1963).

7. OTHER APPLICATIONS

7–1. GENERAL EQUATIONS: OTHER DRIVING FORCES

In Chapters 4 and 5, kinetic equations were derived for several specific driving forces, i.e., those from an electric field, a chemical concentration gradient, and a temperature gradient. Of course, other driving forces are possible. In the present section, general equations that apply to any driving forces are discussed.

An example of an additional driving force is provided by the "electron wind" effect for diffusion in metals. Here an electric field creates a flow of electrons which may transfer some of their momentum to diffusing atoms and hence bias the directions of the individual atom jumps.[1–4] Other driving forces may arise from the centrifugal force on the atoms in a rapidly rotating object, from stress gradients, and from gravitational forces.

General Description of Driving Forces in Terms of Jump Frequencies

From a kinetic viewpoint, very general equations for the atom flux can be written in terms of the atom jump frequencies. These equations provide useful results whenever the influence of the driving forces on the individual atom jumps can be described.

A driving force by definition is any influence which causes a jump in one direction between two given sites to have a higher jump frequency than a jump in the opposite direction between these same two sites. For jumps between planes 1 and 2, one can write

$$\nu_{12} - \nu_{21} = 2\varepsilon\nu_m = \nu_m Fd/kT \tag{7–1}$$

where

$$\nu_m = \tfrac{1}{2}(\nu_{12} + \nu_{21}) \tag{7–2}$$

Here ν_m is defined as the average of ν_{12} and ν_{21}, d is the distance between planes, and F is the force directed normal to these planes. Equation (7–1) serves to define the driving force F for jumps between planes 1 and 2 in terms of the jump frequencies ν_{12} and ν_{21}.

Description of Jump Frequencies in Terms of Energy Barrier Diagrams

If we consider an energy barrier diagram, the effect of a driving force is to alter the base line but not to affect the relative heights of successive barriers above the base line, as in Fig. 1–9b. This effect may be contrasted with the effect from a diffusion coefficient gradient, which leaves the base line unchanged but affects the heights of the barriers above the base line, as in Fig. 1–9c. If the diffusion coefficient increases from left to right, the heights of the barriers show a corresponding decrease. This change in barrier height changes ν_m, but to first order does not change $(\nu_{12} - \nu_{21})/\nu_m$ or ε.

The slope of the base line and the barrier heights above this base line are independent of one another. Thus, any two jump frequencies ν_{12} and ν_{21} can be described in terms of an effective force F for jumps between planes 1 and 2 and a barrier height H, where

$$\nu_m = \nu_{mo} \exp(-H/RT) \tag{7–3}$$

Here T is the temperature associated with the midpoint of the jumps ν_{12} and ν_{21}.

Since two variables F and H are sufficient to describe two different frequencies ν_{12} and ν_{21}, ν_{mo} can be an arbitrary constant. For jumps between planes 2 and 3, ν_{23} and ν_{32} can be expressed in terms of two different values of F and H but with the same ν_{mo}. This picture allows both a variable force and a variable diffusion coefficient but requires no other variables to provide a complete description of jump frequencies along the diffusion direction.

The barrier heights H as defined in Eq. (7–3) do not necessarily equal the actual activation energies. If $\nu_m = \nu_{mu} \times \exp(-H_u/RT)$, where H_u is the true activation energy (enthalpy) and ν_{mu} is a temperature dependent pre-exponential factor, the quantity H in Eq. (7–3) is related to H_u by the equation $H = H_u - R\partial \ln \nu_{mu}/\partial(1/T)$.

Relation of ν_m to Jump Frequencies in Homogeneous Systems

There may be influences which increase ν_{12} above the frequency for a jump normal to the diffusion axis but leave ν_{21} unchanged (or at least changed to a lesser extent than ν_{12}). Then ν_m would not equal the average jump frequency normal to the diffusion axis. Also ν_m would not be the jump frequency in a homogeneous system having the properties associated with the plane midway between planes 1 and 2; and H could not be simply related to the properties of any homogeneous system where there is no preferred direction of jump. This can create a problem if one wishes to relate the average drift velocity $\langle v \rangle$ and atom flux J to properties (such as diffusion coefficients) measured in homogeneous systems.

Usually, however, ν_m differs only slightly from that in a homogeneous system having the properties associated with the midpoint of the jump; and, to first order, jumps normal to the diffusion axis are not affected by forces or gradients along this axis. Then $\langle v \rangle = \partial \langle X \rangle / \partial \tau$ is given quite accurately by (5–31) with D^* assumed equal to the tracer diffusion coefficient for jumps in a homogeneous system having the properties associated with the midpoint of the jump. The error introduced by this assumption will be of the order of $(\nu_m - \nu_{mb})/\nu_{mb}$, where ν_{mb} is the value of ν_m in the absence of a driving force. In most cases, this error will be negligible, but even when it is not, the equations can be corrected by merely replacing the diffusion coefficient D^* in the final equations by a quantity D_m equal to $(\nu_m/\nu_{mb})D^*$.

General Energy Barrier Diagram: Contributions to $\langle v \rangle$ and J

A situation where both F and H depend on position is illustrated in Fig. 7–1. Here F_{12} and H_{12} for jumps between planes

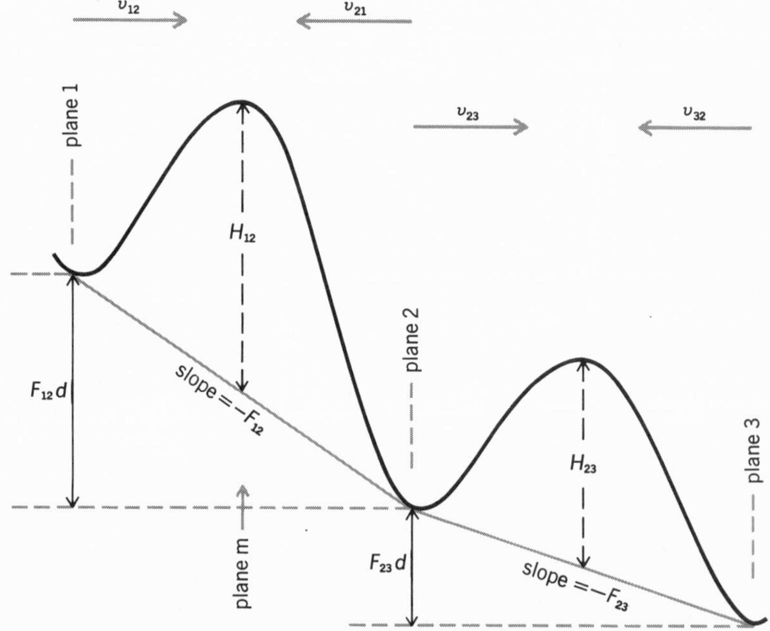

7–1 General energy barrier diagram. Jump frequencies ν_{12} and ν_{21} between planes 1 and 2 can be described in terms of F_{12} and H_{12}; those between planes 2 and 3 in terms of F_{23} and H_{23}. The difference between jump frequencies ν_{12} and ν_{23} depends on all four quantities F_{12}, F_{23}, H_{12}, and H_{23}. Neighboring planes are separated by a distance d.

1 and 2 differ from F_{23} and H_{23} for jumps between planes 2 and 3. From this diagram, we see that an atom on plane 2 has a higher energy barrier on its left than on its right. Both the average force $\frac{1}{2}(F_{12} + F_{23})$ and the term $H_{23} - H_{21}$ from the diffusion coefficient gradient contribute to this difference. The drift velocity $\langle v \rangle$ is proportional to the difference in barrier heights. Hence, the driving forces and diffusion coefficient gradient both contribute to $\langle v \rangle$.

On the other hand, the net atom flux J_{12} between planes 1 and 2 shows a different dependence on F and H. First there is a contribution $-D_m(\partial c/\partial x)$ if the concentration of the diffusing species on 1 differs from that on 2. This contribution is independent of F and dH/dx, since D_m depends only on the average barrier height (H_{12}) on plane m. In addition, there is a contribution because a jump from 1 to 2 across the rather low barrier to the right of 1 is easier than a jump from 2 to 1, where the net barrier height is larger. The sole reason for the difference in barrier height is the nonzero slope in the base line between 1 and 2, proportional to the force F_{12}. The diffusion coefficient gradient (related to $H_{23} - H_{12}$) does not contribute here to the difference in barrier height. Thus, the flux J between planes 1 and 2 depends on the driving force F and the diffusion coefficient D_m, but not on the diffusion coefficient gradient.

General diffusion equations in terms of F, H, and their gradients can be obtained. To apply these equations, one needs only to determine the appropriate values of F and H from the physical circumstances. Contributions from driving forces, as defined in (7–1), and diffusion coefficient gradients can be calculated separately. This allows the equations for J and $\langle v \rangle$ to be presented in a very simple form, as is discussed below.

General Equations for $\langle v \rangle$ and J in Terms of the Diffusion Coefficient Gradient and Driving Forces

The contributions to $\langle v \rangle$ and J can conveniently be expressed in terms of the quantities A and B introduced in Chapter 4.

Both a driving force and a diffusion coefficient gradient can make the barrier on one side of a given plane higher than that on the opposite side of this plane (for example, see plane 2 as discussed above). Thus, there will be two contributions to A, as defined in (4–16) and (4–17)

$$A = A_F + A_D \tag{7–4}$$

where A_F arises from the driving force and A_D from the diffusion coefficient gradient.

Equation (5–30) then can be written as

$$\langle v \rangle = [A_F + A_D + B + \tfrac{1}{2}d(\partial \ln f/\partial x)]2Dd^{-1} \tag{7–5}$$

and Eq. (5–9) as

$$J = -D(\partial c/\partial x) - c(\partial D/\partial x) + c[A_F + A_D + B + \tfrac{1}{2}d(\partial \ln f/\partial x)]2Dd^{-1} \tag{7–6}$$

Here B depends on the vacancy flux, and the vacancy flux is independent of diffusion coefficient gradients.[5] Therefore A_F and B are independent of any diffusion coefficient gradient and depend only on the driving forces, going to zero when these forces go to zero. On the other hand, the correlation factor f was shown in Section 3–8 to be independent of driving forces. Thus, both A_D and $\partial \ln f/\partial x$ are independent of driving forces. The net contribution to J and $\langle v \rangle$ from these terms goes to zero when the diffusion coefficient gradient goes to zero.

When there are no driving forces, A_F and B equal zero, and (7–6) reduces to

$$J = -D(\partial c/\partial x) - c(\partial D/\partial x) + c[A_D + \tfrac{1}{2}d(\partial \ln f/\partial x)]2Dd^{-1} \tag{7–7}$$

However, by definition of the diffusion coefficient, when there are no driving forces, $J = -D(\partial c/\partial x)$. Hence,

$$\partial D/\partial x = 2Dd^{-1}[A_D + \tfrac{1}{2}d(\partial \ln f/\partial x)] \tag{7-8}$$

Equation (7–5) then can be written as

$$\langle v \rangle = \partial D/\partial x + \langle v \rangle_F \tag{7-9}$$

where $\langle v \rangle_F$ is the contribution to $\langle v \rangle$ arising strictly from driving forces, and

$$\langle v \rangle_F = 2Dd^{-1}(A_F + B) \tag{7-10}$$

Then

$$J = -D(\partial c/\partial x) + c\langle v \rangle_F \tag{7-11}$$

as in (5–11), and J shows no dependence on the diffusion coefficient gradient. In general,

$$A_F = \varepsilon = Fd/2kT \tag{7-12}$$

with F and ε defined by Eq. (7–1).

Several Different Forces in One Experiment

If there are several different driving forces, the contribution of each force to A_F and B can be calculated separately and then the results simply added together to give the total contribution. Since we are consistently following a linear approximation, all terms proportional to second order in small quantities may be neglected.

The appearance of several different driving forces in a single experiment is quite common. For example, in electrotransport experiments in metals, an electric potential is applied across the ends of a metal wire. This can give rise to three separate driving forces: (1) The resulting electric field E in the wire exerts a force on the charged ion cores of the metal atoms (charge q) giving a force $F = qE$. (2) The field causes a flow of electrons whose momentum can be transferred to diffusing atoms. This is the electron wind effect mentioned at the beginning of this chapter. (3) The electric current heats the wire. If the ends of the wire are at room temperature, there will be a temperature gradient. One then obtains a driving force from the heat of transport as described in Section 5–7.

In addition, one might consider the vacancy flow term B as arising from still another driving force, as written in Eq. (5–96), for example. However, it is useful to consider this term separately since it merely serves to perturb the effect of the other driving forces and goes to zero when these forces go to zero.

General Expression for the Vacancy Flow Term

In reality, the vacancy flow term B depends on the driving forces acting on the vacancies rather than on those acting on the atoms. In many cases, $\varepsilon_v = -\varepsilon_i$, and therefore this distinction can be unimportant. Examples where this distinction is important, however, are given in Chapter 5. The ε_v can be calculated from Eq. (7–1) if the atom jump frequencies ν in this equation are replaced by the corresponding vacancy jump frequencies w. Equations (4–28) to (4–44) illustrate the calculation of B with a constant driving force and diffusion coefficient. Equations (5–104) and (5–108) provide an example where neither the driving force nor the diffusion coefficient is constant.

Specific Expressions for A_F

In Chapter 4, we explicitly considered effects from an electric field in ionic crystals. There $A_F = q_i Ed/2kT$. In Chapter 5, the driving force from a chemical concentration gradient, where $A_F = \frac{1}{2}d(\partial \ln \gamma/\partial x)$, was considered. Also nonconstant driving forces from the heat of transport in a temperature gradient were discussed. In this case, $A_F = \frac{1}{2}d(q_\alpha{}^* - E_{f\alpha}) \times$

$(kT^2)^{-1}(\partial T/\partial x)$ for an atom jump to site α. Values of A_F for other driving forces can be obtained by first finding the force F or ε from Eq. (7–1). Then, A_F is given by Eq. (7–12).

Once A_F and B have been calculated, $\langle v \rangle$ and the flux J (relative to a given lattice plane) can be calculated from the general equations (7–9) to (7–11).

7–2. PAIR ASSOCIATION METHOD

Tightly Bound Complexes

The equations in Chapter 4 apply even when the vacancy is tightly bound to an impurity. An alternate kinetic calculation, however, can be applied more directly in this case. This alternate approach, first used by Lidiard,[6] can be called the "pair association" approach. Instead of considering the motion of individual vacancies, this method concerns itself with the rates of formation, reorientation, and dissociation of bound vacancy-impurity complexes. The atom flux across a plane 0 is then expressed in terms of the concentration of complexes on plane 0 and on planes to the right and left of plane 0 (see Fig. 7–2).

In ionic crystals, the impurity and the associated vacancy are restricted to a given sublattice (either that for cations or that for anions). In the most tightly bound complexes, the vacancy and impurity are nearest neighbors on a particular sublattice (or next nearest neighbors if both sublattices are included). As an illustration, we shall consider diffusion in NaCl with only tightly bound complexes allowed.

Each sublattice in NaCl is face-centered cubic. For planar diffusion along a $\langle 100 \rangle$ direction in this sublattice, there are only three basic orientations for tightly bound complexes. We define $n_a(x)$ as the concentration of complexes with the impurity on the plane at x and the vacancy at a neighboring site in the forward direction (on the plane at $x + d$, the next plane

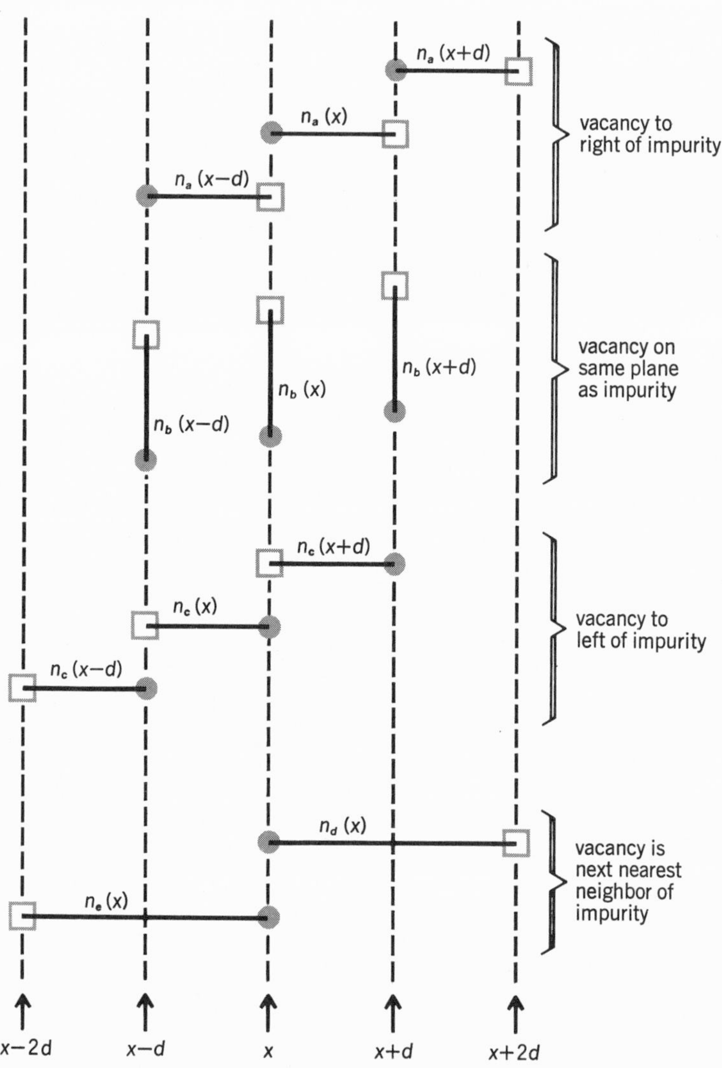

7–2 Vacancy-impurity complexes which influence diffusion at plane x. The lattice planes are shown as dashed lines. Each impurity is shown as a solid circle, connected to its associated vacancy by a solid line. The hollow squares represent vacancies. There are many possible complexes where the vacancy and impurity are not nearest neighbors. Of these, only two are shown. In the other complexes shown, the vacancy and impurity are nearest neighbor.

to the right). Also $n_b(x)$ is the concentration of complexes with the impurity and the neighboring vacancy both on plane x, and $n_c(x)$ is that where the impurity is on plane x and the neighboring vacancy is on plane $x - d$, the next plane to the left. These and similar complexes with the impurity on planes $x + d$ and $x - d$ are illustrated in Fig. 7–2. In each case, subscript a indicates that the vacancy lies in the $+x$-direction from the plane of the impurity; subscript b that it lies on the same plane; and subscript c that the vacancy lies in the $-x$-direction from the impurity.

The net atom flux toward the right at x can be expressed as in Eq. (2–19),

$$J = \tfrac{1}{2}dw_2[n_a(x) + n_a(x - d) - n_c(x) - n_c(x + d)] \quad (7\text{–}13)$$

where w_2 is the frequency of vacancy-impurity exchanges. To first order, this becomes

$$J = dw_2\{[n_a(x) - n_c(x)] - \tfrac{1}{2}d(\partial n_a/\partial x) - \tfrac{1}{2}d(\partial n_c/\partial x)\} \quad (7\text{–}14)$$

When there is a gradient in the concentration of complexes or a net vacancy flux, $n_a(x)$ will not equal $n_c(x)$. The difference $n_a(x) - n_c(x)$ can be determined from kinetic equations for the time rate of change of $n_a(x)$, $n_b(x)$, and $n_c(x)$,

$$\partial n_a(x)/\partial t = -(2w_1 + w_2)n_a(x) + 2w_1n_b(x) + w_2n_c(x + d) \quad (7\text{–}15)$$

$$\partial n_b(x)/\partial t = -2w_1n_b(x) + w_1n_a(x) + w_1n_c(x) \quad (7\text{–}16)$$

$$\partial n_c(x)/\partial t = -(2w_1 + w_2)n_c(x) + 2w_1n_b(x) + w_2n_a(x - d) \quad (7\text{–}17)$$

where w_1 is the frequency for a vacancy jump from one site neighboring on the impurity to another such site by exchange with a solvent atom. In Eq. (7–14), we ignore terms in $\partial^2 n/\partial x^2$. According to the diffusion equation, the time derivatives $\partial n/\partial t$ are of the same order as $\partial^2 n/\partial x^2$. Hence, in this approximation, we can set $\partial n_a/\partial t = \partial n_b/\partial t = \partial n_c/\partial t = 0$. Then (7–16) gives

$$n_b(x) = \tfrac{1}{2}[n_a(x) + n_c(x)] \tag{7–18}$$

and subtracting (7–17) from (7–15) yields

$$n_a(x) - n_c(x) = \frac{w_2 d}{2w_1 + 2w_2}\left(\frac{\partial n_a}{\partial x} + \frac{\partial n_c}{\partial x}\right) \tag{7–19}$$

Substituting this into (7–14) gives

$$J = -d^2 \frac{w_1 w_2}{w_1 + w_2} \frac{\partial n_b}{\partial x} \tag{7–20}$$

Now, $n(x) = n_a(x) + n_b(x) + n_c(x) = 3n_b(x) = p(x)c(x)$, where $c(x)$ is the concentration of impurities at plane x and $p(x)$ is the probability that the impurity will be in a vacancy-impurity complex. If p is constant

$$J = -\left[\tfrac{1}{6}\lambda^2 p w_2 \left(\frac{w_1}{w_1 + w_2}\right)\right]\frac{\partial c}{\partial x} \tag{7–21}$$

where the jump distance λ in the face-centered cubic sublattice is related to the interplanar spacing d by $d^2 = \frac{1}{2}\lambda^2$.

The factor in the square brackets is the diffusion coefficient, and that inside the parentheses is the correlation factor. The correlation factor appears naturally in these equations as a result of the term $n_a(x) - n_c(x)$ in Eq. (7–14).

In ionic crystals, electrical neutrality must be maintained. Introducing a divalent ion into NaCl thus introduces a vacancy on the same sublattice. Except at very small impurity concentrations, the vacancy concentration equals the concentration of divalent impurities. Also the fraction of these atoms and vacancies which are bound in vacancy-impurity pairs is given by

$$p = (1 - p)^2 z N_i \exp(g/kT) \tag{7–22}$$

where g is the binding energy, N_i is the mole fraction of impurity atoms on the sublattice, and z is the number of nearest neighbors on this sublattice. When $N_i \exp(g/kT)$ is small, p is proportional to the concentration N_i of divalent ions. Then $\partial(pN_i)/\partial x = 2p(\partial N_i/\partial x)$ and an additional factor 2 appears in (7–21). Also D in this limit increases linearly as a function of N_i. In the other limit, where $N_i \exp(g/kT) \gg 1$, p is approximately constant and equal to unity. Then (7–21) is valid as it stands (with $p = 1$). Also D is independent of N_i if w_1 and w_2 are independent of N_i. In general, D as a function of N_i is given by

$$D(N_i) = D_\omega \partial(pN_i)/\partial N_i \tag{7–23}$$

where $D_\omega = \frac{1}{6}\lambda^2 w_1 w_2/(w_1 + w_2)$. Here D_ω equals the limiting value of D obtained at large N_i. Values of $D(N_i)/D_\omega$ have been plotted by Lidiard[6] for various values of g/kT.

Equations Allowing Partial or Complete Dissociation of Complexes

Equations (7–15) to (7–17) ignore possible vacancy jumps to or from sites which are second nearest neighbors or farther from the impurity. If the frequency of these jumps is much less than w_1 (as one might expect for a vacancy-divalent impurity complex in an alkali halide), they do not appreciably affect the diffusion coefficient. These jumps, however, are quite significant for diffusion of a monovalent impurity in an alkali halide or for diffusion in an electric field.

There are two general means of including these jumps:

Case (1). Concentrations of partially dissociated complexes, where the vacancy and impurity are not nearest neighbors, may be designated by $n_d(x)$, $n_e(x)$, etc. The time rate of change of these concentrations is given by equations similar to (7–15) to (7–17). However, vacancy jumps to all neighboring sites are now allowed. Subtracting the equations for n_a, n_d, etc., from those for their mirror complexes, n_c, n_e, etc., on the other side of plane x and setting all $\partial n/\partial t$ equal to zero gives a set of m linear equations in m unknowns, $n_a - n_c$, $n_d - n_e$, etc. These may be solved for $n_a - n_c$ and the result substituted into (7–14) to yield the flux. In general, $n_a - n_c$ can be expressed in terms of determinants of infinite order similar to those in Chapter 4.

Case (2). Vacancy concentrations at sites on the second coordination shell from the impurity can arbitrarily be assumed to be maintained at their equilibrium values. When jumps to and from these sites are included in (7–15) to (7–17) and $n_a - n_c$ is calculated from these equations alone, the result[7] is to replace w_1 in (7–21) with $w_1 + \frac{7}{2}w_3$. This yields the same value for the correlation factor as that obtained from the "random walk" approach in Chapter 3 with w_4/w_o set equal to zero. Jump frequencies in face-centered cubic structures are illustrated in Fig. 3–4.

In general, the assumption in the pair association method that vacancy concentrations are maintained at equilibrium at a given site has the same influence on the correlation factor as an assumption in the random-walk method that a vacancy after arriving at such a site cannot return and re-exchange with the impurity. In the random-walk method, such an assumption is equivalent to letting w_4 equal zero, in agreement with the result above.

Case (2) has been considered in detail by Howard and Lidiard.[8,9] When their equations are expressed in terms of chemical potential gradients, as in (6–28) and (6–29), they find for a face-centered cubic sublattice in this approximation,

$$L_{AA} = -\frac{a^2c_p}{3kT}\left[\frac{7w_3w_o}{w_4} - \frac{(80w_3w_1 + 80w_3^2 + 28w_2w_3 + 8w_1w_2)}{2w_1 + 2w_2 + 7w_3}\right] + \frac{4a^2w_o(c_v - c_p)}{kT} \qquad (7\text{–}24)$$

$$L_{AB} = \frac{a^2c_p}{3kT}\frac{w_2(-4w_1 + 6w_3)}{2w_1 + 2w_2 + 7w_3} \qquad (7\text{–}25)$$

$$L_{BB} = \frac{a^2c_p}{3kT}\frac{w_2(2w_1 + 7w_3)}{2w_1 + 2w_2 + 7w_3} \qquad (7\text{–}26)$$

where c_v and c_p are the concentrations of vacancies and of impurity-vacancy pairs, and a is half the length of the cube edge in the face-centered cubic sublattice (the jump distance equals $\sqrt{2}a$).

Effect of Electric Field

When there is a driving force, such as an electric field, Eqs. (7–14) to (7–17) must be modified. Jump frequencies for jumps which move a solvent ion in the direction of the field E are multiplied by $(1 + \varepsilon)$, where $\varepsilon = q_sEd/2kT$ and q_s is the charge of the solvent. Similarly jumps which move a solvent ion in a direction opposite to the field have their jump frequencies multiplied by $(1 - \varepsilon)$. Impurity jump frequencies are changed by a factor by $[1 \pm (q_i/q_s)\varepsilon]$, where q_i is the charge of the impurity. Solving for $(n_a - n_c)$ in terms of mth order determinants, as in case 1 above, then gives the same result for the impurity flux J_i and the drift mobility u_i as that found in Chapter 4.

Nernst Field–Diffusion Potential

Introducing a concentration gradient of divalent ions in a monovalent sublattice will introduce a corresponding concentration of bound vacancies. Such a vacancy gradient normally would give rise to a certain flow of vacancies. Since vacancies are more mobile than ions or atoms, the vacancy gradient would tend to eliminate itself faster than the comparable gradient of divalent impurities. Charge neutrality, however, must be maintained in ionic crystals. Therefore, the net flux of vacancies must equal the net flux of divalent impurities. What actually must happen is that, as the vacancy flow proceeds, an electric field is set up between the impurities (which in a cation sublattice have charge $+e$ with respect to other ions) and the vacancies (which have a charge $-e$ with respect to the ions on this sublattice). This field is called the Nernst field and tends to reduce the vacancy flux while enhancing the impurity flux. The field eventually becomes large enough so that these two fluxes are equal. The field and the associated "diffusion potential" are proportional to $\partial c_i/\partial x$.

Even when there is no external electric field, there can be an internal Nernst field arising from vacancy-divalent impurity dissociation. This may be included in Eqs. (7–14) to (7–17) by introducing factors $(1 \pm \varepsilon)$ and $[1 \pm (q_i/q_\varepsilon)\varepsilon]$ as above. The driving force from the Nernst field will affect the intrinsic diffusion coefficient D_i^I, as defined in Eq. (1–18). Howard and Lidiard find[9]

$$D_i^I = \frac{a^2}{3}\frac{p}{1+p}w_2\left(\frac{4w_1 - 6w_3 + 20w_3\psi}{2w_1 + 2w_2 + 7w_3}\right) \qquad (7\text{–}27)$$

where

$$\psi = \frac{L_{AA} + 2L_{AB}}{L_{AA} + 4(L_{AB} + L_{BB})} \qquad (7\text{–}28)$$

In this approximation L_{AA}, L_{AB}, and L_{BB} are given by Eqs. (7–24) to (7–26).

The homogeneous thermoelectric power in ionic crystals arises from a similar effect. Here two types of imperfections diffuse in a thermal gradient. When there are Schottky defects there are two species of vacancies, one on each sublattice. Since the two species of vacancies usually are affected to different extents by the gradient, there again is a separation of charge. This gives rise to an electric field and creates a potential difference across the crystal.[10–12] When there are Frenkel defects, the situation is very similar, but with the two diffusing species being vacancies and interstitials associated with a single sublattice.

7-3. DETERMINATION OF DIFFUSION MECHANISM

Since the individual atoms inside a crystal cannot be viewed directly as they diffuse, our knowledge of their diffusion mechanisms is necessarily indirect. The kinetic equations often provide strong evidence pointing to a particular mechanism, however.

The dominant diffusion mechanisms will be those with the lowest activation energies and the highest D_o's. Theoretical calculations can be made of these quantities. These results are particularly convincing when they are combined with independent experimental measurements of the energy of formation and energy of motion. These energies can be measured, for example, in quenching experiments, where the defect concentration present at a high temperature is frozen in by rapidly cooling the specimen. By measuring the relative defect concentrations frozen in from various high temperatures one can calculate the energy of formation. Then measurements on the annealing of the frozen-in defects allow the energy of motion to be found. When these results agree with the calculated energies of formation and motion for a particular defect and the sum of E_f and E_m equals the measured activation energy for diffusion, it is very reasonable to conclude that diffusion occurs by means of this defect.[13]

In addition, the relative importance of vacancies and interstitials can be determined experimentally. If the volume (or length) of a given specimen and its lattice parameter are measured as a function of temperature, one can determine the change in the number of lattice sites. An increase in the number of lattice sites indicates that vacancies are being introduced, whereas a decrease indicates that lattice sites are disappearing and lattice atoms are moving to interstitial sites. In the metals which have been studied, these experiments indicate that more vacancies than interstitials are introduced upon heating.[14] The energies of formation for the most part agree with those found from quenching experiments. Thus, it is concluded that volume diffusion in pure metals and substitutional alloys usually occurs by means of vacancies.

The kinetic equations discussed in Chapters 3 and 5 also can help distinguish between possible diffusion mechanisms. For example, the existence of a Kirkendall shift is conclusive proof that diffusion does not occur wholly by an exchange or ring mechanism. These mechanisms require that an atom jump in one direction be accompanied by the jump of a second atom in the opposite direction. Even though individual atoms move through the crystal, there is no net atom flux. On the other hand, both vacancy and interstitial mechanisms allow a net flux of atoms in a given direction. The occurrence of porosity would seem to favor a vacancy mechanism.

The value of u/D in ionic crystals depends strongly on the diffusion mechanism. For self-diffusion by a vacancy mechanism in the NaCl structure, $u/D = q/kTf$, where $f = 0.78$. [See Eq. (4–91).] For self-diffusion by a collinear interstitialcy mechanism in this structure, $u/D = 2q/kTf$, where $f = \frac{2}{3}$. Thus, these two mechanisms can easily be distinguished. Measurements on Ag diffusing in AgCl and AgBr give values of u/D that are too *large* to result from a vacancy mechanism alone.[15–18] This result indicates that interstitialcy diffusion is important in these crystals.[19] On the other hand, u/D is less than $3q/kT$. Thus, diffusion cannot occur solely by a collinear interstitialcy mechanism. Some combination of mechanisms, probably involving noncollinear interstitialcy jumps, is required.[20]

In CsBr, CsI, and TlCl, all of which have the CsCl structure, measured values of σ/D are *smaller*[20–22] than those predicted by the equation $\sigma = \sum c_i u_i q_i$, if $u/D = q/kTf$ as for a single vacancy mechanism. In this case, it is thought that diffusion occurs partially by means of bound anion vacancy–cation vacancy pairs. The pairs have no net charge and hence do not contribute to the conductivity σ. However, they do contribute to the diffusion coefficient D. On the other hand, u/D for diffusion in NaCl agrees well[23–26] with the predicted value of $1.28q/kT$. In this case, it appears that diffusion occurs by means of a single vacancy mechanism alone.

Situations with Two Mechanisms or Activation Energies

In ionic crystals, charge neutrality must be maintained. The creation of cation vacancies removes positive charge from the crystal, leaving a net negative charge in the crystal. This charge can be neutralized either by creating anion vacancies or by introducing charged cation interstitials. In the former case, Schottky defects are formed. This type of disorder is predominant in alkali halides. In the latter case, Frenkel defects are formed. This type of disorder is dominant in AgCl and AgBr. In both types of disorder, two different classes of point defects are introduced: cation vacancies and anion vacancies in Schottky disorder, and vacancies and interstitials in Frenkel disorder.

The measured electrical conductivity σ will contain contributions from all charged species in the crystal, including anions, cations, and electrons. The relative importance of these contributions must be known before σ can be related to u for a particular species. In AgI, the electronic contribution is important. When Schottky defects are present, the relative mobilities of cation and anion vacancies can be determined either by measurement of the transport numbers for cations and anions or by direct measurements of tracer diffusion coefficients.[20,27] In CsBr, CsI, and TlCl, the anion has the higher mobility. However, the Cs cations in CsBr and CsI make appreciable contributions to σ. In alkali halides with the NaCl structure, cation diffusion seems to predominate.

In ionic crystals with Frenkel defects, adding an aliovalent impurity will alter the concentration of interstitials and vacancies. For example, addition of divalent cations to AgBr will create additional vacancies on the cation sublattice to maintain charge neutrality. Through the law of mass action, this reduces the interstitial concentration. Since the ratio of interstitial and vacancy concentrations changes with impurity concentration, measurement of the ionic conductivity as a function of impurity concentration allows the relative mobilities of interstitials and vacancies to be calculated.[27–31]

Addition of sufficient divalent impurities (and vacancies) to an alkali halide at a temperature sufficiently high for the vacancy-impurity complexes to be dissociated will create a large, temperature-independent concentration of free vacancies. Then, the activation energy measured by diffusion or ionic conductivity experiments equals just the energy of motion E_m. At higher temperatures or lower impurity concentrations, thermally generated imperfections dominate. In crystals which normally have Schottky defects, the measured activation energy in the high-temperature "intrinsic" region is $E_m + \frac{1}{2}E_s$, where E_s is the formation energy for a Schottky pair (cation vacancy plus an anion vacancy). Measurements in the intrinsic and impurity regions thus allow E_m and E_s both to be calculated. Measurements at lower temperatures where vacancy-impurity binding becomes important also allow vacancy-impurity binding energies to be calculated.[32]

In noncubic crystals, it is often found that the activation energies for diffusion along the separate principal axes differ from one another. This requires that at least two types of jumps with different energies of motion occur in competition with one another. Methods of excluding possible pairs of mechanisms have been discussed by Huntington and others.[33–43]

7–4. DETERMINATION OF VACANCY JUMP FREQUENCY RATIOS

If the diffusion mechanism is known, the correlation factor for self-diffusion can be calculated and will be a pure number. Then the atom jump frequency can be calculated directly from measurements of the diffusion coefficient. For impurity diffusion, the situation is more complicated. This is especially true for diffusion by a vacancy mechanism. Then, the correlation factor is not a pure number but instead depends on the relative values of the various vacancy jump frequencies in the vicinity of the impurity. This makes the problem of determining impurity jump frequencies more difficult. However, it has the advantage of providing opportunities to calculate the solvent-vacancy exchange frequencies near an impurity.

In a face-centered cubic structure (or in the fcc sublattice in an NaCl structure), the correlation factor f_i for impurity diffusion is given by

$$f_i = \frac{2w_1 + 7Fw_3}{2w_2 + 2w_1 + 7Fw_3} \tag{7–29}$$

where vacancy jump frequencies are w_2 for exchange with the impurity, w_1 for a jump from one site neighboring on the impurity to another such site, w_3 for any vacancy jump from a nearest neighbor to a nonnearest neighbor site, w_4 for the reverse of a w_3 jump, and w_o for any other vacancy jump in the crystal. Here the approximation is made that all w_3 jumps have the same jump frequency whether they are made to second, third, or fourth nearest neighbors of the impurity. The quantity F depends on the ratio w_4/w_o, as illustrated in Fig. 3–5.

Another relation involving these jump frequencies is

$$\frac{u}{D} = \frac{q_t}{kT}\left[1 + \frac{2q_s}{q_t}\langle n_p\rangle\right] \tag{7–30}$$

as in Eq. (4–73). A specific equation for $\langle n_p\rangle$ in a face-centered cubic sublattice is given in (4–78). The ratio of the impurity diffusion coefficient $D_i(0)$ in a crystal where the concentration of impurity is very small to the diffusion coefficient $D_s(0)$ in a pure crystal is given by

$$\frac{D_i(0)}{D_s(0)} = \frac{w_2\, f_i}{w_o\, f_o}\, \frac{w_4}{w_3} \tag{7–31}$$

where w_4/w_3 is the ratio of the vacancy concentration at a site neighboring on an impurity to that for a solvent atom in a pure crystal, as in (3–119).

If the jump frequencies do not change appreciably with impurity concentration, the solvent diffusion coefficient $D_s(N_i)$ in a crystal containing a mole fraction N_i of impurities will for small concentrations N_i (less than $\approx 2\%$) be given by

$$D_s(N_i) = D_s(0)\,(1 + bN_i) \tag{7–32}$$

where

$$b = -18 + 4\,\frac{w_1}{w_3}\,\frac{w_4}{w_o}\,\frac{f_1}{f_o} + 14\,\frac{w_4}{w_o}\,\frac{f_{34}}{f_o} \tag{7–33}$$

as in (3–120).

Equations (7–29), (7–30), (7–31), and (7–33) can be used in various combinations to calculate the ratios w_2/w_1, w_3/w_1, and w_4/w_o. At present, however, there are only a few cases where the necessary data are available. It may be noted that for metals Eq. (7–30) for u/D is not useful in calculating jump frequencies since the "effective charge" of the ions is not known.

When vacancies which are bound to divalent impurities in monovalent ionic crystals are considered, the vacancy jump frequencies can be related to the relaxation times for dielectric and mechanical relaxation of the vacancy-impurity dipoles.[44–59] The relations for these two relaxation times, along with the four relations mentioned above, provide a particularly good opportunity to calculate jump frequency ratios near divalent impurities. In addition, magnetic resonance experiments[60] can yield information about vacancy populations and jump frequencies.

REFERENCES

1. W. Seith and H. Wever, *Z. Electrochem.* **57,** 891 (1953); **59,** 942 (1955).
2. H. Wever, *Z. Electrochem.* **60,** 1170 (1956).
3. H. B. Huntington and A. R. Grone, *J. Phys. Chem. Solids* **20,** 76 (1961); A. R. Grone, *J. Phys. Chem. Solids* **20,** 88 (1961).
4. H. B. Huntington and S. C. Ho, *J. Phys. Soc. Japan* **18** (Suppl. II), 202 (1963).
5. J. R. Manning, *Phys. Rev.* **139,** A126 (1965).
6. A. B. Lidiard, *Phil. Mag.* **46,** 815 (1955).
7. A. B. Lidiard, *Phil. Mag.* **46,** 1218 (1955).
8. R. E. Howard and A. B. Lidiard, *Proceedings of the Sixth Colloquium on Metallurgy*, Relations Between Atomic Defects and Macroscopic Properties, Saclay, July 1962 (Press Universitaires de Francé, Paris, 1962), p. 43.
9. R. E. Howard and A. B. Lidiard, *J. Phys. Soc. Japan* **18** (Suppl. II), 197 (1963).
10. L. Patrick and A. W. Lawson, *J. Chem. Phys.* **22,** 1492 (1954).
11. R. E. Howard and A. B. Lidiard, *Discussions Faraday Soc.* **23,** 113 (1957); *Phil. Mag.* **2,** 1462 (1957); *Reports on Progress in Physics* **27,** 161 (1964).
12. E. Haga, *J. Phys. Soc. Japan* **13,** 1090 (1958); **14,** 992 (1959); **14,** 1176 (1959).
13. See, e.g., "Lattice Defects in Quenched Metals," edited by R. M. J. Cotterill, M. Doyama, J. J. Jackson, and M. Meshii (Academic Press, New York, 1965).
14. R. O. Simmons and R. W. Baluffi, *Phys. Rev.* **117,** 52 (1960); **119,** 600 (1960); **125,** 862 (1962); **129,** 153 (1963).

15. W. D. Compton, *Phys. Rev.* **101,** 1209 (1956).
16. W. D. Compton and R. J. Maurer, *J. Phys. Chem. Solids* **1,** 191 (1956).
17. A. S. Miller and R. J. Maurer, *J. Phys. Chem. Solids* **4,** 196 (1958).
18. R. J. Friauf, *Phys. Rev.* **105,** 843 (1957).
19. C. W. McCombie and A. B. Lidiard, *Phys. Rev.* **101,** 1210 (1956).
20. R. J. Friauf, *J. Appl. Phys.* **33** (Suppl.), 494 (1962).
21. D. W. Lynch, *Phys. Rev.* **118,** 468 (1960).
22. R. J. Friauf, *J. Phys. Chem. Solids* **18,** 203 (1961).
23. D. Mapother, N. H. Crooks, and R. J. Maurer, *J. Chem. Phys.* **18,** 1231 (1950).
24. A. Murin and B. Lur'e, *Doklady Akad. Nauk S.S.S.R.* **73,** 933 (1950).
25. J. F. Laurent and J. Benard, *C.R. Acad. Sci. Paris* **241,** 1204 (1955); *J. Phys. Chem. Solids* **3,** 7 (1957).
26. Y. Haven, Conference on Defects in Crystalline Solids, Bristol, 1954 (The Physical Society, London, 1955), p. 261; K. Compaan and Y. Haven, *Proc. Third Int. Symp. on the Reactivity of Solids, Madrid,* 1956 (C. Bermejo, Madrid, 1957), p. 255.
27. A. B. Lidiard, "Handbuch der Physik," edited by S. Flügge (Springer-Verlag, Berlin, 1957), Vol. 20, p. 246.
28. E. Koch and C. Wagner, *Z. physik. Chem.* **B38,** 295 (1937).
29. J. Teltow, *Ann. Phys. Lpz.* **5,** 63, 71 (1949).
30. I. Ebert and J. Teltow, *Ann. Phys. Lpz.* **15,** 268 (1955).
31. H. C. Abbink and D. S. Martin, Jr., *J. Phys. Chem. Solids* **27,** 205 (1966).
32. R. W. Dreyfus and A. S. Nowick, *J. Appl. Phys.* **33,** 473 (1962); *Phys. Rev.* **126,** 1367 (1962).
33. G. A. Shirn, E. S. Wajda, and H. B. Huntington, *Acta Met.* **1,** 513 (1953).
34. E. S. Wajda, G. A. Shirn, and H. B. Huntington, *Acta Met.* **3,** 39 (1955).
35. G. A. Shirn, *Acta Met.* **3,** 87 (1955).
36. J. E. Dickey, *Acta Met.* **7,** 350 (1959).
37. J. H. Rosolowski, *Phys. Rev.* **124,** 1828 (1961).
38. P. B. Ghate, *Phys. Rev.* **131,** 174 (1963).
39. H. B. Huntington, P. B. Ghate, and J. H. Rosolowski, *J. Appl. Phys.* **35,** 3027 (1964).
40. J. F. Nicholas, *Acta Met.* **3,** 178 (1955).

41. P. G. Shewmon, *Trans. A.I.M.E.* **206,** 918 (1956).
42. J. D. Meakin and E. Klokholm, *Trans. A.I.M.E.* **218,** 463 (1960).
43. C. Coston and N. H. Nachtrieb, *J. Phys. Chem.* **68,** 2219 (1964).
44. R. G. Breckenridge, *J. Chem. Phys.* **16,** 959 (1948); **18,** 913 (1950); "Imperfections in Nearly Perfect Crystals," edited by W. Shockley, J. H. Holloman, R. Maurer, and F. Seitz (John Wiley and Sons, Inc., New York, 1952), p. 219.
45. Y. Haven, *J. Chem. Phys.* **21,** 171 (1953); Conference on Defects in Crystalline Solids, Bristol, 1954 (The Physical Society, London, 1955), p. 261.
46. Y. Haven and J. H. van Santen, *J. Chem. Phys.* **22,** 1146 (1954); *Nuovo Cimento* **7** (Suppl.), 605 (1958).
47. A. B. Lidiard, Conference on Defects in Crystalline Solids, Bristol, 1954 (The Physical Society, London, 1955), p. 283; "Handbuch der Physik," edited by S. Flügge (Springer-Verlag, Berlin, 1957), Vol. 20, p. 246.
48. G. Jacobs, *Naturwiss.* **42,** 575 (1955); *J. Chem. Phys.* **27,** 217 (1957).
49. J. S. Dryden and R. J. Meakins, *Discussions Faraday Soc.* **23,** 39 (1957).
50. G. D. Watkins, *Phys. Rev.* **113,** 91 (1959).
51. V. N. Lozovskii, *Izv. Akad. Nauk S.S.S.R.* **24,** 161 (1960).
52. J. S. Cook and J. S. Dryden, *Australian J. Phys.* **13,** 260 (1960).
53. R. W. Dreyfus, *Phys. Rev.* **121,** 1675 (1961).
54. G. Jacobs, L. G. Vandewiele, and A. Hamerlinck, *J. Chem. Phys.* **36,** 2946 (1962).
55. J. B. Wachtman, Jr., *Phys. Rev.* **131,** 517 (1963).
56. A. D. Franklin, *J. Res. Nat. Bur. Standards* **67A,** 291 (1963).
57. R. W. Dreyfus and R. B. Laibowitz, *Phys. Rev.* **135,** A1413 (1964).
58. A. D. Franklin, A. Shorb, and J. B. Wachtman, Jr., *J. Res. Nat. Bur. Standards* **68A,** 425 (1964).
59. A. S. Nowick, *Bull. Amer. Phys. Soc. Ser. II* **10,** 394 (1965).
60. G. D. Watkins, *Phys. Rev.* **113,** 79, 91 (1959).

Index